W HEN we build, let us think that we build forever. Let it not be for present delight nor for present use alone. Let it be such work as our descendants will thank us for; and let us think, as we lay stone on stone, that a time is to come when those stones will be held sacred because our hands have touched them, and that men will say, as they look upon the labor and wrought substance of them, "See! This our father did for us."

—*John Ruskin.*

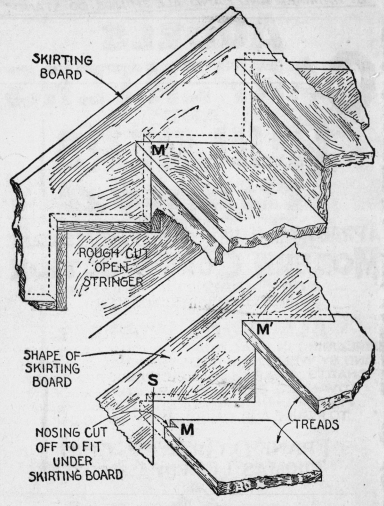

SKIRTING
BOARD

M'

ROUGH CUT
OPEN
STRINGER

SHAPE OF
SKIRTING
BOARD

M'

S

M

NOSING CUT
OFF TO FIT
UNDER
SKIRTING BOARD

TREADS

Detail of Stair Construction

Views showing stairs with skirting board and form of joint. *To simplify fitting* the board, the nosing of the treads is cut off as at **M**. When the board is in place, the cutaway part **M**, fits under **S**, of the board, indicated in position by the tread in dotted lines at **M'**. Here note how the skirting board fits on top of the tread and against the riser. For full treatment of stair construction see Chapter on Stairs in this volume.

"BY HAMMER AND HAND ALL THINGS DO STAND"

AUDELS
CARPENTERS
AND
BUILDERS
GUIDE #4

A PRACTICAL ILLUSTRATED TRADE ASSISTANT
ON
MODERN CONSTRUCTION

FOR CARPENTERS- JOINERS
BUILDERS-MECHANICS
AND
ALL WOOD WORKERS

EXPLAINING IN PRACTICAL, CONCISE LANGUAGE
AND BY WELL DONE ILLUSTRATIONS, DIAGRAMS
CHARTS, GRAPHS AND PICTURES, PRINCIPLES
ADVANCES, SHORT CUTS-BASED ON MODERN
PRACTICE-INCLUDING INSTRUCTIONS ON HOW
TO FIGURE AND CALCULATE VARIOUS JOBS

BY
FRANK D. GRAHAM-CHIEF
THOMAS J. EMERY-ASSOCIATE

THEO. AUDEL & CO - PUBLISHERS
49 WEST 23RD ST , NEW YORK, U.S.A.

Foreword

"The Audel's Guides to the Building Trades" are a practical series of educators on the various branches of Modern Building Construction and are dedicated to Master Builders and their Associates.

These Guides are designed to give technical trade information in concise, accurate, plain language.

The Guides illustrate the hows and whys, short cuts, modern ways and methods of the foundation principles of the art.

Each book in the series is fully illustrated and indexed for readiest form of reference and study.

The Guides will speak for themselves—and help to increase the reader's knowledge and skill in the Building Trades.

—Publishers.

OUTLINE OF CHAPTERS

READY REFERENCE INDEX

How to Use the Index.—By intelligent use of the index, the reader will have no difficulty in finding any item, and if he will carefully read the index he will be amazed at the vast amount of information to be found in this book, and will in this way find numerous items he would like to look up. This constitutes one method of study—*a reference method.*

The making of an index is an art which requires long experience, the indexes for these Guides being made by specialists in that line.

An index is said to be "full" when each item is indexed in two or more ways. For a practical example, the item "Rip saw," may be indexed either as "Rip saw," or "Saw(s), rip." This method of entering each item in two or more ways constitutes a *full index.*

In the *Carpenters' and Builders' Guides* the author has *abridged* the index to gain more space for the main text, by largely avoiding the unnecessary cross indexing.

Accordingly, if you do not find the item "Rip saw" in the letter R, turn over to S, and look for "Saw(s), rip."

In case the item be not found under either heading, look up some *associated heading*, as, for instance, "Tools," and follow down the indented items under this heading, looking for the desired item, "rip saw."

It should be noted that when there is a main heading with comma, followed by indented items, the main heading should be connected with each indented item, thus:

Plane(s), ills., 259-290
block, ills., 265, 284

the last item being read in full, "Plane, block, 265, 284."

Finally, if an item be not found in one Guide, look for it in the other volumes of the set. For instance, the *steel square* is explained in Guide No. 1, and its application to roof framing treated at length in Guide No. 3.

CHAPTER 47

Roofing

The term *roofing* as here used means *the water proof covering placed on the rafters.* It includes the supporting and fastening undersurface as the ribs or shingles, roof boards, etc., and the

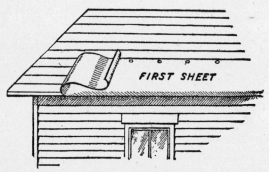

FIG. 2,239.—Paper roofing *1.* Starting the work with the first sheet.

outer or water proof covering as shingles or other roofing material.

There are numerous forms of roofing. They may be classified:

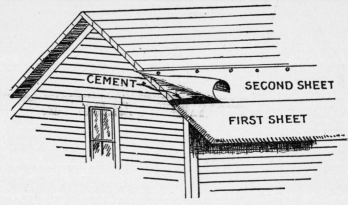

FIG. 2,240.—Paper roofing 2. Method of making laps.

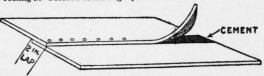

FIG. 2,241.—Paper roofing 3. Width of lap and surface to be cemented.

FIG. 2,242.—Paper roofing 4. Nailing, showing completion of roofing ridge being put on.

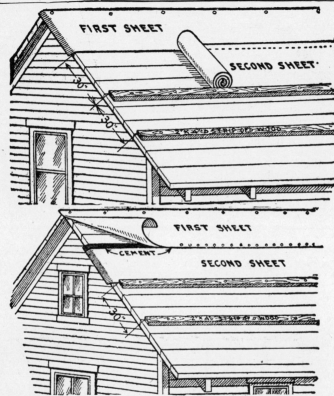

Figs. 2,243 and 2,244.—Paper roofing 5. Laying roofing on roof too steep to work on without slipping. Lay the first sheet along the ridge, holding it in place with a few nails driven in upper edge about half inch from it. Be sure that it lays smooth and even, the end extending over edge of roof or gable end 1⅜ in. if the end has been squared; if not, enough farther to admit of trimming it so that it will show 1⅜ in. over the edge when nailed. Nail a strip of 2 × 4 in. joist over the roof boards 30 ins. from the lower edge of first sheet as shown and another 30 ins. below that; these are to stand or kneel upon when working and by moving them as the sheets are laid mechanics will not have to stand on the roofing. By this means there is no danger of tearing it. Unroll the second sheet, allowing it to rest against the 2 × 4 in. joist, its upper edge temporarily overlapping the lower edge of first sheet 2 inches. Lift the upper edge of second sheet with one hand to drop it beneath the lower edge of first, and so on, thus reversing their positions and making the lap in the proper way to shed water as seen in fig. 2,244. Now lift lower edge of first sheet again and apply the cement as before. Begin nailing at the middle of roof and work out to the ends. Place nails 2 ins. apart and avoid nailing in cracks, joints or knot holes. Continue laying as in fig. 2,245. Cement surface at end.

1. With respect to the material, as

    a. Fibre
    b. Wood
    c. Metal
    d. Slate
    e. Tile
    f. Gravel, etc.

2. With respect to shape, as

    a. Plain
    b. Corrugated
    c. Thatched

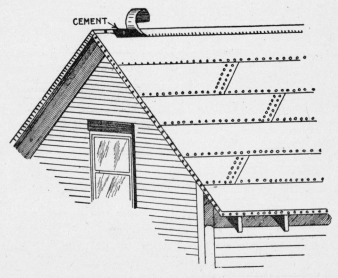

CEMENT

FIG. 2,245.—Paper roofing 7. Cap being bent to cover ridge.

Fibre Roofing.—A cheap form of roofing material is tar felt or other paper. Such material comes in rolls and is made in many varieties, some being surfaced with ground slate, etc.

FIG. 2,246.—Paper roofing *8.* Method of splicing sheets when they do not reach the **full** length. Cut preferably on bevel so that water will run off the joint rather than along **the** joint. These laps should be 4 ins. for double nailing as shown. Note at the bottom **edge** of ends where turned down over and nailed into edge of deck or roof covering are cut so **that** there is a uniform line, no one end below another and an equal width on all edges. **It is** important that this edge drop below the bottom of nailing edge about ⅜″ so that **water** will drop clear of the wood finish and avoid the bad discoloration to paint by not **running** down over it.

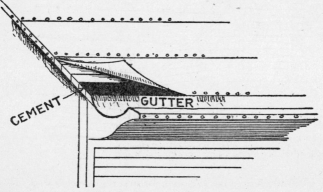

FIG. 2,247.—Paper roofing *9.* Method of laying gutters by laying a strip of roofing **lengthwise** of the gutters and bending to the shape desired. *Never drive nails in the gutter.* **Overlap** each sheet at least 6″ and cement betwe n. These details require extra care in the work

Fig. 2,248.—Paper roofing *10*. Method of laying valleys. The sheets on each side should overlap 6 ins. well and carefully cemented. Nails must not be driven in them or they will leak.

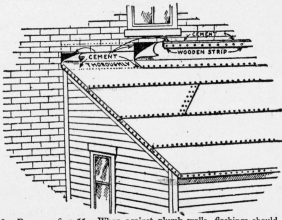

Fig. 2,249.—Paper roofing *11*. When against plumb walls, flashings should be made by bending the roofing up about 4 ins. and fitting it snugly in the angle. Cement turned-up part to wooden wall and cut a strip of roofing 12 ins. wide, fit it over the turned up edge as shown. Cement the upper part of this strip to the wall so that no water can get down behind it, and the lower part to the sheet where it over-laps, and fasten it in place with a strip of wood having its upper edge beveled, in brick work scrape the mortar out of a level joint about 1 in. deep and turn the upper edge of the paper into this open, or a "raggle" block joint and pack up with Portland cement. However, it is always better to use tin, zinc or copper flashings in brick work. A better way is shown in fig. 2.250.

In laying, for best results a good under surface is necessary; do not use unseasoned lumber for this, as the heat will cause the boards to warp and split, eventually tearing the roofing. Tongue and grooved boards are best for the under surface, well nailed with 8*d* nails.

Never try to pull a strip of roofing or sheathing paper after it is unrolled. Unroll it straight to start with.

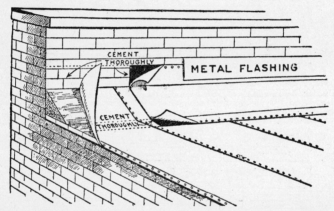

FIG. 2,250.—Paper roofing *12*. Approved method of flashing over a wood strip of triangular section. Raggle block is a tile manufactured especially for this purpose. Flashing is turned into it, calked and cemented and cannot leak. This block can be laid in a brick as well as tile wall.

When cutting for roofs that are very steep, it is best, and sometimes necessary to cut the material to the desired lengths, in the building on the floor. It can then be rerolled for convenience in carrying to the roof. The material should be cut to desired shape as it will not tear straight. Do not attempt to cut one length on top of another already laid.

To insure uniform laps of proper parallel widths, mark roofing with a chalk line the same as laying shingles.

In nailing on the paper use galvanized nails with a big head and short enough so as not to penetrate the under side of the board.

Never nail through a single sheet or through the middle between laps. Nails *must* be driven through *cemented* and other laps *only*.

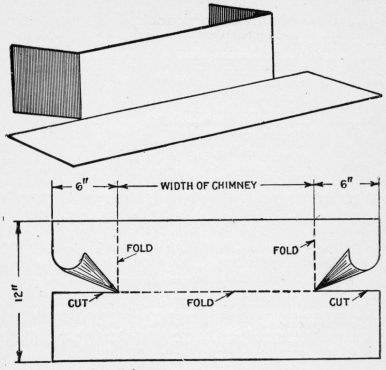

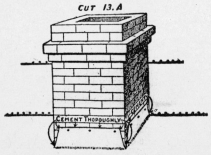

FIGS. 2,251 to 2,253.—Paper roofing **13.** Flashing for chimneys, skylights, etc. Turn up the roofing, fitting it closely in the angles as in fig. 2,251, and cement it against the chimney, being careful not to tear it at the corners or crack it. Next cut a strip 12 ins. wide for each side of the chimney, making each strip 12 ins. longer than the side to be flashed, measuring along the slope of roof as shown in figs. 2,252 and 2,253.

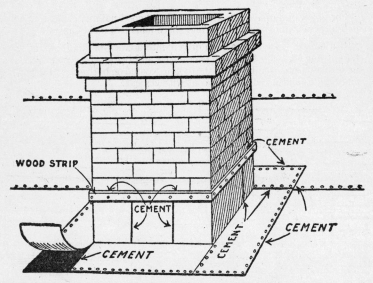

FIG. 2,254.—Paper roofing *14*. Flashing for chimney on steep roof. Cut the strips to suit the angles and thus folded, fit them snugly around the chimney as shown, with ample overlaps at corners; and cement close to chimney and roofing which they overlap. A wood strip with its upper edge beveled must be nailed into the brick joints all around and well cement coated. Flashing of skylights is done in the same manner. There is no better method for temporary work, but for permanent construction metal flashings should be used and join the felt, rubberoid, asphalt or canvas to it in the same manner as though of tar paper.

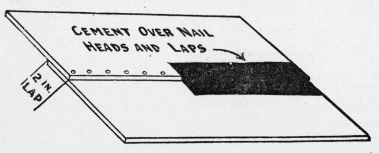

FIG. 2,255.—Paper roofing *15*. Detail showing two inch lap and cement covering over nail head and laps.

For good joints have lap wide enough for good nailing, cementing back two inches from exposed edges, and space nails two inches apart.

If a nail be loose or has been driven into a crack or knothole, at once take it out carefully lest it be overlooked and before the cement sets slip under the sheet a small piece of the roofing, coated on both sides with cement and nail around its edge; then coat with cement.

Fig. 2,256.—Laying canvas roofing.

In closing and cementing lap do not apply the cement too thin and don't skip any places in laps or behind flashings. Apply the cement with a fairly stiff brush. The accompanying cuts, figs. 2,239 to 2,255, show the various operations in laying paper roofing.

Canvas Roofing.—This form of covering is extensively used for water proofing decks of excursion steam boats.

On a smooth deck it can be just as well laid without paper under it. It is made in weights from 12 to 18 ozs. per yard of 27″ wide. The 12 oz. is most generally used.

Canvas can be obtained with a treatment of oil so that when laid it is ready for paint. However, it can just as well be treated after laid.

There is a blue line woven in it about one inch from the edge. This is the distance of lap and a guide. Nail with 1-inch galvanized or copper tacks ¾″ apart.

Before laying, it should be dampened, drawn evenly taut, raw edges con-

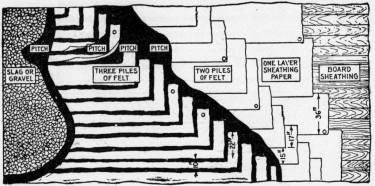

Fig. 2,257.—Sectional plan of gravel roof.

cealed and nailed. Many workmen first use a 75% oil paint for first coat and then paint as floors.

Where the canvas is to be walked on, as on decks, its durability depends on frequent painting.

One method of treating canvas after laying is to first give it a heavy coat of raw linseed oil which saturates. While wet sprinkle all over with calcined plaster of Paris and then with a stiff broom or scrubbing brush on a handle thoroughly brush it over uniformly, removing the superfluous plaster. This process holds the canvas against contraction and expansion, increases wear resistance and makes the best base for paint.

Gravel Roofing.—This form of roofing is used upon flat roofs. A good smooth undersurface to lay this roofing upon is necessary. There should be four thicknesses of roofing felt, laid with a lap of ⅔ of the width, starting with ⅛ of the first course of the second layer of felt at the eaves.

All the layers except the first should be well mopped with pitch. The

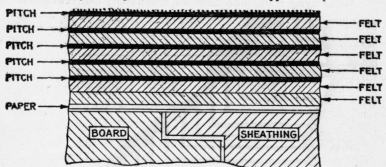

FIG. 2,258.—Enlarged cross section of gravel roof showing construction.

first layer is laid dry so as not to cement it to the undersurface which, because of shrinkage of the roofing boards, might break the paper. The last layer should be nailed with 3*d* common nails, driven through tin discs about 30 inches apart. A thick coat of moderately hot pitch is then applied, over which is spread clean, well screened gravel, which, if laid in cold weather, should be thoroughly warmed.

In flashing the felt is turned up from 4 to 6 inches and held to a brick wall by nails driven through wooden laths, or to wood with nails driven through discs of tin, the whole being carefully bedded in thick pitch and thoroughly doped.

Shingle Roofing.—For roof covering shingles are extensively used. They may be divided into three general classes: 1, wood, 2, fibre, and 3, metal. Treating first of wooden shingles, the best are made from cypress, cedar, or red wood, cypress being the most durable; pine, cedar and red wood coming next in order. They are cut out with the saw regularly in the following sizes:

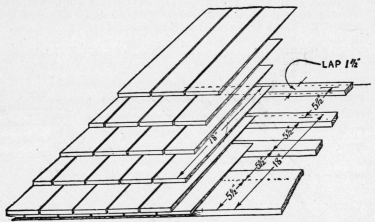

FIG. 2,259.—Section of shingle roof illustrating the amount of shingle which may be exposed to weather as governed by the *"lap."*

Stock Shingle Sizes

Length..................	16	18	20	24
Thickness at butt..........	$5/16$	$7/16$	$1/2$	$1/2$

They usually come in bundles of approximately 250 in random widths from $2\frac{1}{2}$ to 12 or more inches, though they may be had cut to uniform widths.

An important requirement in shingling is that *each shingle should lap over the two courses below it*, that is, *there should always be the three layers of shingle at every point on the roof.*

This requires that the amount of shingle exposed to weather, that is, the spacing of the courses should be less than ⅓ the length of the shingle. Thus in fig. 2,259, 5½ inches is the maximum amount that 18 inch shingles can be laid to weather and have an adequate amount of lap. This is further shown in fig. 2,260.

In case shingles be laid more than ⅓ of their length to weather there will be a space as MS in fig. 2,261, where only two layers of shingles will cover the roof, which is objectionable because, if the top shingle split above the edge of the shingle below, water will leak through.

The following table gives the maximum spacing to weather

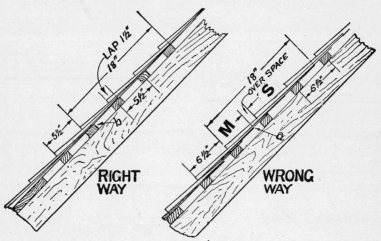

Figs. 2,260 and 2,261.—Right and wrong way to lay shingles illustrating ap and no lap.

for the various sizes of shingles for approximately ½ inch lap:

Spacing of Shingles

Length of shingle........	16	18	20	24
Exposure to weather.....	4⅞	5½	6⅛	7½

Strictly speaking the amount of lap should be governed by the pitch of the roof. The above table may be followed for roofs of moderate pitch; for roofs of small pitch more lap should be allowed and for steep pitch the lap may be reduced somewhat but it is not advisable to do so. The spacing in the above table may be regarded as the maximum for good construction.

The following table shows the number of sq. ft. 1,000 or four bundles of shingles will cover for various exposures.

Space Covered by 1,000 Shingles

Exposure to weather..	4¼	4½	4¾	5	5½	6
Area covered in sq. ft.	118	125	131	138	152	166

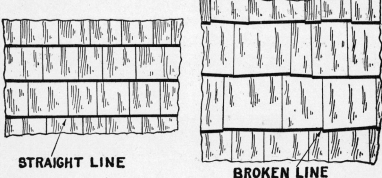

STRAIGHT LINE

BROKEN LINE

FIG. 2,262.—Appearance of shingles laid with butts squared, tight joint and nailed under first butt.

FIG. 2,263.—Appearance of shingles of promiscuous widths with log butts, laid to a line with closed joints. Most shingle butts touching a line.

This table does not allow for waste on hip and valley roofs. See chapter on Estimating in Guide No. 3 for allowances.

Shingles should not be laid too close together, for they will swell when wet, bulge and split. Seasoned shingles should not be laid with their edges nearer than 3⁄16 inches when laid by the American method.

Great care must be used in nailing wide shingles; when they are over 8 inches wide they should be split and laid as two shingles especially on roofs.

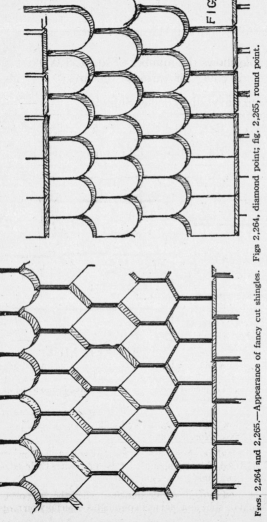

Figs. 2,264 and 2,265.—Appearance of fancy cut shingles. Figs 2,264, diamond point; fig, 2,265, round point.

The nails should be spaced as nearly as possible in the position that will narrow the space between them to the smallest possible distance, thus directing the contraction and expansion toward the edges, lessening the danger of wide shingles splitting in or near the center over joints beneath.

Shingling is always started from the bottom and laid from the eaves or cornice up.

There are various methods of laying shingles, those most generally used are known as:

1. The straight edge
2. The chalk line
3. The gauge and hatchet

The straight edge method is one of the oldest. At first **any** straight edge was used, and then the method was improved **upon** by using a straight edge having a width equal to the spacing to weather or distance between courses.

This eliminated measuring, it being only necessary to keep the lower **edge** flush with the lower edge of the course of shingles just laid, the upper **edge**

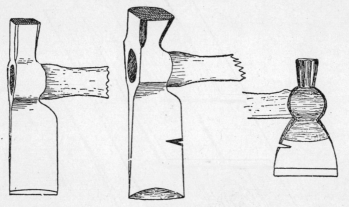

Figs. 2,266 to 2,268.—Various hatchets. Fig. 2,266, lathing hatchet; fig. 2,267, box maker's hatchet; fig. 2,268, ordinary or so called shingling hatchet.

of the straight edge then being in line for the next course. This is about the slowest method.

The chalk line method consists in snapping a chalk line **for** each course, and to save time two lines may be snapped, making it possible to carry two courses at once because the second line could be seen through the spaces between the shingles.

This method is still extensively used. It is faster than the straight **edge** method but not as fast as the gauge and hatchet method. This method **is** extensively used in the Western states. The hatchet used is either a lathing or a box maker's hatchet, as shown in figs. 2,266 and 2,267. The hatchet put out by the manufacturer shown in fig. 2,268, and called a shingling hatchet, should never be used.

Hatchet gauges to measure the space between courses are shown in figs.

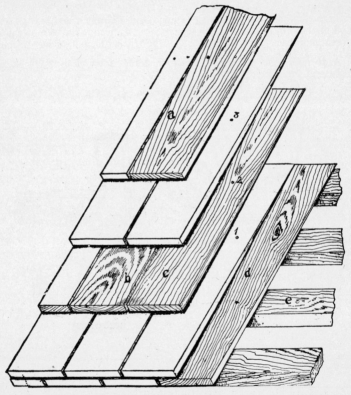

Fɪɢ. 2,269.—One method of nailing shingles. The starting course, *d* should be nailed in the second rib *e*. The distinctive character produced by this method is shown in this detail. *a* represents a shingle with flat grain laid the right side up. If it were turned over the water would run against the grain, as at *b* producing earlier decay. *c* and *d* show nearer edge grain which may well be laid either side up. However, it is well to observe in laying sawed shingles that there is a right and a wrong side. Here again observe that the shingles overhang the eaves and at the sides.

2,270 to 2,273.   The gauge is set at a distance from the end equal to the exposure.

There are various theories as to the best method of nailing shingles: Some say nail near the butt, others near the thin end.

In the first instance the shingle is much more securely nailed but the second method, by not holding the butts down so firmly, leaves a so-called "breathing space" between layers, allowing ventilation and quicker drying.

As to nails, only galvanized nails should be used.   Fig. 2,274 shows right and wrong methods of nailing.

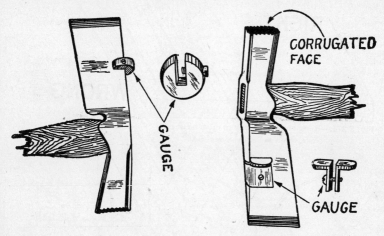

FIGS. 2,270 to 2,273.—Hatchet gauges.   Fig. 2,271, adjustable gauge; fig. 2,270, hatchet with adjustable gauge in place; figs. 2,272 and 2,273, hatchet with fixed gauge in place and view of fixed gauge.

Hips.—The hip is less liable to leak than any other part of the roof as the water runs away from it.   However, since it is so prominent, the work should be well done.

There are several methods of shingling hips.

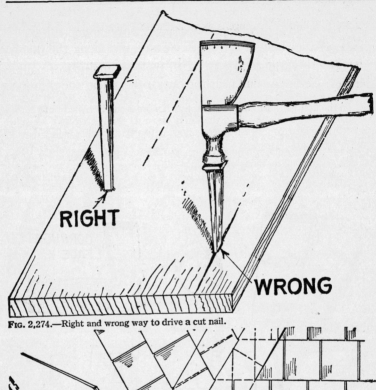

FIG. 2,274.—Right and wrong way to drive a cut nail.

BEST METHOD OF WOVEN HIP,
ILLUSTRATES CUT OF SHINGLE.

FIGS. 2,275 and 2,276.—Shape of shingle as cut for hip and general appearance of shingled hip.

Fig. 2,276 shows general appearance of a shingled hip. The ends of the shingles are sawed at an angle along the line MS, so that they will be in line with the other shingles.

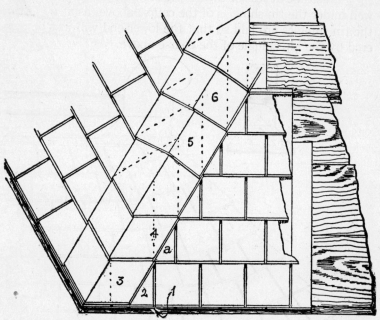

FIG. 2,277.—Hip shingling. After the courses 1 and 2 are laid, the top corners over the hip are trimmed off with a sharp shingling hatchet kept keen for that purpose and shingle 3 with the butt cut (see fig. 2,275) so as to continue the straight line of courses and again on the dotted line 4, so that shingle *a*, of the second course squares against it and so on from side to side, each alternately lapping the other at the hip joint. 5 and 6 show the less attractive way by laying the courses leaving the butts square. The sole reason for cutting them is for looks and the ultimate result is well worth more than the difference in labor. Able mechanics fail to see, or neglect this important acquisition to the hip roof. It is sometimes made to look very clumsy by laying this, so called Boston ridge on top of the finished roof. It is only a makeshift and should never be done.

Fig. 2,277 shows two methods of cutting shingle butts for hips and described under the illustration.

For best construction tin shingles should be laid under the hip shingles, as shown in figs. 2,280 and 2,281. These tin shingles should correspond in shape to that of hip shingles; they should be at least 7 inches wide and large enough to reach well under the tin shingles of the course above, as at *w*. At *a*, the tin shingles are laid so that the lower end will just be covered by the hip shingle of the course above.

FIGS. 2,278 and 2,279.—Half pitch hip without ridge; method avoiding short grain. What is the first course at the eaves is the second course on the hip, producing a curve upward with a pergoda effect. It is readily seen in the drawing how this is done. 1, 2 and 3 show, by a dotted line how pleasing the effect would be if the butts were not cut, creating a saw tooth, rustic appearance. Or how one pattern would cut all the butts. In either case only a slight tapering of about 4 shingles to the course with a hatchet to fit the radius, is all that remains to be done to produce an uncommon and pleasing roof. If the shingle spacing be properly done it cannot leak.

This method is not so serviceable as that shown at *b*, fig. 2,281, as the short grain of the hip shingles at Z (fig. 2,280) will in time split off, and the

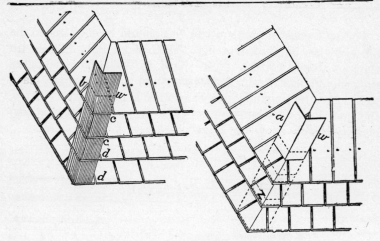

Figs. 2,280 and 2,281.—Method of laying tin shingles in hip shingling.

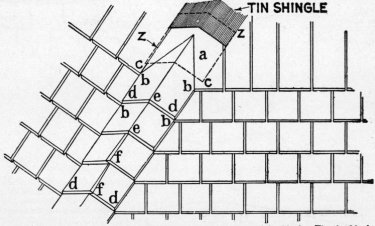

Fig. 2,282.—Square method of hip shingling showing treatment of tin shingle. The tin shingle Z, may be cut square at both ends and laid under the hip shingle out of sight, as at a, the hip shingle forming a row of raised shingles along the hip, the hip shingles being nailed at the butt end d, as the upper end of the "sight" at b, or that part of the shingle to the weather is not so thick as the lower end of the course it fits against as at c, which may leave a space between the back side of the hip shingle d, and the face side of b, unless the upper shingle is nailed down to a joint. The hip joint may be mitred as at e, or lapped as at f.

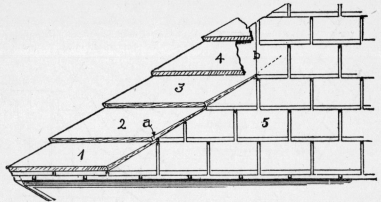

Fig. 2,283.—General appearance of "Boston hip" from side, showing that after shingle 1 of the woven hip, with the butts cut to line with the shingle courses to the apex is laid flush with the two under or first courses, shingle 2 may be laid enough lower as at *a*, for its top axis (edge) to line with that of the rest of the course. Sometimes when a roof is seen at angle much lower than the average, that is the house is somewhat elevated, it is an improvement to its looks to increase the distance down at *a*, or they may all be laid as 1 and 3 Shingle 3, is uncovered at the top to show how it is cut to join the succeeding course as at *b*. There is no objection to the difference in thickness.

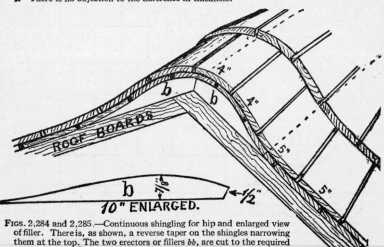

Figs. 2,284 and 2,285.—Continuous shingling for hip and enlarged view of filler. There is, as shown, a reverse taper on the shingles narrowing them at the top. The two erectors or fillers *bb*, are cut to the required shape. Unless the pitch be under 4 to 12 it will not leak if the distance to weather be not increased.

hip be destroyed, though the former makes the better looking hip when first laid. At *b*, fig. 2,281, the tin shingles are laid over the hip shingles flush with the lower edge of each course; this protects the short grain.

Valleys.—In shingling a valley, first a strip of tin, lead, zinc

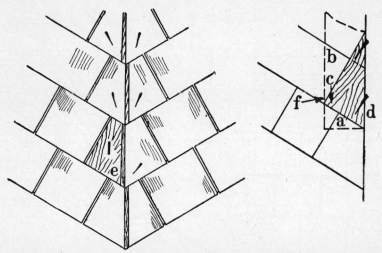

FIGS. 2,286 and 2,287.—Detail of hip without ridge showing two ways of cutting and method of nailing. In fig. 2,286, the point of the shingles as at *e*, curl up and often split off producing a ragged unsightly line against the sky, causing leaks. With proper precautions this can be largely avoided. First a good heart seasoned shingle must be used, those to be cut selected for grain that will favor its length at the acute angle *e*, they must be nailed right with small headed nails which must not be driven in until it draws and at the points indicated so that at the butt the contraction and expansion will not be hindered. The dotted lines, fig. 2,287, show the whole shingle and indicates how that the parts *a* and *b*, may be taken off and leave the short grain at *c*, in which case the butt nail may be nearer the center, and should a piece of the point at *c*, come off it will not be near as noticeable. Again *a* and *b*, may be left on and the whole shingle laid with the point *a*, dropping below the course making the short grain on the point of the next shingle at f. This shingle having but one cut, is left with the grain longer at *f*, than at *c*, where there are two cuts. Again the shingle may have the part *b*, taken off only and laid with the point *a*, left on. By this method there will be no short grain corner to split off. When a method has been decided upon, the shingles for hip can be selected and sawed several at a time in bunches.

or copper ordinarily 20 inches wide is laid in the valley. Fig. 2,288 illustrates an open type valley.

Here the dotted lines show the tin or other material used as flashing under the shingles. If the pitch be above 30° then a width of 16 inches is sufficient, if flatter, widen in proportion. In a long valley its width between shingles should increase in width from top to bottom about 1 inch, and at the top

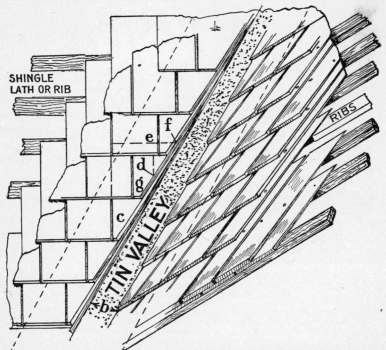

SHINGLE LATH OR RIB

RIBS

TIN VALLEY

Fig. 2,288.—General appearance of shingled valley showing tin flashing. *If tin be used* for the flashing it must be painted and dry on the under side before laid and should have a second coat on the top and dry before shingles are laid. A good method of applying the paint is to dip the shingles; this applies the paint quickly to both sides in one operation. Allow the paint to dry thoroughly and be careful not to scratch the paint in laying the tin and shingling.

2 inches is ample width. It is to prevent ice or objects wedging when slipping down. It is seen that the shingles taper to the butt, the reverse of the hip, and need no reinforcing, as the thin edge is held and protected from splitting off by the shingle above it. Care must always be taken to nail the shingle nearest the valley as far from it as practical by placing the nail higher up.

It is seen in fig. 2,294 that the shingles are nailed on a solid deck, and in fig. 2,269 on shingle lath or ribs which requires that ⅛-inch boards shall be laid in the valley wide enough for the tin to lay on solid its full width.

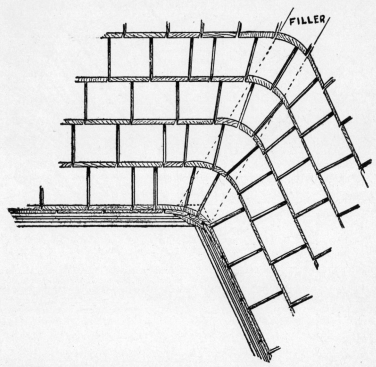

FILLER

FIG. 2,289.—Continuous shingling for valley with large valley filler and *without* flashing. The filler is made to fit the pitch of valley by ripping the two back edges of a board as shown, in this case the dimensions are to fit a valley where the pitch is 7 to 12 (30°). When placed in the valley it provides a surface that can be readily shingled over by using say 4 to 5″ shingles, tapering them toward the butt so that they will conform to the radius and meet at the top ends. When done thus, with joints properly broken it will make a perfectly tight job and when understood develops that it is easy and simple to do with the added cost much less in proportion to the improved looks, and permanency of the job.

Shingles should not be laid in a valley beyond the place where those of the course above will meet them.

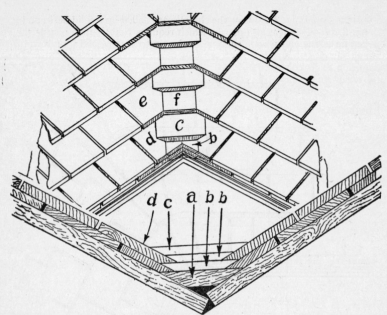

FIGS. 2,290 and 2,291.—Least expensive safe valley without flashing. First a filler *a*, is beveled into the valley. Starting the first course which is double, shingles *b*, are beveled into the valley, then a shingle enough wider *c*, has the under side corners taken off until it fits down on *d* and *b*. In the second course *e*, chamfers on *f*, etc.

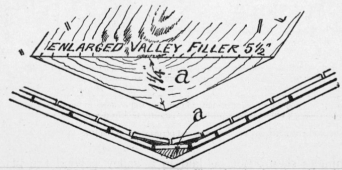

FIGS. 2,292 and 2,293.—Enlarged section of valley filler and section through continuously shingled valley showing filler in position.

For instance, course *c*, need not be continued beyond *d*, where it meets the course above. This leaves a triangular space, *def*, in which the shingles do not lie closely against the tin, but which allows the air to enter under the valley shingles of course *g*, thus assisting the shingles in drying out, and requiring less number of nails to be driven through the tin especially near the water zone.

Flashing.—By definition *flashing* is *the process of making a*

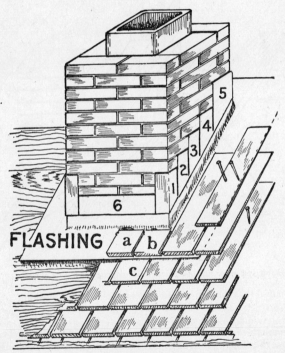

FLASHING

Fig. 2,294.—Flashing and counter flashing chimney located in one side of the roof.

joint water tight by fitting tin, lead, zinc or other material in such a way as to prevent the water penetrating the joint.

On every roof that has valleys, dormer windows, chimneys or other projections, joints occur which require flashing.

In the case of chimneys or other brick work strips of flashing material (tin, zinc, etc.) is inserted into a "raked out joint" about 1½ inches deep into the joints of the brick work on the pitch of the roof.

If built in they are not to be turned down until other pieces are laid flat

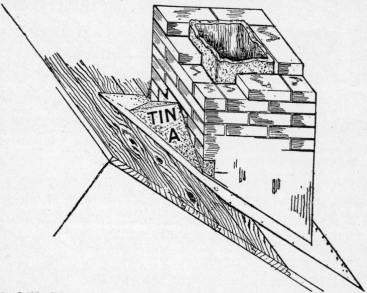

FIG. 2,295.—Bridge on upper side of chimney when coming out of side of roof.

on the roof so that those in the wall or chimney (counter flashing) overlap in every way as seen in figs. 2,294 and 2,295.

When the shingles, slates or other roof coverings are all on, these counter flashings are turned down and their seams or edges soldered tightly together all around the chimneys, so as to exclude all dampness and be air tight.

Fig. 2,295 shows how a bridge or ridge is built against the upper (back) side of the chimney to shed the water in both directions as at A. This is covered by durable metal, turned up against the chimney and counter flashed as shown and out on the roof far enough to be lapped by two courses of shingles.

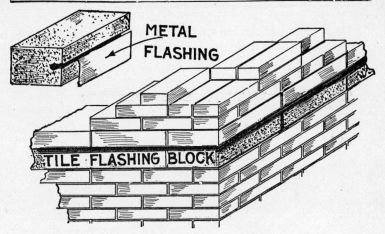

FIGS. 2,296 and 2,297.—"Raggle" or flashing block showing flashing inserted in groove, and view how laid in brick work. The groove is sealed with cement, or calked and sealed with any plastic material, as the case may require. It shows also how that a metal counter may be sealed in with it if desired. It may be used in chimneys as well as in wall breasts where it saves continuing flashing or roofing up to and under coping.

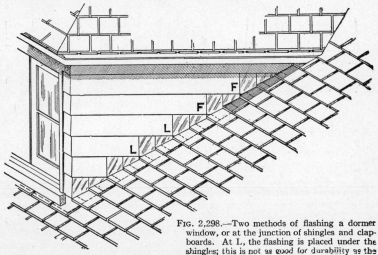

FIG. 2,298.—Two methods of flashing a dormer window, or at the junction of shingles and clap-boards. At L, the flashing is placed under the shingles; this is not as good for durability as the method shown at F, where the flashing is bent over the shingles.

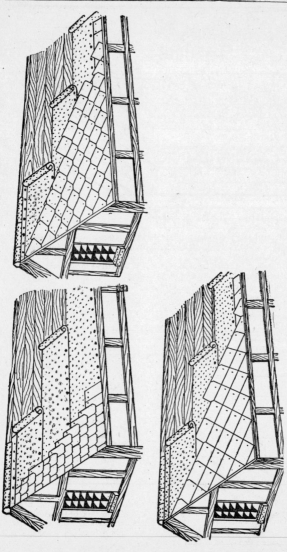

FIGS. 2,299 to 3,001.—Method of laying fibre shingles of various shapes.

Flashing is required not only on roofs but over all doors, windows and other projections exposed to weather, hence a thorough knowledge of flashing is essential. If tin be used, it should be noted that there is no economy in using poor tin.

If tin be used, use only the best made in charcoal iron sheets; it is much more lasting than steel.

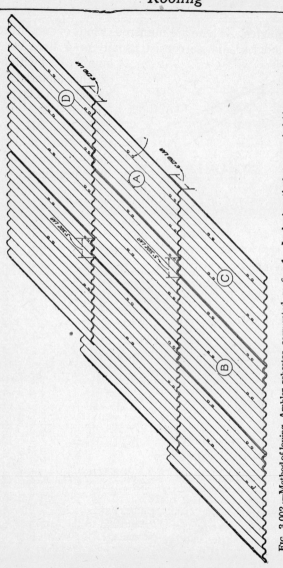

FIG. 3,002.—Method of laying Ambler asbestos corrugated roofing 1. *In laying,* the *first course* is laid, commencing at the right with a full width sheet 27½ ins. wide, and working to the left, lapping each new sheet (2 corrugations) over the sheet just laid. The *second course* laps 6 ins. over the first course. In starting the second course the first sheet **A** is fitted snugly against the *second sheet* of the *first course* (sheet **B**). Now work across the roof to the left as before, this will leave sheet **A**, projecting 5 ins. (2 corrugations) further beyond the end of the roof than sheet **C**. This 5 in. piece must be cut off. On the *third course,* the first sheet will project 10 ins. (4 corrugations). This of course must be cut off also (see sheet **D**.) On the *fourth course,* the first sheet will project 15 ins. (6 corrugations). This must be cut off, and so on.

Artificial Shingles.—There are numerous kinds of substitutes for wooden shingles. These consist usually of a fibre board impregnated with tar or other material and coated with a layer of ground slate. Figs. 2,299 to 3,001 show the method of laying these shingles cut to various shapes.

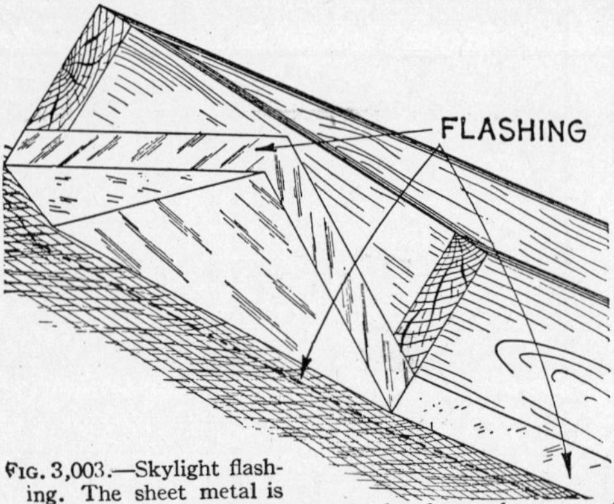

FLASHING

FIG. 3,003.—Skylight flashing. The sheet metal is fitted as shown, bedded in white lead and securely nailed. A cricket or saddle is provided at the upper end similarly as with chimneys located on one side of the roof.

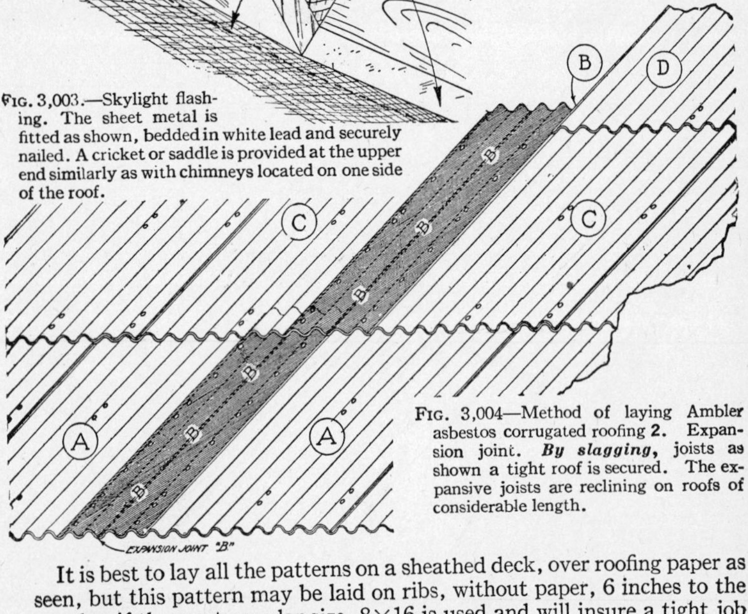

EXPANSION JOINT "B"

FIG. 3,004—Method of laying Ambler asbestos corrugated roofing 2. Expansion joint. *By slagging,* joists as shown a tight roof is secured. The expansive joists are reclining on roofs of considerable length.

It is best to lay all the patterns on a sheathed deck, over roofing paper as seen, but this pattern may be laid on ribs, without paper, 6 inches to the weather if the most popular size, 8×16 is used and will insure a tight job if the directions with and for laying them be followed.

For every two nails to a shingle fastening them to the roof there is one inverted copper nail that binds the extremity to the course beneath so that they must lay close

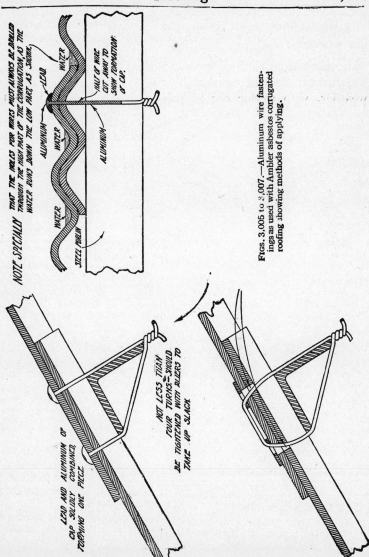

NOTE SPECIALLY THAT THE HOLES FOR WIRES MUST ALWAYS BE DRILLED THROUGH THE HIGH PART OF THE CORRUGATION AS THE WATER RUNS DOWN THE LOW PART AS SHOWN.

WATER

WATER LEAD

ALUMINUM

WATER

WATER

STEEL PURLIN

HALF OF WIRE CUT AWAY TO SHOW FORMATION OF CAP.

ALUMINUM

LEAD AND ALUMINUM OF CAP SOLIDLY COMBINED FORMING ONE PIECE.

NOT LESS THAN FOUR TURNS—SHOULD BE TIGHTENED WITH PLIERS TO TAKE UP SLACK

FIGS. 3,005 to 3,007.—Aluminum wire fastenings as used with Ambler asbestos corrugated roofing showing methods of applying.

There are also flexible asphalt shingles, mostly made in 8″×13″ size. They are covered on the face with crushed slate taken from slate quarries. Red, green, gray, black, &c. They must be laid on sheathing ¼″ apart and 4″ to the weather, with a zinc coated nail having a large flat head

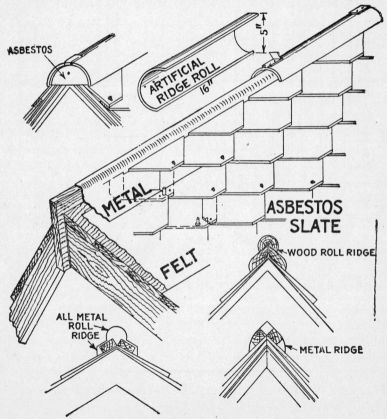

FIGS. 3,008 to 3,013.—Details of ridge roofing showing method of laying shingles with the various types of ridge roofing or "ridge roll."

They can be laid continuous over valleys and hips to a level line without break. No flashings are required. In fitting, they are readily cut by heavy shears or a tinsmith's snips. Their longevity is not determined. Those longest in use show no signs of depreciation.

This same material is made up in what is called strip

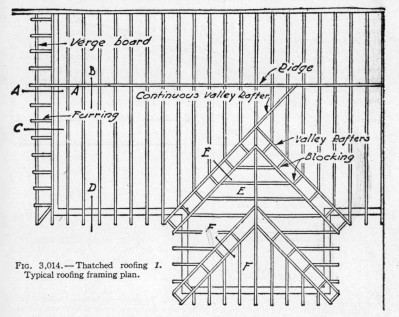

Fig. 3,014.— Thatched roofing 1. Typical roofing framing plan.

shingling, several shingles in one strip, so cut as to represent separate shingles after laid. It is also made in roll lengths for covering old shingle roofs, on this the shingle is marked off instead of cut by scraping off the top dressing and showing a black line.

NOTE.—The instructions on thatched roofing as shown in the accompanying cuts are given by the Creo-dipt Co., specialists on thatched roofs.

Slate Shingles.—Roofs of natural slate are usually laid by professional roofers who make that a specialty. However, sometimes circumstances or conditions may place this responsibility upon the contractor or carpenter and he should equip himself with few simple tools necessary and learn that slate is

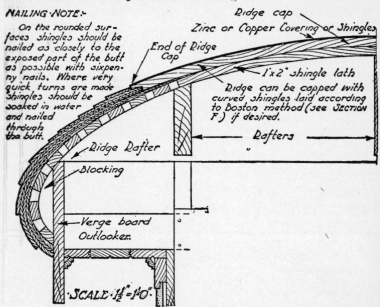

NAILING NOTE:-

On the rounded surfaces shingles should be nailed as closely to the exposed part of the butt as possible with sixpenny nails. Where very quick turns are made shingles should be soaked in water and nailed through the butt.

Ridge cap
Zinc or Copper Covering or Shingles

End of Ridge Cap

1"x2" shingle lath
Ridge can be capped with curved shingles laid according to Boston method (see SECTION F) if desired.

Rafters

Ridge Rafter

Blocking

Verge board
Outlooker.

SCALE 1½"=1'-0"

FIG. 3,015.—Thatched roofing 2. Section end of ridge. To obtain the best results for the roll of the gables, the furring should project well beyond the verge board at the apex and this projection should be gradually reduced toward the eaves. The drop from the ridge to the verge board should start three or four feet back from the face of the verge board and curve down gradually.

better laid on a sheathed rather than ribbed roof. That it is best not to recommend it on a roof of wooden houses where there

NOTE.—Slate is quarried principally in Vermont and Pennsylvania, black slate coming from the latter state almost exclusively, while sea green, purple, variegated and red can all be secured in Vermont. All sizes are cut in width just one-half their length. The size 11×22 can be used almost exclusively as it is not too large for a dwelling and can be laid almost as fast as 12×24 on a barn.

is a chance for vibration, for it readily cracks off the shingle if nailed tight or cemented.

Nails should not be driven hard down but left so that there is visible play, or space between the face of the slate and under side of nail head.

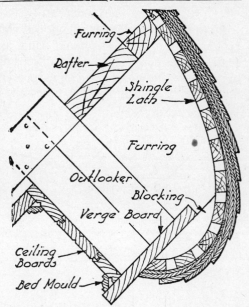

FIG. 3,016.—Thatched roofing 3. Typical ridge section.

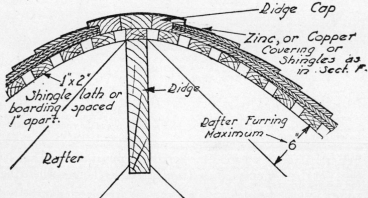

FIG. 3,017.—Thatched roofing 4. Typical rake section. The radius of the roll on the rake should never be less than 10". The blocking projects well beyond the verge at the ridge and decreases toward the eaves.

Valleys should be laid, open, but may be closed by using regular flashings and slaters' cement, the same as at the hips.

Up to 16 feet rafter lengths the roof framing for shingles is ample with the additional strength provided by the sheathing for slate.

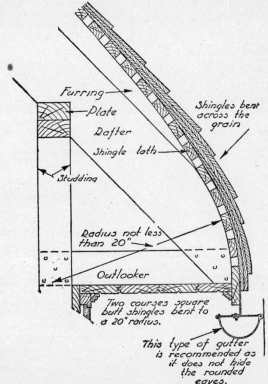

Furring

Plate

Rafter

Shingle lath

Studding

Shingles bent across the grain

Radius not less than 20″

Outlooker

Two courses square butt shingles bent to a 20″ radius.

This type of gutter is recommended as it does not hide the rounded eaves.

FIG. 3,018.—Thatched roofing 5. Typical eaves section. Shingle laths 1″ × 2″ are laid in usual manner except on gable ends, hips and valleys. On gable ends laths run parallel to rafters. On hips and valleys the laths run from eaves to ridge. *Furring.* All rafters are furred from 4″ to 6″ at the center diminishing to nothing at the eaves and ridge giving the roof a slightly convex surface.

Oftentimes insufficient nailing of roof boards allow them to warp, raise the joints of shingles and sometimes break them. A slate roof shows every imperfection after it is laid. It may be laid as flat as a quarter pitch and be tight. Snow sliding off a roof and falling to one below always breaks the slate and causes leaks.

Approaching the ridge, courses may be varied in distance (shorter) to weather to make them come out right. If the starting course be over a gutter it should have a cant strip about ⅜ inch thick placed under it.

FIG. 3,019.—Thatched roofing 6. Typical roof framing perspective. *As shown* each rafter is furred. This is to give a general rounded effect to the roof, but there are some very excellent examples of thatched roof houses where this furring has been omitted and just straight rafters, rounded at the ridges and eaves, used. This will eliminate a great deal of expense and still permit of a very beautiful thatched effect.

Single nailing and double nailing is an important point in slating.

There is no doubt that a double nailed slate is more securely fixed than one with a single nail, but the difficulty of repairing a double nailed slated roof has caused many to pause before adopting this method. On the other hand, a single nailed roof can be easily repaired at any damaged part by simply turning round the slates immediately above, taking out the broken

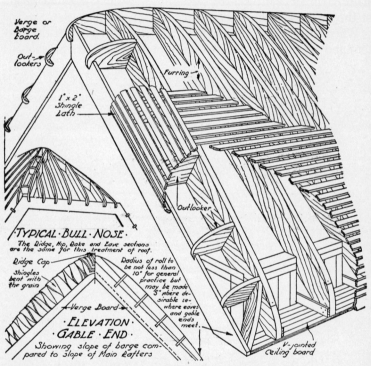

Verge or Barge Board.

Out-lookers

Furring

1" x 2" Shingle Lath

Outlooker

·TYPICAL·BULL·NOSE·
The Ridge, Hip, Rake and Eave sections are the same for this treatment of roof.

Ridge Cap

Shingles bent with the grain

Radius of roll to be not less than 10" for general practice but may be made 5" where desirable to where eaves and gable ends meet.

Verge Board

·ELEVATION· ·GABLE·END·
Showing slope of barge compared to slope of Main Rafters

V-jointed Ceiling board

FIG. 3,020.—Thatched roofing **6.** Typical roof framing perspective·
FIG. 3,021.—Thatched roofing **7.** Typical bull nose.
FIG. 3,022.—Thatched roofing **8.** Elevation of gable end.

part, replacing with a new slate and turning those disturbed into their original place.

Repair of Slate Roofs.—When slate roofs are damaged by falling chimneys or other accidents they can be repaired so as to be tight and durable. First the roof is cleared of all cracked or broken pieces. Nails of the top row may be cut with the slater's ripper, slate pulled out, thus exposing the nail heads of the next row, going on down the roof as far as necessary.

When the roof is clean, as in fig. 3,030, commence at the bottom and lay up in the ordinary way until good slate is reached,

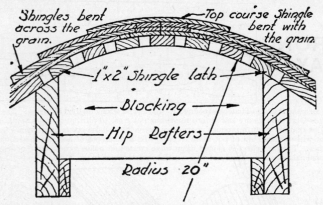

FIG. 3,023.—Thatched roofing 9. Typical hip section.

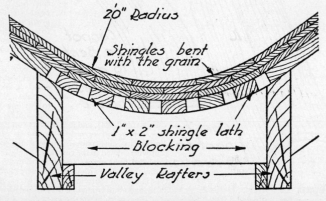

FIG. 3,024.—Thatched roofing 10. Typical valley section.

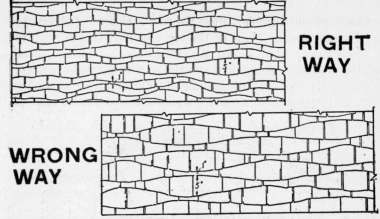

RIGHT WAY

WRONG WAY

FIGS. 3,025 and 3,026.—Thatched roofing *11*. Right and wrong method of laying. The butts of Creo-Dipt shingles are sawed into numerous patterns, so all that is necessary is to lay shingles that their butts produce continuous wavy lines whose crests and hollows vary in height with a maximum of not more than 5″ and a minimum of not less than 1″ to the weather. The best effect is gained when wave crests and hollows come more or less on a diagonal axis (see above) and not on a vertical axis as shown in fig. 3,026.

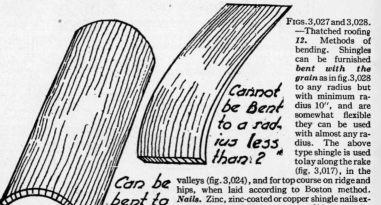

Cannot be Bent to a radius less than 2″

Can be bent to 10″ radius

FIGS. 3,027 and 3,028.—Thatched roofing *12*. Methods of bending. Shingles can be furnished *bent with the grain* as in fig. 3,028 to any radius but with minimum radius 10″, and are somewhat flexible they can be used with almost any radius. The above type shingle is used to lay along the rake (fig. 3,017), in the valleys (fig. 3,024), and for top course on ridge and hips, when laid according to Boston method. *Nails*. Zinc, zinc-coated or copper shingle nails except where noted to the contrary. Shingles can be furnished *bent across the grain* as in fig. 3,027, to any radius but with minimum radius 20″. This type is used on the rounding of the eaves, as in fig. 3,018, and on the rounding of ridge and hips except top course (figs. 3,016 and 3,023). Shingles 16″ long, random widths, extra clear are recommended for use on thatched roofs. They are furnished already stained with any color desired.

as will be noted in fig. 3,030. Nail the last row close up to the butts a course above, as shown by dots in fig. 3,031, and cover nail heads with putty, or, better yet, make a cement as follows. as it has been used for years with best results:

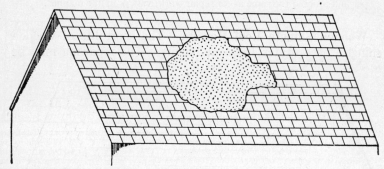

FIG. 3,029.—Hole in slate roof.

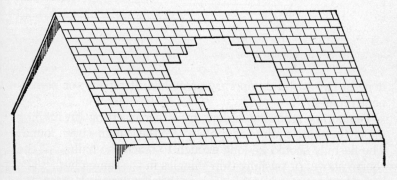

FIG. 3,030.—Broken slate removed for repairs.

Thin oxide of iron to a dry paste with coal tar. Thin this to the consistency of putty with boiled linseed oil.

Leaks have been stopped in the bottom seam of large water tanks with this combination used continually where needed.

When a leak occurs in the body of a roof and its precise location cannot be determined, strips of well painted roofing tin may be slipped under the slate reaching from the bottom to nails a course above. Apply these strips 5 to 6 inches wide under the seam for a considerable area, and they will probably stop the leak.

In renewing roof gutters remove the second or third row of slate with ripper and proceed the same as for repair work, valleys in like manner.

Wooden Shingle Roof Repairs.—The short life of wooden shingles necessitates frequent repairs. The repairing may be

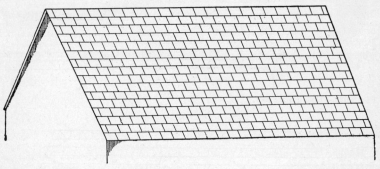

Fig. 3,031.—Nail through slate at top finish.

done in two ways: temporary or makeshift repairs, or permanent repairs.

Temporary repairing is done by either inserting tin flashing under the shingle joints or splits where the leak has been found. The flashing should be long enough to reach the nailing of the course above, or pushing thin shingles in the same place. The latter leaves a rough looking job as the shingles reach below the courses and look rough and bunchy.

The better and permanent way is to take out all the bad shingles and nails by use of an instrument specially made for that purpose, as shown in fig. 3,033.

It reaches up under the shingle and with a nail cutting edge hooks over the nail and is then drawn down and the nail cut off by a blow with the hammer on a lug at its extremity. By this means only the shingles to be replaced need be removed. And the last course will go to place under the old with nail obstruction. It is often possible to find old weathered shingles for this purpose, thus avoiding unsightly new patches.

Tin roofing.—Tin for roofing is extensively used. Under no

FIG. 3,032.—Shingle repair cutter. L, F, cutting edges. The length of the tool is **from 24** to 30 ins.

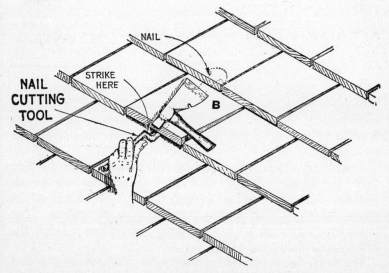

FIG. 3,033.—Method of using the nail cutting tool. The long thin blade is thrust under the shingle and the surface of shingle **B**, explored until the cutting edge engages with the nail The latter is cut by a few sharp blows as shown, allowing the old shingle **B** to be removed circumstances should tin on steel plate be used. Unless the plates be of genuine iron it is advisable to use some other form of roofing.

The following instructions on how to lay a tin roof are in accordance with the standard working specifications adopted by the National Association of Sheet Metal Contractors.

FIG. 3,034.—Flat **seam tin** roofing. Sheets of tin put together in long lengths, with edges turned ready to lay on the roof.

FIG. 3,035. — Flat seam tin roofing 1. Method of fastening the tin to the roof, cleat in position. The adjoining sheet is hooked over this and the seam hammered down and soldered, locking the cleat firmly into the seam. One end of the cleat is turned over the nail heads to prevent them scratching the under side of the tin.

Slope of Roof.—If the tin be laid flat seam or flat lock, the roof should have an incline of one-half inch or more to the foot. If laid standing seam, an incline of not less than two inches to the foot. Of course, good tin is constantly being used with entire success on roofs of less pitch than this, some of them almost flat, but a good pitch is desirable to prevent any accumulation of water and dirt in shallow puddles. Gutters, valleys, etc., should have sufficient incline to prevent water standing in them or backing up in any case far enough to reach standing seams.

Tongue and groove sheathing boards are recommended, of well-seasoned dry lumber, narrow widths preferred, free from holes, and of even thickness.

A new tin roof should never be laid over old tin, rotten shingles, or tar roofs.

Sheathing paper is not necessary where the boards are laid as specified above. If steam, fumes or gases be likely to reach the under side of the tin,

FIG. 3,036.—Flat seam tin roofing 2. Sheets in position before seam is hammered down and soldered. One cleat is shown (magnified), with faint lines indicating the various folds of tin in the seam.

use some good water proof sheathing paper such as black Neponset. Never use tar paper.

Seams should be made as shown in the accompanying illustrations. No nails should be driven through the sheets.

Flat Seam Tin Roofing.— When the sheets are laid singly, they should be fastened to the sheathing boards by cleats (see fig. 3,037), using three to each sheet, two on the long side and one on the short side. Two 1-inch barbed wire nails to each cleat.

If the tin be put on in rolls the sheets should be made up into long lengths in the shop, the cross seams locked together and well soaked with solder.

Fig. 3,037.—Tin roofing cleat. Used for fastening the sheets to the roof boards.

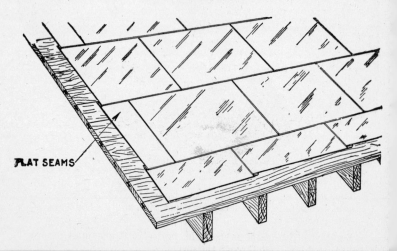

FLAT SEAMS

Fig. 3,038.—Flat seam tin roofing 3. Appearance of finished roof. Edges cut away to show the flat seams.

The sheets should be edged ½ inch, fastened to the roof with cleats spaced 8 inches apart, cleats locked into the seam and fastened to the roof with two 1-inch barbed wire nails to each cleat, as in figs. 3,034 to 3,038.

Standing Seam Tin Roofing.—The sheets should be put together in long lengths in the shop, the cross seams locked together and well soaked with solder. The sheets should be applied to the roof the narrow way, fas-

FIG. 3,039.—Standing seam tin roofing *1*. First operation: adjoining sheets turned up at right angles with cleat installed.

FIG. 3,040.—Standing seam tin roofing *2*. Second operation: projecting edge turned over.

tened with cleats spaced one foot apart. One edge of the course is turned up 1¼ inches at a right angle, and the cleats are installed, as in fig. 3,039.

The adjoining edge of the next course is turned up 1½ inches, and these edges locked together, as in fig. 3,040, turned over, as in fig. 3,041, and the seam flattened to a rounded edge, as in figs. 3,042 and 3,043. Valleys and gutters should be formed with flat seams, applying the sheets the narrow way.

In soldering use nothing but rosin as a flux. The solder should be well sweated into all seams and joints. The tin should be painted one coat on the

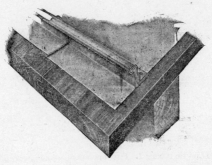

FIG. 3,041.—Standing seam tin roofing 3. Third operation: entire seam turned partly over.

FIGS. 3,042 and 3,043.—Standing seam tin roofing 4. Fourth operation: Standing seam completed, showing cleat in position. Thickness of seam magnified to show the folds of the metal.

under side before it is laid on the roof. After laying, the upper surface should be immediately cleaned of rosin and dirt and painted. Apply a second coat two weeks after the first coat; the third coat a year after.

Zinc Shingle Roofing.—These shingles, as claimed by the Illinois Zinc Co., the makers, can be safely laid on roofs having

FIG. 3,043.—Standing seam tin roofing 5. Appearance of finished roof with one seam unfinished to show application of cleats; thickness of sheets and joints exaggerated in the latter.

a pitch of five inches or more to the foot, or any roof where wood or slate shingles can be used. The following instructions in the text and accompanying illustrations are given by the manufacturer.

Sheathing.—The sheathing under shingles should be free from sap, rosin or other defects, which will tend to shorten the life of the roof. We recommend square edge sheathing boards, either rough or dressed.

If dressed and matched stock be used, care should be taken that they be not driven up tight, so as to prevent warping and buckling at the joint, either before or after the shingles are laid. Do not lay shingles over wet sheathing. If yellow pine sheathing be used, it should be covered with plain unsized or oiled building paper. *Do not use tarred or rosin sized paper of any description.*

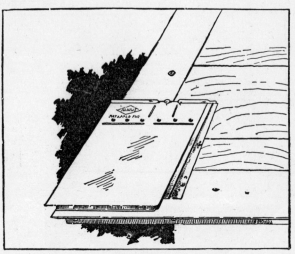

Fɪɢ. 3,044.—Laying zinc shingles *1.* Zinc shingles are laid from left to right. After roof is prepared with zinc starting strip on all eaves and gables and with zinc valleys in place, begin at the lower left hand corner to lay the first row of shingles. The first shingle is cut to extend over the starting strip of the gable about ¾″, with lower edge of shingle about ¾″ above edge of starting strip of eave. The shingle is then nailed with one zinc clad nail in hole punched in the lower right hand corner. If lower hole come over crack in sheathing, use hole above it.

Sheathing paper is always worth more than what it costs, and it is desirable on any roof.

Nails.—Use the nails furnished with the shingles as they have been found to be the most satisfactory for the purpose. There is but one nail to each shingle, which should be driven up tight through nail hole provided in shingle in lower right hand corner. If this hole come over a crack in sheathing, nail above it. The half shingle at right hand eave should have nail driven through the shingle at upper left hand corner but not through the under shingle.

Each shingle or one-half shingle should contain but one nail to hold in place, except those formed at hip joints; when these are cut on a diagonal and bent over the hip, an additional nail is necessary to hold in place.

Starting Strip.—Place starting strip on all eaves, gables, etc., butting ends together securely, nailing same to sheathing with zinc clad nails supplied with shingles, spacing nails about 8 inches apart.

BEND UP LUG BY PRESSING DOWN ON SHINGLE AND SHOVE INTO PLACE.

Fɪɢ. 3,045.—Laying zinc shingles **2.** The next shingle is laid by slipping the projecting lug on lower left hand corner of shingle under the lower right hand corner of first shingle and bringing in position, with butt of shingle on line with the butt of the first shingle. The left hand edge of second shingle should fit snugly in the gutter of the first shingle and lay flat on the roof sheathing.

If ordinary gutter hangers are to be used they should be nailed in place when eave piece is laid.

Valleys.—Place all formed valley sheets, if purchased with the shingles, where required, nailing sheets with zinc clad nails at the top, lapping sheets at least 6 inches. Sheets are formed narrow at the lower end to slide into upper end of lower section.

Do not solder sheets together.

Fig. 3,046.—Laying zinc shingles **3**. Second shingle is now nailed at the bottom as before. This holds the first shingle securely in place so that the left hand edge of first shingle, which projects over the starting strip, may be bent down over the starting strip of the gable to make a finished edge. If starting at a hip, bend first shingle over hip and nail. After second shingle is nailed in position proceed as before for rest of row.

UPPER SHINGLE **MUST NOT OVERLAP** THE RIB ON LOWER SHINGLE

THE NAIL MUST PENETRATE **ONE** SHINGLE ONLY

Fig. 3,047. — Laying zinc shingles **4**. The next course of shingles is laid the same as the first, using a cut half shingle to start with. This new course should be lapped over the lower course, so that the lower edge of the upper course covers the bottoms or indentations of the lower course just above the raised rib on each shingle Use the raised rib as a guide for laying. *This rib, however, should not be covered by the shingle above it.*

Care should be taken that valley sheets lay smoothly in place. Lower end of sheets should be extended over starting strip at eaves, to be bent under after shingles are laid. Valley is supplied in lengths of 48 inches formed.

Hips.—If hip frame has not been built up to permit a flashing of shingles against it, then snip edge of shingle to a flat position and lap over the hip joint and nail in place. Use same method on opposite side of hip, lapping edge of shingle over the joint. Then apply hip cap the same as explained under ridge, fig. 3,049.

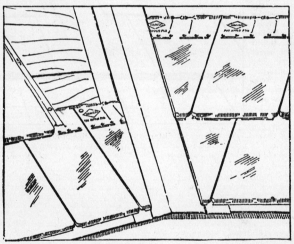

‹IG. 3,048.—Laying zinc shingles 5. Where roof is intersected by valleys, the shingles should be cut to line of valley sheets so that when they are in position the edge of shingle will project about ¾″ over rib of valley. After shingle is in position, the projecting edge should be bent under rib of valley sheet. Where necessary at valleys, the shingle may be nailed at the top to hold in position.

Flashing.—The shingle can be snipped and easily flashed to dormers, chimneys, etc., by bending shingle up and counterflashing, or by using special flashing strips.

Don't use solder. If these instructions be followed, solder is not required.

Don't expose nails or nail through ridge strip

Don't use any other metal in contact with zinc. Always use zinc against zinc to obtain best results.

Don't use any less care with this roof than with any other good roof.

Don't nail through two shingles at any place.

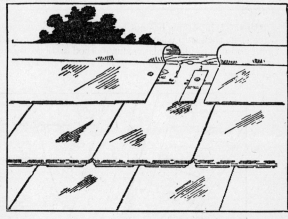

F‍IG. 3,049. — Laying zinc shingles **6.** *Ridge.* The formed ridge cap is furnished in 3 ft. lengths with an expansion joint or lap of 3 ins. The under lap not exposed to the weather should be nailed in place after the ridge cap has been slipped under the small zinc lugs. The lugs are furnished with the ridge cap and should be nailed over and through the shingle at ridge, with lower end projecting toward eave the proper distance from center line of ridge to hook into and to hold ridge cap in place. There should be three of these lugs on each side of the ridge to each section of ridge cap.

NOTE.—*Physical Properties of Zinc.* Sheet zinc has practically no magnetic qualities, being classed as a diamagnetic substance. The following is a summary of tests on zinc: Zinc, either rolled or cast, has no well-defined yield point and its elastic limit is very low. Zinc possesses a relatively high degree of plasticity. The ultimate strength of rolled zinc plate (thicker than .05 inch) is about 21,000 lbs. per square inch. The electrical conductivity of zinc is 25.6 to 29.9 according to determinations of several observers, and its thermal conductivity 28.1 compared in both cases with silver as 100. Zinc melts at a comparatively low temperature, its melting point being 419 degrees C.; it boils at 950 deg. C., the vapor burning in air with a characteristic brilliant bluish green flame. According to Ingalls, zinc burns in the air at a temperature as low as 500 deg. C. When it passes from cold solid to the molten condition zinc increases in volume 11.1 per cent. It contracts but slightly on cooling from the molten stage, and is thus well adapted for castings. The ductility of rolled zinc is much less than that of mild steel and the ductility of zinc plates with the grain is greater than the ductility across the grain. Zinc responds very little to hardening or annealing treatments. The coefficient of expansion of zinc is .000029 per degree Centigrade. The expansion and contraction of zinc by heating and cooling is about 2.6 times that of iron and about 1.3 times of tin. Due to its fibrous structure, sheet zinc does not tend to crystallize or crack from vibration. Zinc is not affected in dry air at ordinary temperatures. In damp air it becomes coated with a very thing layer of hydrated basic zinc carbonate (due to carbon dioxide in the air), which layer is sufficiently dense to protect the metal from any further atmospheric action; consequently, it is not necessary under normal conditions to protect zinc with paint or other protective coatings. It is possible to braze or weld sheet zinc under very limited conditions, as the welded portion is of a coarse crystalline structure and easily fractured along the weld. Sheet zinc is more readily folded across the grain than with the grain and up to .05 inch thick will fold flat either across or with the grain, without cracking. Sheets of greater thickness will fold across the grain.

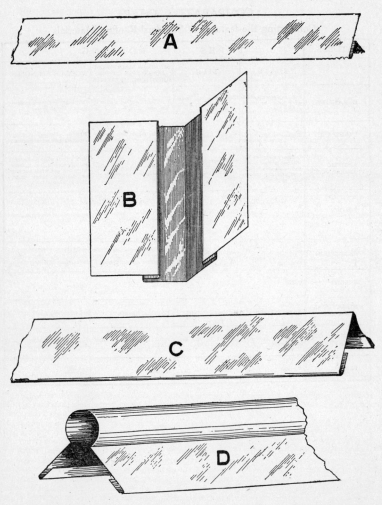

Figs. 3,050 to 3,053.—Fittings for Illinois zinc shingles. **A**, starting piece; **B**, zinc valley; **C**, ridge and hip piece; **D**, ridge roll.

COMPARATIVE CHART
Contrasting the features of Standard Roofing Materials

FEATURES	TYPES OF ROOFING			
	SLATE	TILE	SHINGLES MADE FROM ASPHALT OR OTHER SUBSTITUTE MATERIALS	WOODEN SHINGLES
DURABILITY	Apt to crack, chip, work loose, or break at any time.	Apt to crack, chip, work loose, or break at any time.	Curl, warp and work loose in few years' time.	Curl, warp and work loose; average life 10 years.
UPKEEP COST	Require repairs.	Require repairs.	Require repairs and replacements.	Require painting, staining, repairing and replacements.
ARTISTIC APPEARANCE	Ordinary slate lies flat without a butt. Artistic slate very high in cost and not universally applicable.	Good artistic effects, but only suitable for certain types of buildings.	Lie flat without a butt. Warping destroys effect.	Very artistic when weathered to right degree, but homely when new and when warping or patching takes place. Shabby when old.
COLORS	A hard dull gray except in expensive varieties.	Pleasing color effects.	Restricted in colors. Color not always pleasing.	Beautiful when properly weathered, or can be painted any desired color.
PROTECTION	Fire-safe. Not always weather-tight. No protection against lightning.	Fire-safe. Not always weather-tight. No protection against lightning.	Not always fire-safe. Not always weather-tight. No protection against lightning.	Combustible. Not always weather-tight. No protection against lightning.
WEIGHT	Varies.	Varies.	Varies.	Varies.
STRUCTURAL FEATURES	No special features.	No special features.	No special features.	No special features.
EASE AND COST IN LAYING	Difficult to lay, and hence expensive.	Difficult to lay, and hence expensive.	Fairly easy to lay. Inexpensive.	Must be fitted, marked, etc., and hence expensive.
PRICE	Variable.	Variable.	Variable.	Variable.

CHAPTER 48

Cornice Work

By definition, a cornice is *a group of mouldings surmounting a wall; the projecting mouldings which crown the entablature in architecture, surmounting the frieze.*

The cornice or eave finish is undertaken after the house is boarded in and the roof covered, it being essential that the roofing be put on as soon as possible, not only to protect the house, but to allow the men to work during stormy weather upon partitions, rough floors, etc.

In general there are two kinds of cornice.

1. Open
2. Closed

Figs. 3,054 and 3,055 shows the open type which is simply an overhanging roof with the rafters exposed.

In this section is shown a 3×5 rafter end which, of course by reason of its being exposed, must be dressed (planed) and is often made with the ends cut to some design, or they may be plain. Any smaller would look too light for the size of "over-shot" which in this case is 3 ft., taken on a level line from the house. It does not follow that the rafter shall be so large.

In many instances a 2×4 rafter is ample in this style if they be spaced 14 to 16 inches apart, so, not only for the economy in material, but for convenience of sawing, this rafter end is a separate piece made long enough to be securely spliced to the common rafter inside the plate line. These would have to be 4 feet long, and for hips and valleys six feet long.

It also shows a spring at the start of roof but that is not in the rafter. it is produced as at 1 in., fig. 3,054, and is seen to be very simple and easy to do and adds greatly to the appearance. The only added cost would be, if, as at *a*, an opening should be required opposite a window for the admission of sun light, or if at another part of the roof the over shot should be shorter, then the moulding under the spring would have to conform, either by being curved and sprung or worked to the shape; ordinarily there would not be any returns on the pitch, then the moulding would mitre at angles and

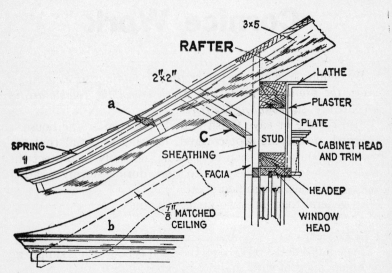

Figs. 3,054 and 3,055.—Open cornice, or section of overhang to a hip (umbrella) roof with a spring at eaves, showing fascia outshoot.

corners and continue on a level line as at *b*, in fig. 3,055. It will be seen in this section that the top of window is capped by the fascia and that from it to *a*, is the line for the admission of light, or indicates the ordinary over-shot of roofs.

C, shows how the fascia is continued by a cant board out between the rafters on a level held securely in place by nailings as indicated by strip back of it marked 2″×2″. These are securely nailed to the rafter and sheathing, materially strengthening the roof and greatly improving the appearance by closing (killing) the deep angle.

If the job be a small one, with less over-hang or if the workman be building his own house he can select the best end of his 2×4 rafters, dress them and hand saw to any of the shapes shown, and indicated by dotted lines in figs. 3,056 to 3,058, leave them plain or beveled. In any case the feathers or rough edges usually left after the compass saw should be cleaned off. Figs. 3,057 and 3,058 show the roof starting straight; in fig. 3,057, the ceiling extends

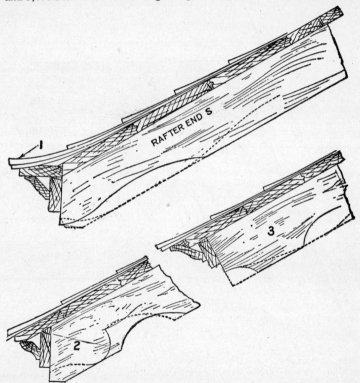

RAFTER END S

FIGS. 3,056 to 3,058.—Three types of open cornice.

out over the moulding, in fig. 3,058 the shingles rest on the moulding. To any of these cornices may be fastened the conventional half round galvanized iron gutters, but one of the things sought to accomplish by the wide over-hang is doing away with the unsightly gutter.

The box cornice may be constructed in a variety of forms, with, and without gutter. One form of box cornice of frail construction is shown in fig. 3,060. Here the outrigger or lookout is sawn out for gutter, and that its shape will accumulate a large load of snow and that it is unsightly, in that it hides so much of the roof in perspective and has no redeeming feature to commend its use; it is only shown to safeguard the novice against its use.

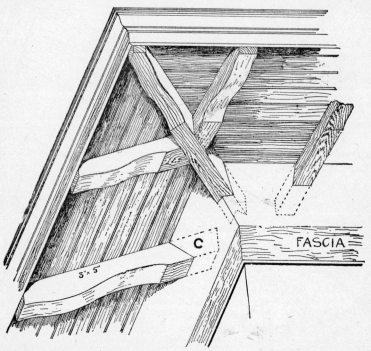

FASCIA

C

3" x 5"

FIG. 3,059.—View of open cornice looking under umbrella roof and showing how rafters come through fascia at C.

Fig. 3,061 shows a box cornice of better and more substantial construction. With this type it should be noted that unless the fascia is very narrow and the ceiling high it may compel a shorter window than is desired, and prevent its reaching well up toward the ceiling for ventilation, as is the general practice when no other means of ventilation is provided for.

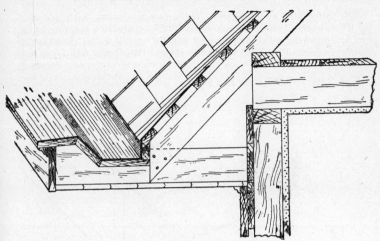

FIG. 3,060. —Box cornice of frail and objectionable construction.

FIG. 3,061.—Box cornice of better and more substantial construction than the design shown in fig. 3,060.

The half around metal gutter shown is to take the place of the built-on or "Philadelphia" gutter as an economy. Unless they are amply anchored and strapped the snow, if in a cold climate, sliding down the roof soon destroys them. Fig. 3,062 shows the gutter at the eaves where the same trouble will occur.

Figs. 3,063 to 3,065 show how a gutter is built on top the roof above the

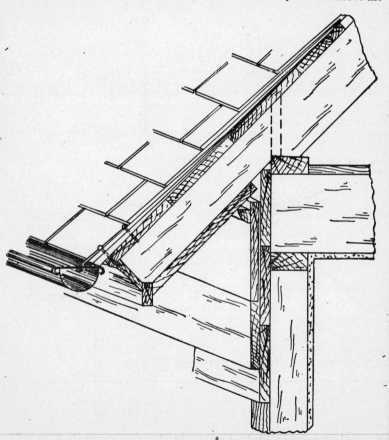

FIG. 3,062.—Cornice with exposed gutter subject to sliding snow which causes trouble.

shingles at a small cost. Board A, is set up at right angles to roof, of a depth sufficient to insure a fall from end to end, according to the distance water is to travel to reach leader, and the surface provided by pitch, and held in place by either a moulding or brackets. By placing it on top of shingles there is no need of flashing the outside. If the gutter be built to a true line with but one inch of fall in fifty feet, and there can be no settlement, it is just as good as though it has 2½ inches as shown in section.

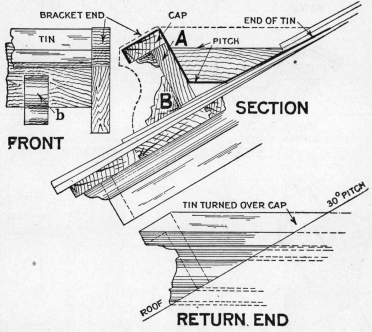

FIGS. 3,063 to 30,65.—"Philadelphia" or flush gutter on a pitch roof.

The heavy black line indicates the metal lining of gutter turned over face of cap and nailed, and its ending under shingles. The brackets B, should not be spaced more than 18 ins. apart. Dotted lines, fig. 3,065, show how return end would continue if roof pitch were also a hip. The plumb bracket end is cheaper than the return and is just as good but does not look as well. If possible all designing of pitch roofs should be so done as to admit of the

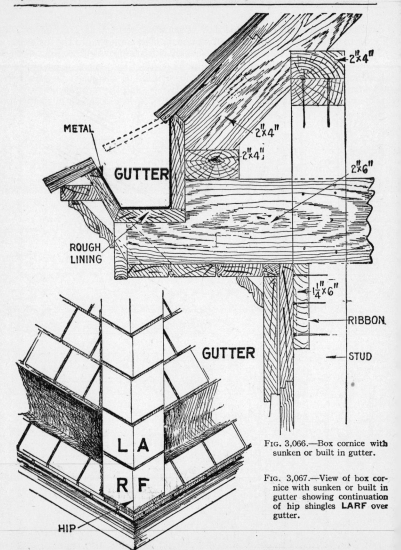

METAL

GUTTER

ROUGH LINING

2"x4"

2"x4"

2"x4"

2"x6"

$\frac{1}{4}$"x6"

RIBBON

STUD

GUTTER

L A
R F

HIP

Fig. 3,066.—Box cornice with sunken or built in gutter.

Fig. 3,067.—View of box cornice with sunken or built in gutter showing continuation of hip shingles **LARF** over gutter.

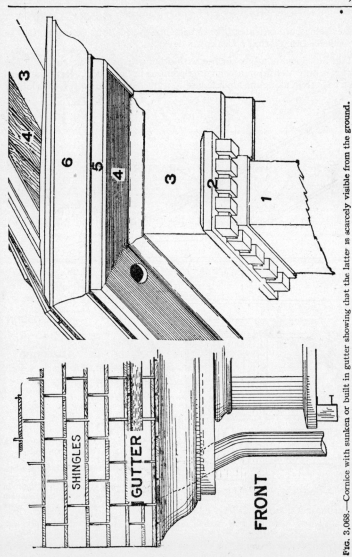

FIG. 3,068.—Cornice with sunken or built in gutter showing that the latter is scarcely visible from the ground.

FIG. 3,069.—Colonial cornice. 1, corner board; 2, dental cap; 3, fascia or architrave; 4, plancher or soffit; 5, cornice; 6, crown moulding.

gutter being built outside of the outside line of wall of house unless they be so well constructed that no leaks can develop.

Fig. 3,066 shows a box cornice with a built in or sunken gutter. The gutter is only seen from an elevated point as in fig. 3,067. Here the shingles, as LARF, along the hip line, are continued over the gutter thus killing

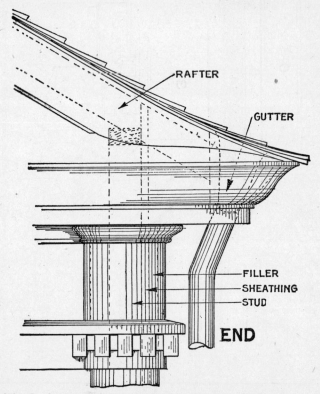

Fig. 3,070.—General appearance of Colonial cornice shown in fig. 3,069.

the crude break so often left, and at the same time giving the roo. the appearance of having a bell-cast or spring at its start as indicated by the dotted lines over gutter, fig. 3,066. In shingling around a built in gutter, no nails should be driven nearer than 7 inches of butt of starting course, or in valleys, otherwise leaks may occur. As viewed from the ground, in fig. 3,068, the built in gutter is scarcely visible. Fig. 3,069 shows a colonial cornice that can be applied to hip or gable roofs of any suitable pitch. In this instance it is fitted to a gable with the roof pitched on an angle of 15 degrees; has a plancher or soffit 4, ten inches wide, which may be increased or lessened as desired. This distance is outside of fascia or architrave 3, which finish line is 2⅞ inches outside of sheathing. The corner

Fig. 3,071.—General appearance of corner of open cornice from below.

board 1, forms a pilaster (here 8 inches wide) which may be any width to suit building proportions, has a dental cap 2, suggesting support to the whole entablature or superstructure; it may be paneled, fluted, ribbed or left plain, as shown.

A box cornice does not dry out so quickly as an open cornice and will accordingly need repairs more often. In the design of a box cornice the following points, essential for good construction, should be noted: The frieze should extend a little above the top side of the plancher or soffit, a space of ¼ in. being left between the frieze and the soffit. With this construction any water which enters into the cornice will drop behind the bed mould outside of the house.

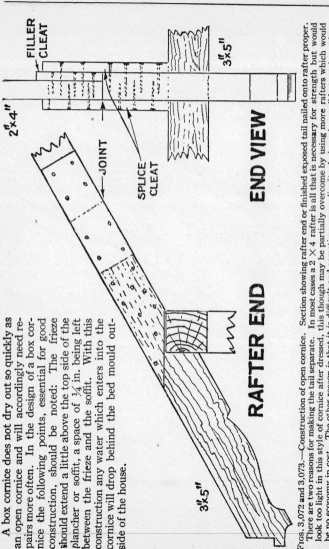

FILLER CLEAT

2″×4″

3″×5″

JOINT

SPLICE CLEAT

RAFTER END

END VIEW

3″×5″

FIGS. 3,072 and 3,073.—Construction of open cornice. Section showing rafter end or finished exposed tail nailed onto rafter proper. In most cases a 2 × 4 rafter is all that is necessary for strength but would look too light in this style of cornice after dressed, this though may be partially overcome by using more rafters which would be no economy in cost. The other reason is that it is difficult and sometimes according to design—impossible to swing a long stick far enough on the land saw table to reach the curves. When it is possible it involves more labor. Another cause may well be considered, it is that with separate ends, the pieces being short better selections of material may be made at the same cost. When possible it is well to consider placing most of the rafters so that the end may be spiked to its side, except, of course, hips. In roof framing it will be seen that their location cannot be changed.

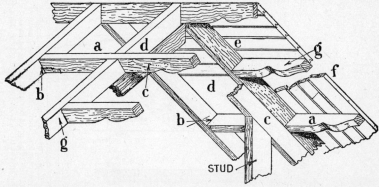

FIG. 3,074.—Construction of open cornice in gable. The sheathing is not depended upon to prevent sag, but the "out riggers" (rafter ends) are made long enough to frame against the second rafter as at *b*, and rest on a false gable rafter *c*, with the main rafter *d*, cut in between them. Notice that there is no hip rafter showing, nor is it necessary; that by this method the deck boards may be mitred at the corner and return up the gable at right angles to eaves. The cheap way is to lay these finish boards as at *e*, breaking joints on the first and second rafter and nailing the rafter ends into them squared against the outside rafter as at *g*, instead of through it. The only objection to this is the possibility of sagging, especially if the over-shot be wide.

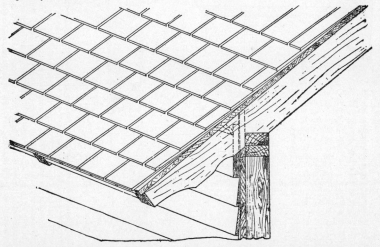

FIG. 3,075.—Open cornice. The tail of the rafter may be cut to any ornamental shape desired. Where the tail and rafter is in one piece the wood must be dressed to form a finish.

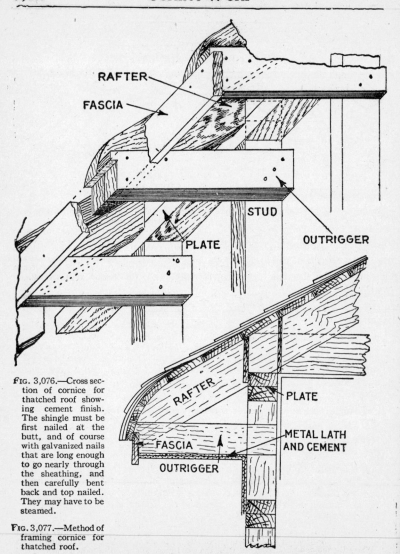

FIG. 3,076.—Cross section of cornice for thatched roof showing cement finish. The shingle must be first nailed at the butt, and of course with galvanized nails that are long enough to go nearly through the sheathing, and then carefully bent back and top nailed. They may have to be steamed.

FIG. 3,077.—Method of framing cornice for thatched roof.

CHAPTER 49

Mitre Work

In treating of this important branch of carpentry, it is advisable to mention some of its elements because it has its own peculiar characteristics.

By definition a mitre is *the joint formed by two pieces of moulding, each sawed at an angle so as to match when joined angularly;* also, to mitre, means *to meet and match together on a line bisecting the angle of junction, especially at a right angle*, in other words, *to cut and join together the ends of two pieces obliquely at an angle.* To do this with precision the proper tools are necessary.

The first is, of course, the saw, which should be a good twenty inch back of panel saw of about ten or eleven teeth to the inch, filed to a keen edge and rubbed off on sides with the face of an oil stone, to give a clean cutting edge and a smooth surface of joint (a wrinkle, by the way, which is not generally known).

To make the cuts at the proper angles a mitre box is used.

For precision a manufactured metal box should be used. However, a serviceable box can be made of wood by the carpenter such as shown in figs. 3,078 and 3,079.

For ordinary mouldings or strips, up to $3\frac{1}{2}$ inches in width, the length may be not less than 18 inches nor more than 30 inches; the bottom piece $1\frac{1}{2}$ to 2 inches thick by 4 inches wide, so as to insure the sides being firmly glued, screwed or nailed to its edges, and the sides 1 inch to $1\frac{1}{2}$ inches by 6 inches wide.

Either white pine or oak are the preferable woods to use, as most other woods are too liable to warp and split, through climatic changes, steam heat.

etc., so that the cuts will vary and become out of true. While the oak box is heavy, it has at least the virtue of wearing well, but pine is most popular.

There are two or more ways by which the box can be marked for accurate sawing. One consists in taking a drawing board or a clean piece of stuff with a straight edge as in fig. 3,080 and laying out on it a square figure, whose side is equal to 6 or 8 inches, and drawing two diagonal lines from

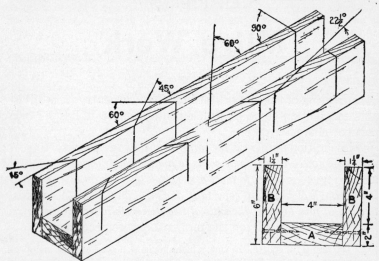

Figs. 3,078 and 3,079.—Home made mitre box. *In construction,* the bottom piece A (fig. 3,079) must be taken out of wind, with the fore plane or jointer, by using "winding sticks" or two short straight edges, one across each end of the surface, and keep planing until they show parallel or as one line, or by closing one eye and sighting across the surface until one makes sure it is perfectly flat, and not twisted or in-wind. The edges are next squared and the piece gauged to an exact parallel width. The sides, BB must be similarly worked, and for a very good box they should be surface gauged to a set thickness ⅞ inch to 1¼ inches as needed. The sides are now gauged with a line 4 inches down on the face (inside) and edge, and a small wire nail driven close to each end exactly on this line and the sides placed on the edges of the bottom piece and nailed or glued, and nailed fast and close thereto, keeping the fastening screws or nails about the middle of the edges. Should the above work be properly done, the inside of the box will be exactly 4 inches square and geometically parallel square and true, and on looking across the top edges and gradually lowering the farthest they will show as one line.

corner to corner, as shown; then by setting a bevel to one of the diagonals and screwing the blade fast in the stock. Now, by taking the tool, and laying it across the edges of the sides of the box and applying it from the outside, holding the blade firmly down with the left hand, the cut can be marked with a sharp penknife on the edges with the right hand. Next reverse the bevel for the other cut as in fig. 3,081 and mark it the same, which being done, square down from the top edges on the outside faces to the bottom, also with the knife, watching that the square does not move, and that all lines are perfectly straight.

Another method is to set on the edges the width of the box inside, viz., 4 inches, and lay it off on the inside arrises, square and with a steel square and knife mark the direction of the angle of 45 degrees. Again two equal numbers, as 10 and 10, 12 and 12, from the heel of a steel square can be used.

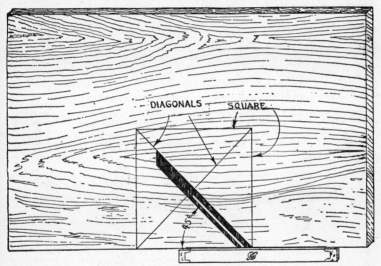

FIG. 3,080.—Method of setting the bevel to mark out mitre box. When the box has been properly marked, the next thing is to saw into the sides exactly to the knife marks and the saw should not be run down at the center of each mark, but to one side, so that the line may be distinctly seen to the right of the blade and reversing the box to make sure it follows all lines.

It will be seen by plan, or fig. 3,081, that any angle for mitre may be cut. It is well to always have the box long enough to be able, when cutting many short pieces of one length to tack a stop in the box for ending against, thus insuring exact duplicates.

Though several patent mitre boxes are now in use, the wooden box will always have its place where the most common mitres are to be cut, not because it is better, except that it may be more carelessly used and is not readily broken.

The steel mitre box is liable to rust out in the weather or on damp jobs, otherwise it is to be commended where the position or work will warrant the expense.

Some of the metal mitre boxes have attachments whereby frames may be held firmly in position while the mitre is nailed.

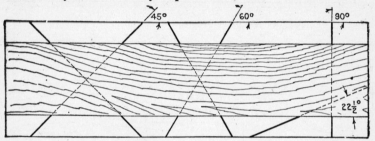

FIG. 3,081.—Top view of mitre box.

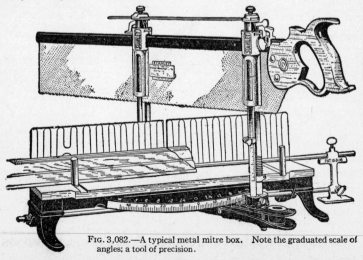

FIG. 3,082.—A typical metal mitre box. Note the graduated scale of angles; a tool of precision.

There are also hand and foot power mitre cutters by which both mitres are rapidly cut by one operation.

Mouldings.—In the ornamental side of carpentry construction various forms of fancy shaped strips called *mouldings* are used.

Some of these are designed to lay flush or flat against the surfaces to which they are attached, as in fig. 3,083; others are shaped to lie inclined at an angle to the nailing surfaces as in fig. 3,084. It is the latter kind that are the more puzzling in cutting mitres.

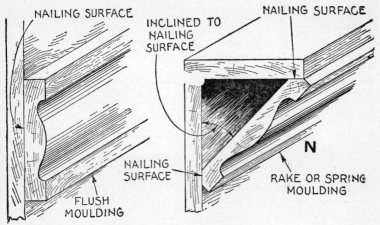

FIGS. 3,083 and 3,084.—Flush and spring or rake mouldings.

Mitring Flush Mouldings.—Where the two pieces of moulding join at right angles, as for instance sides of a picture frame the mitre angle is 45°. The term "mitre angle" means *the angle formed by the mitre cut and edge of the moulding*, as in fig. 3,085.

In paneling for stair work mouldings are joined at various angles as in fig. 3,086, this is known as *varying mitres*, and a problem arises to find the mitre angles. This is easily done by remembering that *the mitre angle is always half of the joint angle* hence to find the mitre cut, that is the angle at which

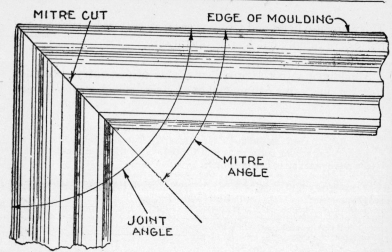

FIG. 3,085.—Two pieces of flush moulding joined at 90° illustrating the terms mitre angle, and joint angle.

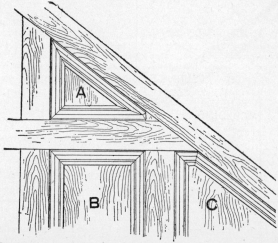

FIG. 3,086.—Panel work on side of stairs illustrating varying mitres. In panel A, each mitre angle is different. Both mitres in panel B are 45° to the edge of the moulding. Panel C. has two mitres at different angles.

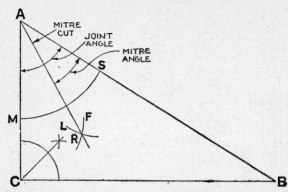

FIG. 3,087.—Method of finding mitre angle for varying mitres. The triangle ABC, corresponds to the triangular panel of fig. 3,086. To find the mitre cut at A, describe the arc MS, of any radius, with A as centre. With M and S as centres and equi-radii, describe arcs L and F, intersecting at R. Draw AR which is the mitre cut required. By similar construction (as indicated) the mitre cut for B and C are obtained.

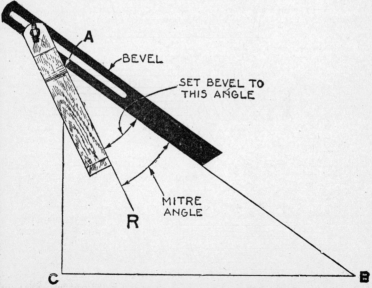

FIG. 3,088.—Bevel set to mitre angle preliminary to marking mitre box.

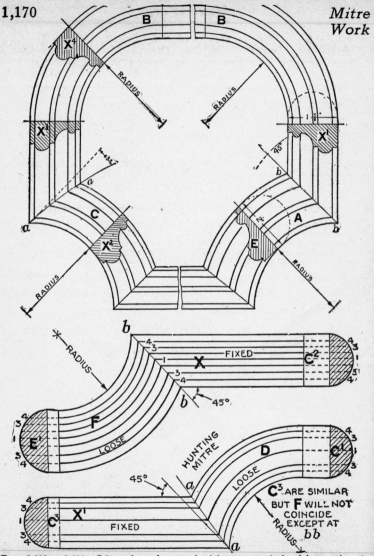

FIGS. 3,089 to 3,091.—Scheme for a door panel, giving two methods of intersecting the angles and illustrating a "*hunting mitre.*"

the mitre cut is to be made, *bisect the joint angle*.   This is done as explained in fig. 3,087.

"Hunting" Mitre.

"**Hunting**" **Mitre.**—A scheme for a door panel is shown in figs. 3,089 to 3,091, giving two methods of intersecting the angles.

The cross sections of the moulding X4 are similar, but the shape of the opening varies according to the arc used, whether internal or external.

The circular mouldings B, B, C, are alike and of the same section as the straight parts, but A, is widened to conform to the conditions laid down in the scheme that all the intersections should be true mitres (45 degrees).

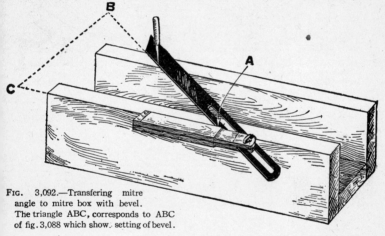

Fig.   3,092.—Transfering   mitre
angle to mitre box with bevel.
The triangle ABC, corresponds to ABC
of fig. 3,088 which shows setting of bevel.

B, B, joins the straight parts with a butt joint. C, is the same section and would intersect in the same manner as B, if it were in that position.

It will be seen that it does not intersect on a true mitre, but the joint is not a straight line and is impossible to make in a box, so it is often called a hunting "mitre," and must be chiseled to its true shape, as the two ends are curved. This will seem clearer by examining figs. 3,090 and 3,091, and if a model be made from it, a curious result will develop.

X, X, are straight lengths of mouldings (any section—in this case half round for simplicity). D, is a quadrant of a circle, same section as X, X, joined so that the marginal lines intersect.

The form of the curved mitre *dd*, is found by a series of straight and curved auxiliary planes drawn parallel to the axes of D, and X'.

F, is a similar arc to D, internally, which intersects X, at *bb*, at an angle of 45 degrees, with the result that the point where the angular line cuts the horizontal is the position where the arc must join the straight line; therefore F, is widened and its exact section shown at E.

This explains why many mechanics cannot get turned and straight mouldings to intersect when both are of similar cross section.

When making a model alternate the positions of D, and F, with X, and X'.

Mitring Spring Mouldings.—A spring moulding is *one that*

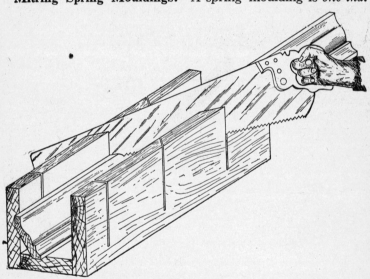

Fig. 3,093.—Mitre box with spring moulding in position for making mitre cut.

is made of thin stuff, and is leaned or inclined away from the nailing surface as before explained in fig. 3,084.

These mouldings are difficult to mitre, especially when the joint is made with a gable or raking moulding that springs also.

The best method is to place the length in the box against the farthest side upside down so that the side, that side which is to be nailed plumb against the fascia will be up and also plumb or perpendicular as in fig. 3,093.

The two usual forms of mitres made on spring mouldings are those on the inside and outside angles as A, and B, in fig. 3,093, where the pieces are represented as they will appear from the top sill looking down.

When one has to be cut on an outside mitre, say for the corner of a building, closet, etc., it is measured and started from the first, left hand as B, fig. 3,078, and the direction of the cut will be outside the right angle made on the building, but if it be an inside mitre, the joint will be contained within

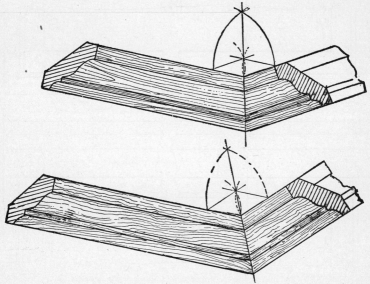

FIGS. 3,094 and 3,095.—Method of finding the intersection of spring mouldings.

the angle of the building and will bisect it. However, inside angles as A, are usually coped.

Fig. 3,079 explains the manner of mitring a crown mold running on the bevel with one set on a pitch on the same surface, which can be done by taking any two points and striking arcs cutting each other, and the point of intersection being joined the upturned apex of the angle will give the direction of the mitre joint.

As it may perchance happen that there is one or two gables or pediments on a building, or two of different pitches, it would scarcely be necessary to make a box for four or eight cuts; a very simple method which will be found to work out well is to lay out the direction of the kerf on the plumb side, which nails against the wall or fascia, and then square across the bottom edge.

Any carpenter with a steady hand and well filed saw can make this joint from the back of the moulding clean and straight.

Another way which some prefer is to lay down on a board the running directions of the moulding, and set up each piece on the laid out lines, then

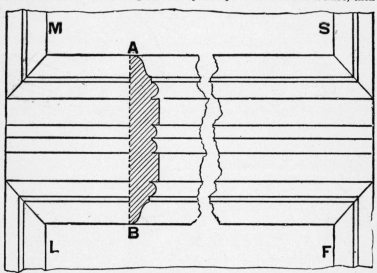

Fig. 3,096.—Chair rail mitred into the wall mould of a door or window trim.

to place the moulding to these and square up with a try square from the intersection of the mitre as set down. This method saves more time than by making a box.

Regarding the mitering of spring mouldings on a curve much the same conditions prevail as with those stuck flat.

Fig. 3,096 shows the elevation and section of a length of chair rail mitered into the wall mould of a door or window trim. AB, is the section, and it will be noticed that the two lower and upper members MS and LF, though run solid on and are part of the chair rail are of the same profile and mitre with their fellows on the wall moulding or back moulding D.

Mitring Spring and Rake Mouldings.—A difficult operation for most carpenters is the cutting of a spring moulding when the horizontal portion has to mitre with a gable or raking moulding.

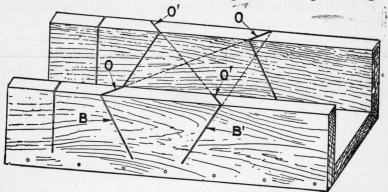

FIG. 3,097.—Mitre box lay out for cutting a spring moulding when the horizontal portion has to mitre with a gable or raking moulding.

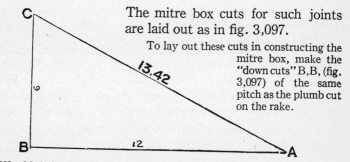

The mitre box cuts for such joints are laid out as in fig. 3,097.

To lay out these cuts in constructing the mitre box, make the "down cuts" B,B, (fig. 3,097) of the same pitch as the plumb cut on the rake.

FIG. 3,098.—Method of finding angle for over cuts 0, 0, 0′,0′, of fig. 3,097.

The "over cuts" O,O, O′O′, should be obtained as follows: Suppose the roof to have say a quarter pitch, find the rafter inclination as in fig. 3,098 by laying off AB = 12 ins. run and BC, = 6 ins. rise, giving roof angle CAB, for ¼ pitch and rafter length AC = 13.42 ins. per foot run.

With the setting 13.42 and 12, lay the steel square on top of mitre box **as** shown in fig. 3,099.

The side marked 13.42 is the side to mark four, using this bevel for both cuts.

Mitring Polygonal Figures.—Preliminary to mitring of any kind, all mouldings ought to be carefully examined to make sure they come from the machines the full thickness; that if rabbetted, the rabbet is square and fully fit for the job intended, although it is best to plane off the back a little on the bevel, so that it will fit easily into place, and tighten as tapped down.

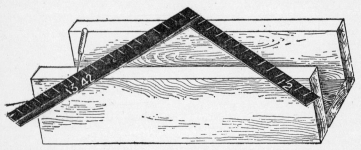

FIG. 3,099.—Steel square applied to mitre box with 13.42, 12 setting to mark over cuts.

When the moulding is too thick for the sinkage, it must be planed off until the distance from the lip to the bottom is slightly less than from the face of the frame to the fillet or panel.

In mill work moulding cutters vary in their sectional outlines and thicknesses—especially from separate lots, so that when the mechanic cuts one joint from 2 pieces, or separate run lengths, he often finds that one sticks above its fellow and requires trimming off to make the joint exact and the profile of the members even and continuous, thus the importance of discovering this before forcing and fastening into place.

Figs. 3,100 to 3,107 show various polygonal figures and the following table will give the cuts for all.

Properties of Polygons

NAME	NUMBER OF SIDES	SETTING		EXTERNAL ANGLE	INTERNAL ANGLE	MITRE ANGLE	AREA FOR UNITY SIDE
TRIANGLE	3	7	4	120	60	30	.433
SQUARE	4	12	12	90	90	45	1.
PENTAGON	5	13¾	10	72	108	54	1.72
HEXAGON	6	4	7	60	120	60	2.6
HEPTAGON	7	12½	6	51.43	128.57	64.29	3.63
OCTAGON	8	18	7½	45	135	67.5	4.82
NONAGON	9	22½	9	40	140	70	6.18
DECAGON	10	9½	3	36	144	72	7.69
UNDECAGON	11	10¾	3	32.7	147.3	73.65	9.37
DUODECAGON	12	11¼	3	30	150	75	11.2

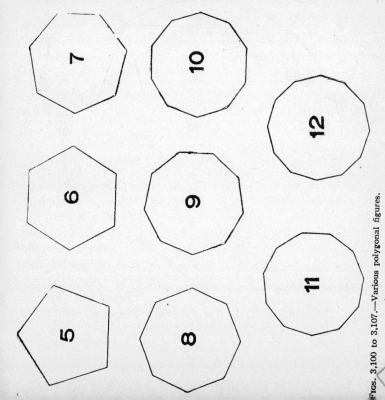

FIGS. 3,100 to 3,107.—Various polygonal figures.

The hexagon, fig. 3,109, is *circumscribed* about a 14 foot circle, making the distance from extremity to extremity of mitres, cutting at B 16 feet 4 inches. No matter what the diameter may be the cut is the same. The radii, dotted lines at once show how the 6 points are established and when the timber is 12 inches wide, the length of each piece is shown to be 7 feet inside and 8 feet 2 inches outside.

Further considering mitres other than those of 45°, the mitre

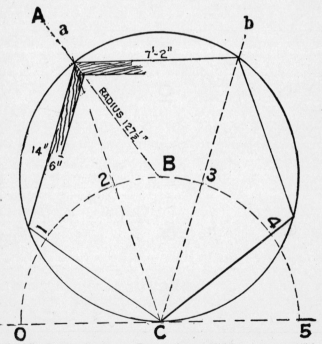

Fig. 3,108.—Mitre lay out of pentagon. The fine pieces cut 7′ 2″ on the outside will frame a pentagon with its greatest diameter from any of the 5 points cutting at B, 10′ 10″. It is seen that it is laid out with the compass. The dotted lines show that the diameter of the circle is used in describing a half circle. A straight line is struck as 0-5, from this a right angle is drawn establishing the center at B. The half circle is divided into 5 equal parts, 1 and 4 making two of the sides, and c, a, and c, b, establish the other two points from which the other 3 sides are laid. In both illustrations AB is the radius that cuts the joint.

box as with 45° mitres is necessary, and the method of kerfing for the cuts being the same, with the exception that the direction of the cuts across the top edges of the box is different, that, for example, for the octagon cut being 22½ degrees instead of 45 degrees.

Mitring Panel and Raised Mouldings.—The following instructions illustrate how raised and rabbetted mouldings may be cut and inserted in panels.

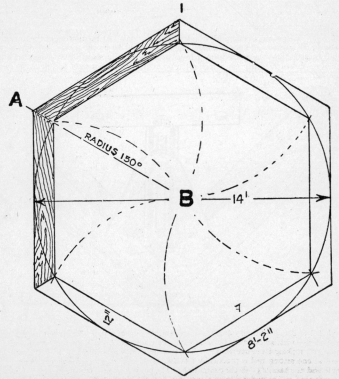

Fig. 3,109.—Mitre lay out of hexagon *circumscribed* about a 14 ft. circle.

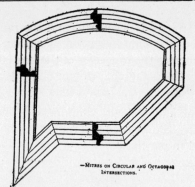

—Mitres on Circular and Octagonal
Intersections.

Fig. 3,110.—Mitres on circular and octagonal intersections. At the bottom of the illustration
is shown the section and lines of a moulding mitred together on the inside and outside cuts
of an octagon; also the mitre formed by a straight piece intersecting with another on the
octagonal cut of 22½ degrees, which often occurs in practical joinery and demands care in
making.

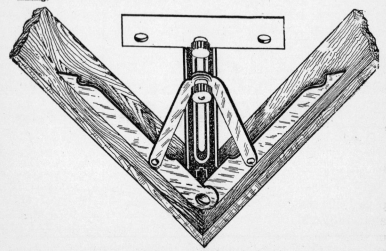

Figs. 3,111 to 3,113.—Stanley angle dividers, and method of using. To lay out the cut bisecting an angle with an ordinary bevel necessitates the use of dividers and a second hanging of
the bevel, making three operations. The tool here shown is designed for performing this
work at one setting and is practically a double bevel. The two blades each fit one side of an
angle and the handle gives the center line. The cut is marked from the center. The handle
is graduated on the under side for laying out, 4, 6 or 8-sided work, and, by means of a removable "T" head. it can also be used as a "T" square.

Fig. 3,114 shows a panel and moulding designed for a room or wardrobe door AB, being the section, denoting the two stiles or rails A, and B; C, the raised panel; D, and E, the pine fillets inserted in the plowing; and F, the panel moulding which has to be mitred round the inside edges of the framing and cover the joint at the arrises as G, by the rabbet or lips on the moulding F.

Should the framing be so carefully done, and the surfaces

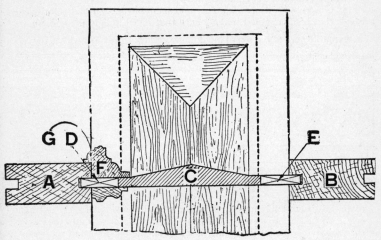

Fig. 3,114.—Panel and moulding.

planed off, that the sinkage down to panel will be equal all around, then all that is necessary is to make a hard wood strip or saddle equal in width, to the depth of the sinkage down from the arris, which is here approximately one-half inch, sucn strip to be one-quarter or three-eighths of an inch thick and to set it on the bottom and corner of the mitre box, so that the lips of the moulding may rest upon it as at F, in fig. 3,114.

Fig. 3,115 being a plan of the box, illustrates this more clearly also, how the marks for determining the exact length of each piece are scratched with a penknife on the bottom by squaring out from the mitre points where the saw intersects and cuts them.

Should there be any difference in the sinkage between each angle or corner, then a separate saddle or strip the width in the box of which is equal to the neat depth in the panel must be used when cutting the right and left mitres for each individual corner.

When this is being done the best method is to first mitre all four or more pieces, to place them gently around in the panel opening just catching, making the profiles intersect equally, each to each, then commencing at the left to tap down easily, using a hammer and small block, so as not to bruise or break the mouldings and making sure that all fit snugly in their places.

To mark this description of moulding correctly the proper way is to place

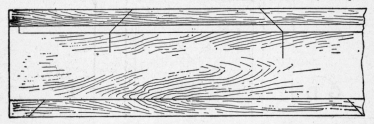

FIG. 3,115.—Plan of box with saddle.

each piece, sawed about one inch longer on its intended place, the left hand end being first cut to its miter joint keeping this end closely into the corner, then marking with a sharp knife or chisel on the back bottom arris as X in fig. 3,116.

This mark is set to the square line at fig. 3,115, and when sawed, will be found to be the exact length required.

The front door seen in figs. 3,117 and 3,118, has both flush and raised panels, namely, a raised one inch moulding on the outside or street side and an ordinary O-gee and chamfer on the inside. The enlarged section is as shown in fig. 3,116.

This door is a good example of mitred mouldings done as described in the foregoing with the addition of having a central bottom panel with L panels grouped around to form an attractive design of door and which develops and provokes outside mitres, all cut.

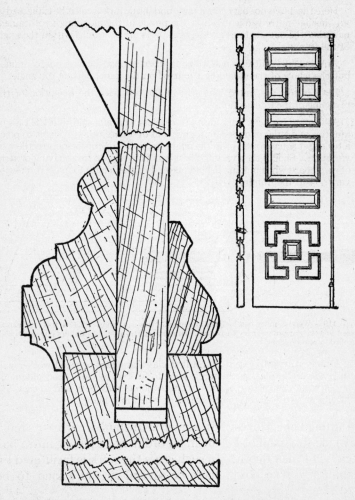

FIG. 3,116.—Enlarged section of the door shown in figs. 3,117 and 3,118.

FIGS. 3,117 and 3,118.—End and side view of door with raised mouldings.

Here the difference between outside and inside mitres must be explained— an "inside" mitre is one in which the profile of the moulding is contained, or rather the outside lines and highest parts are contained within the angle of the framing.

An "outside" mitre is one which is directly opposite and not contained but the whole of the moulding is mitred on the panel outside the angle.

Both mitres are sawed similarly in the box with the exception of the reversing of the intersections.

As it often happens from faulty or careless workmanship that the rails or muntins and stiles of doors are slightly out of square, it is advisable to place a try or set square over, or in the angles to make sure of their correctness or variation. Should they vary the best way is to place a thin shaving or strip of card board when mitring behind one end of the length to make it likewise vary to suit the framing.

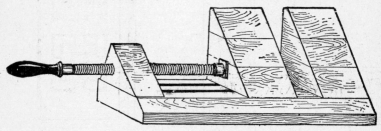

Fig. 3,119.—Wooden mitre box for planing mitres. This is a cabinet makers' tool, but can be used to advantage in ordinary carpentry. *In construction* one block slides in grooves controlled by a wood screw.

Finally it might be said that a first class carpenter or wood worker will rarely resort to planing the mitre joint to fit, but by care, good judgment and accuracy in the use of the box, mitre joints may be sawed so they will fit almost to invisibility when nailed or glued into place.

Cutting Long Mitres.—In numerous instances mitre cuts must be made that cannot be cut in an ordinary or patent mitre box because of their depth. In such cases the work is facilitated by making a special box if there be several cuts of a kind to be made.

Figs. 3.120 and 3.121, a box 13 inches high and having a flare of 3¼ inches, its construction requiring mitres which cannot be cut in an ordinary mitre box. The bevel is shown at *b*, set to the correct angle to cut the flare, and the dotted lines show how readily it is found without the use of a protractor.

If to be a butt joint, here shown at *c*, as rabbetted into its next piece, then this bevel and a square is all that is required to lay it out, but if a neat cabinet finish is to be obtained by the use of a mitred corner, then, as shown at *a*, on plan and *d*, fig. 3,123, a bevel must be set at 45 degrees to complete

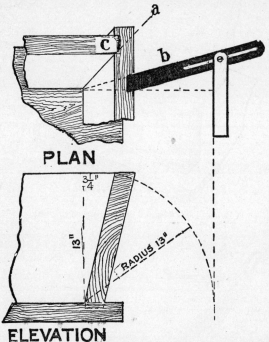

PLAN

ELEVATION

Figs. 3,120 and 3,121.—Box illustrating how to cut mitres that are not right angles.

the layout. If only a few joints are to be made, such as possibly making one box, the two bevels would be used to lay out the cut and make it without the use of a mitre box.

Coping.—The word *coping* is used in contradistinction to mitring.

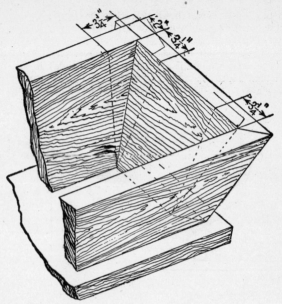

Fig. 3,122.—View of the two joints described in the accompanying text.

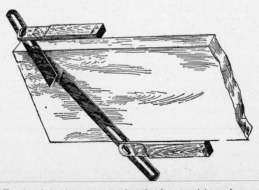

Fig. 3,123.—Two bevels in place to cut a mitre that is not a right angle.

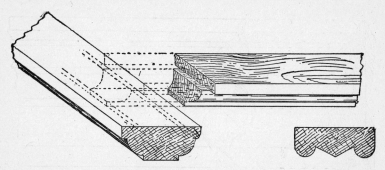

FIGS. 3,124 and 3,125.—Horizontal cope consisting of a ceiling strip or piece of astragal coped to a quarter round or oval. Fig. 3,125 is the coped end, done by placing the moulding with its back against wall of mitre box and each on the side square across the piece, after cutting and chiseling the end out to the profiles made by the saw in the mitring until it appears as in fig. 3,124, so it will fit closely against the section as in fig. 3,125. This cope ought to be slightly hollow so as to press against the surface of the moulding.

FIG. 3,126.—Form of moulding that cannot be coped, as some of its members sink below the others, which will be seen at a glance and the moulding mitred, and it is in sections of this form where the art cannot be profitably applied.

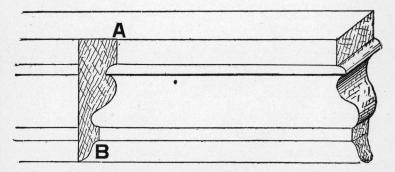

FIG. 3,127.—Coping an architrave moulding whose profile is a series of compound curves and flats, the mitre box is again brought into requisition and the end wrought to the mitred face line, always beveling slightly under to bring the coped joint close on the line of AB. A sharp pen knife is essential and a great aid in coping mouldings to cut away the wood on the curves exactly to the mitred line, which can scarcely be done correctly with the compass saw, gouge or chisel, as in soft wood the arises are very liable to break under the pressure of the hand even though the edge be keen, whereas the small blade of a good pocket knife, if reasonably sharp, can be very handily drawn around the quick curves and will also cut obliquely against the grain without injuring the edge of the end wood, which is often cross and brittle.

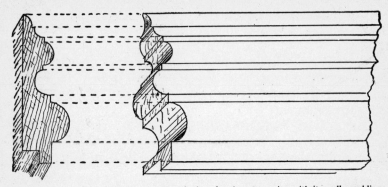

Figs. 3,128 and 3,129.—Coping a section of rebated wainscot capping with its wall moulding and another piece coped to it on the left hand and at right angles. *To do this,* the coping is mitred in the left hand cut in the box, and then sawed out to mitre line with a fine compass or coping saw and trimmed smooth with a pocket knife. The wall moulding is similarly wrought but for all mouldings when coping, pieces of same thickness and material should be selected.

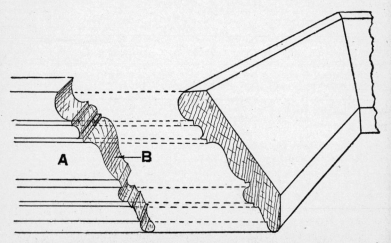

Figs. 3,130 and 3,131.—Simple cope joint consisting of a common shelf cleat with a chamfered edge. As will be seen at A, looking underneath from the inside shows the finished, or face side. At B, is seen the coped end from the back, looking down ready to butt against its next part, cut to fit over and against it so as to appear as if mitred.

By definition *cope* means *to cover, or match against, a covering.* Hence, when a carpenter copes he really "covers and matches against."

Coping is generally used for mouldings, square and flat surfaces being fitted together, one piece abutting against the other but curved or moulded profiles and surfaces can only be coped to a successful joint.

Mitring interior angles is often faulty and is rarely done by mechanics of ability, on account of one or the other joints slipping past its fellow, spoiling the intersection and exposing end-

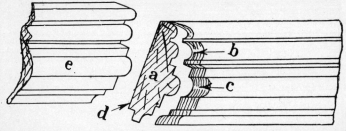

Figs. 3,132 and 3,133.—Method of kerfing by cutting the mitre until fitted. In the figures *b* and *d*, are the two lines showing when the mitre is cut, the end wood *c* how it appears when the line is sawn to *A* or *e*, its fellow to which it fits.

wood added to the difference of the profiles of machine run mouldings.

Against plaster the inside mitre is useless, as one piece is almost certain to draw away and open the joint as it is being nailed into the studding.

If it can be mitred tight enough by cutting the lengths a little full and springing them into place, it is not advisable, except possibly in solid corners. If against plastered walls it is sure to crack them. The best way then to make this joint is to cope it.

Figs. 3,132 and 3,133 show a simple cope joint. In order to gain this joint the piece is first placed in a mitre box and cut on the side to which the joint fits—in this case the left-hand side. When this is done the piece is sawn through from the face kerf line and slightly under so that the joint may close on every point. When fitted on an obtuse angle it must be beveled back to suit the angle.

Placed in position if cut slightly, a hair long, the joint will be close and fit well, but the strip coped to must always be nailed well back and solid before marking the piece to be coped, as it is certain to yield to the concussive blows of the hammer. The above is a plumb or vertical cope.

Acute angle pieces are easily coped and obtuse angles may also be, taking care that the end is beveled well back to clear the piece passing behind it, otherwise the joint will rest and the back be open.

Coping obtuse angles gives a good chance to bring the joint close by nailing through the cope into the piece behind, which can never be done with an inside mitre.

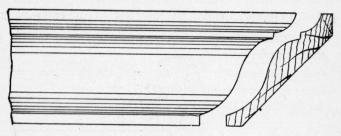

FIGS. 3,134 and 3,135.—Coped crown or spring moulding.

Figs. 3,134 and 3,135 show that *when a moulding is cut in a mitre box for coping it is always the reverse of the profile*, and when cut out to the line thus formed, preferably with a coping saw, it fits to it at every inside corner so as to be invisible.

In brief, each curved line and members joining and intersecting each to each without interruption at any point.

Oftentimes mechanics prefer to mitre this and save the work of "coping" and invariably, or at least generally, with possibly some exceptions, the joint is not a tight closure, thus not a perfect fit; hence, the coped joint is and must be very generally used in corners of all interior and cabinet finish to represent a perfect mitre. Applies particularly to membered base and chair rail.

CHAPTER 50

Doors

There is a great multiplicity of types of doors to meet the varied requirements. They may be classified:

1. According to operation, as

   a. Swinging
   b. Sliding
   c. Telescoping
   d. Folding

2. According to units, as

   a. Single
   b. Double

3. According to method of construction, as

   a. Hand made
   b. Mill made

4. According to construction, as

   a. Mortised
   b. Dowel
   c. Solid
   d. Laminated (veneer)

Batten Doors.—Fig. 3,136 shows a pair of batten doors with sash in top. There are two styles shown. One has the bottom half divided into two panels, the middle, cross rail is so spaced from the top as to form the rabbet to receive a sash divided by 1¾ inches cross rails into six squares requiring 12½×12½ glass. The other door is made to receive same style sash in top with nine lights the same size, below the middle cross rail is divided into two triangular panels.

It will be noticed that the stiles and rails of bottom panels only are chamfered, while in the other the panel receiving sash is

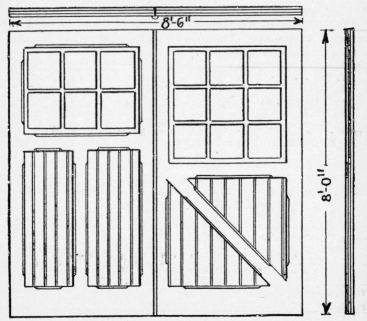

Fɪɢ. 3,316.—Batten doors with sash in top suitable for a garage.

also chamfered, and when neatly done—with spoke shave, chisel and block plane makes an attractive looking door.

If it be desired to build this door at the smallest cost the chamfering may be omitted.

As shown in fig. 3,137, cross battens are placed on the back, forming panels for the purpose of adding strength and better retaining the shape. This, too, can be omitted and show panels inside of stiles and rails.

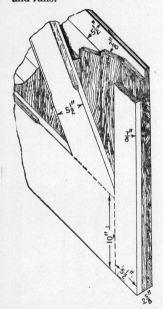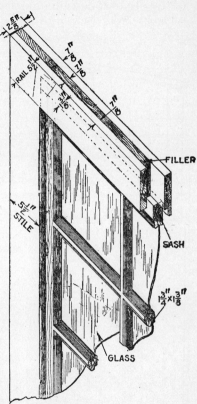

FIG. 3,137.—Detail of batten door showing three ply construction.

FIG. 3,138.—Detail of batten door showing method of securing sash. Here the sash is shown (see dotted lines) to be 1⅜ in. thick, requiring the rabbet to be ½ in. deep, but it can as well be used 1⅛ in. thick. As shown the sash rails are 1¾ in. wide, but this is special and more expensive than standard moulded size or ⅞ in. Sometimes the filler—the board showing in the panels—is put on in diagonal or herring-bone. Sometimes the fronts tiles and rails are put on with screws. When put on with wrought nails they should be large enough (6d.) to clinch or tack about ¼ in. In nailing the back on care must be taken to drive all the nails opposite the stiles, rails and mullions, so that no nails will show through in panels.

In fig. 3,138 it is seen that the back rails and stiles are rabbetted to hold the sash. Sometimes instead of a rabbet, a quarter round is used to fasten the sash, but that shows the stiles and rails narrower at the top and does not look so well.

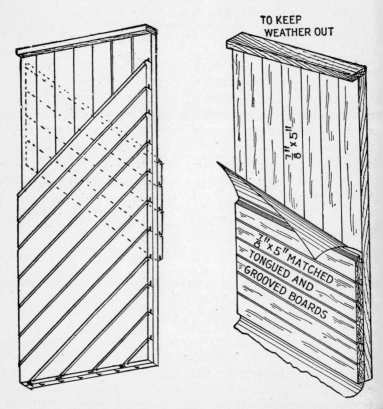

TO KEEP
WEATHER OUT

$\frac{7''}{8} \times 5''$

$\frac{7''}{8} \times 5''$ MATCHED
TONGUED AND
GROOVED BOARDS

F‌ɪɢ. 3,139.—Plain ledger or batten door, two or three ply. The third ply is indicated by the boards shown in dotted lines.

F‌ɪɢ. 3,140.—Two ply batten door with paper between the layers and layers at right angles. The water proof paper, should be three ply to effectively guard against dampness. In applying the paper the sides in contact with the paper should first be painted.

A second example of batten door, which can be easily hand made is shown in fig. 3,139. It may be either two or three thicknesses of ⅞ inch matched tongue and groove boards.

The illustration shows a two ply door 2 feet 10 inches wide and 7 feet high. The dotted lines show how, when it is important to hold the door in shape, a third thickness is added especially when the door is much larger.

It is the opinion of the author that, when the door is to be of two thicknesses it is better to put it together at right angles, vertical and horizontal, as shown in fig. 3,140.

Manufactured or Mill-made Doors.—For all ordinary purposes, doors can be obtained from the mill in stock sizes much cheaper than they can be made by hand and also less expensive than special sizes not listed as standard in manufacturers' catalogues.

Stock sizes of doors cover a wide range but those most commonly used are.

$$2'\ \ 6'' \times 6'\ \ 6''$$
$$2'\ \ 8'' \times 6'\ \ 8''$$
$$2'\ 10'' \times 6'\ 10''$$
$$3'\ \ \ \ \ \ \times 7'$$

These sizes either 1⅜ or 1¾ inches thick. The following table gives full list of standard sizes:

Door Construction.—There are usually three grades of doors, Nos. 1, 2 and 3, the No. 1 door being the best. It is poor economy to select cheap doors; get only the best—No. 1. This grade has mortised joints, whereas the cheaper doors are doweled. The dowel joint, if *well made*, will give as good satisfaction as the mortised joint. Fig. 3,141 shows position of dowels, and fig. 3,142 mortise construction.

It is claimed that veneered doors, if well made will hold their shape better than solid doors. Fig. 3,143 shows the method of constructing a laminated or veneered door.

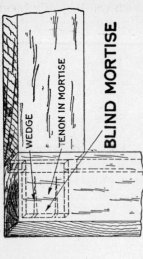

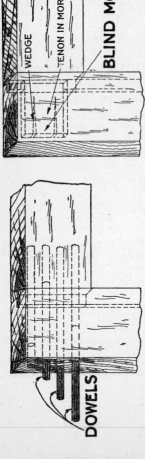

DOWELS

WEDGE

TENON IN MORTISE

BLIND MORTISE

FIGS. 3,141 and 3,142.—Door construction. Fig. 3,141, dowel joint; fig. 3,142, mortise joint. In fig. 3,141, for a 1⅜ in. door, ½ in. dowels, staggered as shown, it is claimed will make a stronger job than a mortised joint, other things being equal. In dowel joints the doors are usually coped after the dowel holes are bored, as otherwise there will be no center for a bit. The grooves for the panels should be ⁹⁄₁₆ in. deep, to allow the panels which enter ½ in. to swell ⅛ in. without opening the joint between the rails and stiles. The joints in the doors are made by machinery and are forced to their places and held there by clamps while the glue sets.

Door Frames.—As with doors there are numerous ways in which a door frame may be constructed. A door frame consists of the following essential parts:

1. Sill
2. Threshold
3. Side jambs } frame proper
4. Top jamb
5. Casing

These essential parts are shown in fig. 3,144. As usually constructed the sill will have its ends housed into the jambs.

The jambs will be assembled first, and nailed together.

Next the side casings are fitted at their lower ends, cut to length and nailed.

Frequently they are nailed and then cut to length. The head casing with its cap is next fitted and nailed.

The threshold is fitted after the door is hung. Figs. 3,144 to 3,146 show the general construction of a door frame.

Single Inside Door Jambs.

On architects' plans figures for doors are generally given so that it will be easy to get the sizes.

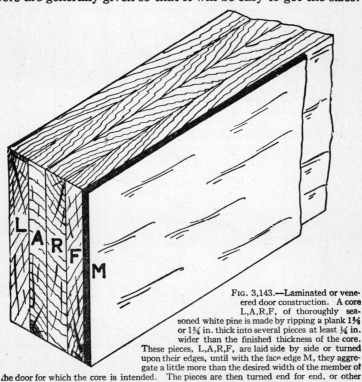

FIG. 3,143.—Laminated or veneered door construction. A core L,A,R,F, of thoroughly seasoned white pine is made by ripping a plank 1⅝ or 1¾ in. thick into several pieces at least ¼ in. wider than the finished thickness of the core. These pieces, L,A,R,F, are laid side by side or turned upon their edges, until with the face edge M, they aggregate a little more than the desired width of the member of the door for which the core is intended. The pieces are then turned end for end, or other edge up, to cross the grain, thus counteracting the tendency of the different pieces to change their shape. A piece of the finish wood or veneer M, should be glued upon one edge of the stile at the same time. After the glue sets, all the cores of the door should be jointed straight and dressed to the desired thickness. Use a scratch or tooth plane on back of veneer to make the glue hold better.

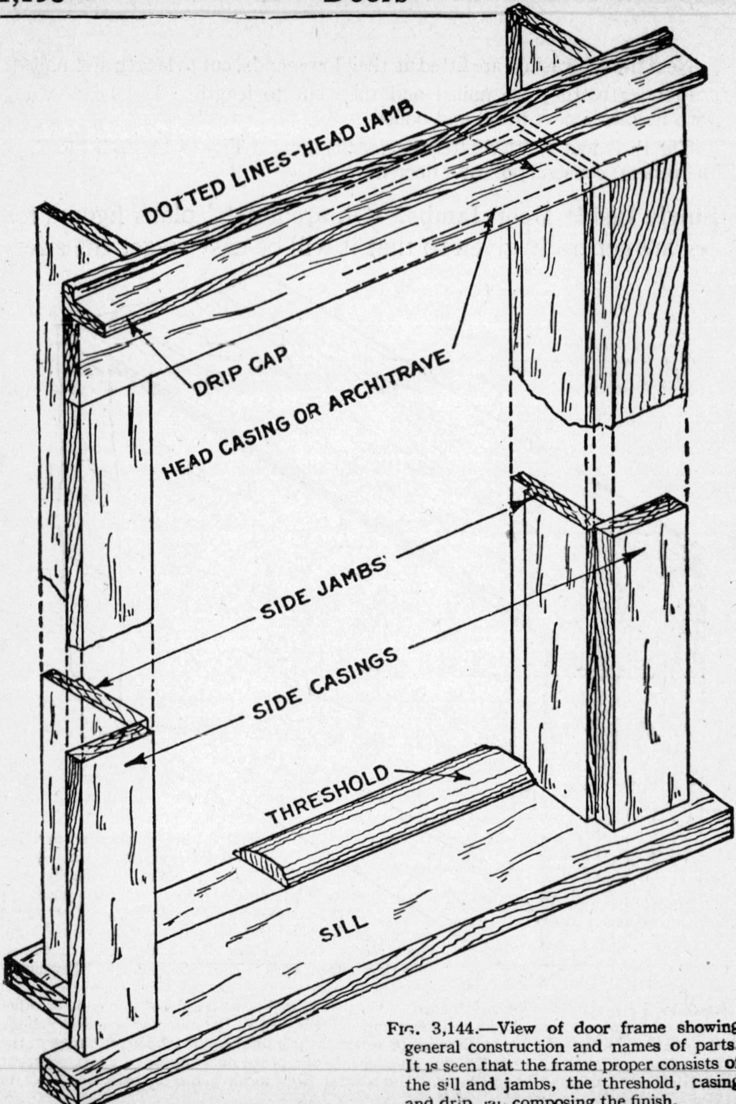

DOTTED LINES-HEAD JAMB

DRIP CAP

HEAD CASING OR ARCHITRAVE

SIDE JAMBS

SIDE CASINGS

THRESHOLD

SILL

Fig. 3,144.—View of door frame showing general construction and names of parts. It is seen that the frame proper consists of the sill and jambs, the threshold, casing and drip cap composing the finish.

For example, to measure or copy: commence by listing all the different widths of doors, say, 2' 4", 2' 6", and 3' 0". Then take the different heights, as, 6' 6", 6' 8", 6' 10", etc., as may be shown on plans, and make a list as follows:

Door Jambs

$$2' 4'' \begin{cases} 2—6' \; 6'' \\ 7—6' \; 10'' \\ 10—7' \\ 15—7' \; 6'' \\ 9—7' \; 8'' \end{cases} \quad 2' 6'' \begin{cases} 10—6' \; 10'' \\ 5—7' \; 4'' \\ 12—7' \; 2'' \\ 9—7' \; 6'' \\ 6—7' \; 8'' \end{cases} \quad 3' \begin{cases} 25—7' \\ 15—7' \; 6'' \\ 20—7' \; 8'' \\ 24—7' \; 10'' \end{cases}$$

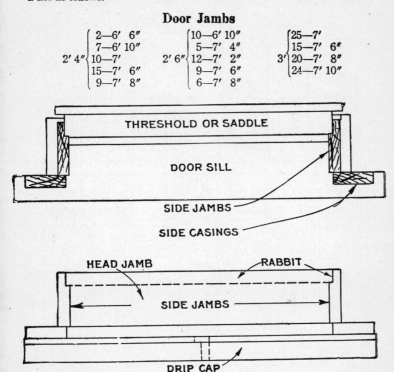

Fig. 3,145.—Plan of lower section of door frame.
Fig. 3,146.—Plan of top of door frame.

The side jambs as seen in figs. 3,145 and 3,146 should be allowed 1½ or 2 inches longer than the height of the door and the head should be dadoed the exact width of the door size, as in fig. 3,149.

Each door will require two side jambs and a top or head jamb, or as they are called collectively, a set of jambs.

Great care must be taken in determining the width of the jamb to span the thickness of the studding lath and plaster: 2-inch stud partitions will

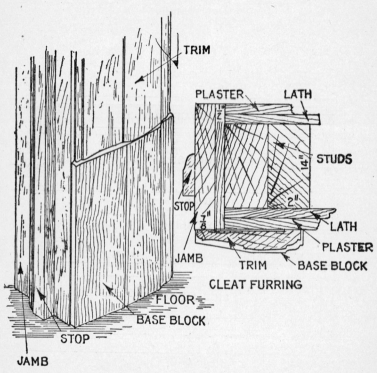

FIGS. 3,417 and 3,148.—Detail of jamb in place showing base block, trim and stop in place.

require 4-inch jambs; 2½-inch stud partitions will require 4½-inch jambs, and so on up, according to the thickness of the wall. If the wall be very wide, it is best to screw cleats or battens on the back of the jambs to prevent warping.

Figs. 3,150 to 3,156 show rabbetted door jambs, as commonly

used, being provided with *door stop* or strip as seen in figs. 3,417 and 3,418 to "stop" the door.

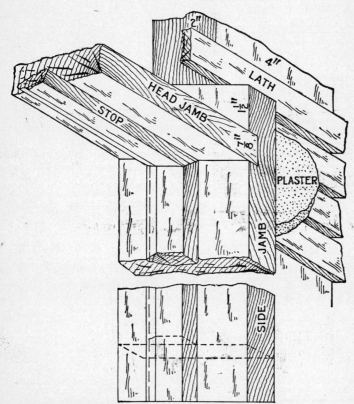

Fig. 3,149.—Detail showing upper or head jamb dadoed into side jamb.

Figs. 3,150 to 3,156 show rebated (rabbetted) jambs for brick or cement wall window and door frames. The rabbet or groove is ½ inch deep, so that the frame will be made ½ inch shorter

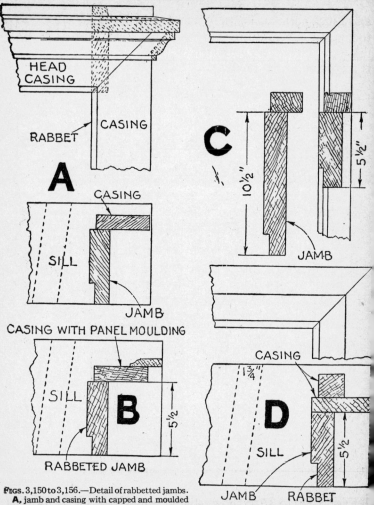

FIGS. 3,150 to 3,156.—Detail of rabbetted jambs. **A,** jamb and casing with capped and moulded head; **B,** same without moulded cap, provided with a moulded bead for covering mortar joint, continuous across top; **C,** shows a narrow casing against which the masonry finishes with its axis 4 in. out; **D,** jamb with casing against which the outside course is laid. This is very safe against leaks.

and 1 inch narrower between jambs than the size of door or sash to be used. The width of the rabbet is governed by the thickness of door or sash and the trim to be used. The width of jamb is according to the thickness of wall. Five and one-half inches

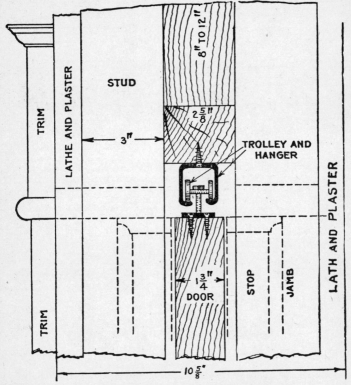

Fig. 3,157.—Parlor sliding door in position with a trolley sliding door hanger.

is required for a 9-inch wall and 10½ inches for a 13-inch wall, etc.

Measurements for partition jambs can always be taken after finish walls

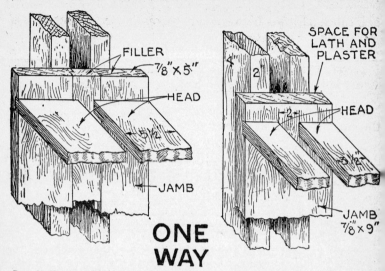

FILLER
7/8" x 5"

HEAD

5 1/2"

JAMB

SPACE FOR LATH AND PLASTER

4" 2

HEAD

JAMB
7/8" x 9"

ONE WAY

Figs. 3,158 and 3,159.—One way sliding door jambs (closed side). Fig. 3,158, studs set 2 in. way; fig. 3,159, studs set 4 in. way.

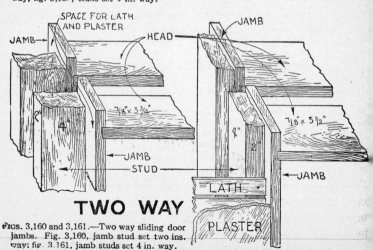

SPACE FOR LATH AND PLASTER

JAMB

HEAD

JAMB

7/8" x 3 3/4"

7/8" x 5 1/2"

JAMB
STUD

JAMB

LATH

TWO WAY

PLASTER

Figs. 3,160 and 3,161.—Two way sliding door jambs. Fig. 3,160, jamb stud set two ins. way; fig. 3,161, jamb studs set 4 in. way.

are in, however, grounds should be set before plastering and these should furnish exact size and thus the builder be able to make and have ready his jambs at will without waiting for plastering to be done. Frame walls being thin, the jamb or pulley stile of window frame is always made wide enough to trim on, but where box frames are used in masonry walls, extra jambs have to be provided of a width to finish out to plaster finish.

Sliding Door Jambs.—The accompanying illustrations show the construction and setting of sliding door jambs in double

POOR   GOOD   REVERSIBLE

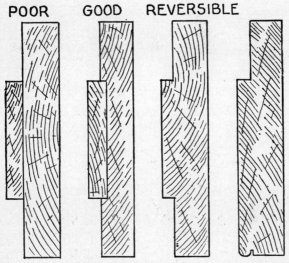

Figs. 3,162 to 3,165.—Various door jambs. Upon corner work the door jamb is often made of 1½ in. stock. However, when rabbetted, this is not thick enough to hold the screws of the hinges properly. If this thickness of stock be used, a stop is sometimes nailed on to form the rabbet as in fig. 3,162. This is poor construction as the stop is apt to be loosened by slamming the door; the stop should be let into a groove as in fig. 3,163. The jamb shown in fig. 3,162 permits the door to be hung on either side, whereas, this cannot be done with the type jamb shown in fig. 3,165.

partition doorways. Thus it is seen that two sets of jambs are required, one for each side of the slot or pocket. The heads are dadoed into the jamb.

One inch is usually allowed for lath and plaster, thus the jamb must be that much wider than the stud on the outside and enough wider on the inside to close the aperture or slot on each side within a ¼ in. of the thickness of the door, thus the distance between the jambs will usually be ½ in. greater than the thickness of the door. This can vary some as the opening is finally closed by door stops, leaving only clearance for the doors to move without rubbing.

Fitting Any Hanging Doors.—In hanging doors they may be

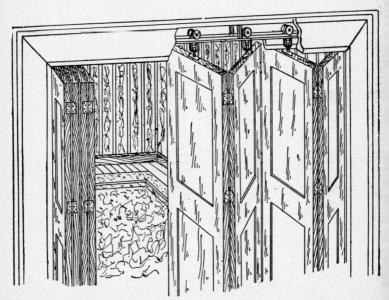

FIG. 3,166.—Accordion folding doors. They are hinged and travel on an invisible trotter track so that they fold together like the bellows of an accordion.

hung *right hand* or *left hand*. The distinction between a right, and a left hand door is shown in figs. 3,167 and 3,168.

When a catalogue indicates that a lock is "reversible," it means that it may be used on doors of either hand except where the edge of the door is beveled which seldom becomes necessary

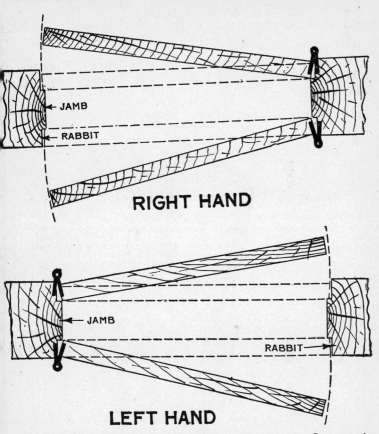

RIGHT HAND

LEFT HAND

FIGS. 3,167 and 3,168.—**Right** and **left** hand doors hung on one way hinges. Contrary to the impression of many mechanics that the hand of door means the knob or hand side, which has been the cause of expensive mistakes, and thus this plan showing that the hand of door always means the hinge side or edge, whether opening from or toward you. So let it be understood that when a lay out man goes through a job and marks the door openings R, it means that the door is to be hung with the hinges to the right, and swinging in (from you). If marked R. R. it means that the door is hung on the same stile or jamb, but opening toward you. If it is marked L, it means that the hinges are to be placed on the left stile as you face it from the outside, and is to open natural, from you. If marked L. R. it means that the hinges are placed on the opposite edge of same jamb so that the door will open (reversed) toward you.

except in narrow, thick doors, or ordinary widths when a very deep hinge is used for some purpose such as clearing the architrave of a deep door trim.

When this becomes necessary a reversible lock will not do and a bevel front lock must be used to make the work satisfactory, especially for appearance.

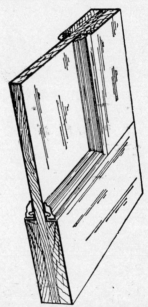

Fig. 3,169.—Detail sectiona lview of a wood core metal covered door; a type used where fire protection is desired.

1. The hand of a door is determined from the *outside*. 2. The outside is the street side of an entrance door, and the corridor side of a room door. The outside of a communicating door, from one room to another, is the side from which, when door is closed, the hinges are not visible, and it opens from you. The outside of a pair of twin doors is the space between them. The outside of a closet door, opening either hand, is the room side, and applies to sliding as well as hinged doors.

3. If standing outside of a door the butts be on the right, it is a right hand door; if on the left, a left hand door (except as to casement sashes, where the joint of view is always from the inside). If, standing outside, the door open from you, or outward, it takes a square faced lock with a regular bevel bolt; if opening outward, the bevel of the bolt must be the opposite, which means reversing the bolt.

As closet, book case and furniture doors necessarily always open out, locks for them are always made with reverse bevel bolts.

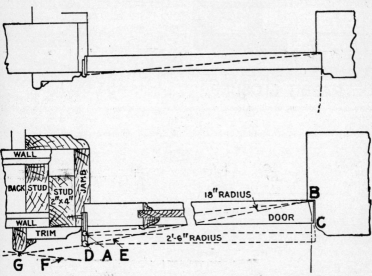

FIGS. 3,170 and 3,171.—Practical explanation of why a bevel to the lock edge of a door is sometimes used. The opening between jamb rabbet is for a 2′ 6″ radius and an 18″ radius. On the 2′ 6″ radius, A, B and C, if a very close joint between door and jamb be not required, the edge can be square, unless a very wide hinge is used to throw the door clear of wide (deep) trim as at G, at which point door should never bind, and to prevent it, or the knob marring the wall a door stop of wood to match, should be screwed to the base or floor or into the bottom rail of door. A good door stop is turned, fitted with a screw in a flat end and a rubber tip or bumper inserted in the finished or outside end. D, indicates a 1½ in. wider hinge throwing the door around to wall as at F. E, shows the position of the opened door with the narrower, 3½ in. hinge, A. With the wide hinge and the 18 in. radius the need of a bevels shown at B. The cut shows the importance of selectng one stud with a straght axis and setting it flush with outside of hanging stile, insuring strong screw holds for hinge screws. It is readily seen how much better this is than the mere ⅝ to ¾ in. that remains of the jamb after rabbetted. Even when the full thickness of the ⅞ or 1⅛ in. jamb remains and a stop is used, it permits of a much more permanent job by the use of longer (1¾ in.) screws. The back stud set in the center provides wall and trim fastening.

4. The hand of a lock varies according to the type of door on which it is to be used.

5. A door is beveled when its outside edge is not at a right angle with its face as seen in figs. 3,170 and 3,171.

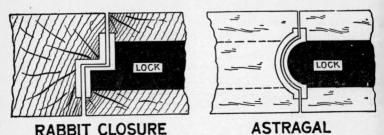

RABBIT CLOSURE   ASTRAGAL

FIG. 3,172.—Meeting of rabbet in folding doors showing position of lock, lock face and striking plate.

FIG. 3,173.—Plan of astragal front lock fitting the astragal on door.

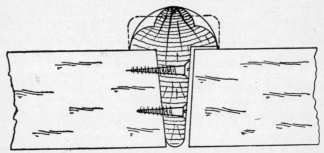

FIG. 3,174.—Plan of tongued astragal stop bead attached to one of a pair of folding doors. Its tongue is beveled to fit the level of the door. In the half round is shown a second and dotted line indicating the possibility of varying the design.

6. Mortise locks as commonly made have reversible bolts, thus suiting them to either right or left hand doors. In the case of locks which are not "reversible" such as front and vestibule door locks, they can only be used on the hand of door for which they are made.

7. Mortise locks used on double or sliding doors are made with a standard rabbet or astragal and therefore doors should be rabbetted or have astragal to match.

Ordinary house doors are hung on butts (hinges) made of iron, steel, brass or bronze, or of steel, coppered, nickeled, enameled, bronzed or oxidized, for cheaper work.

Figs. 3,175 and 3,176 show the ordinary butt of the most used style and another door that is hung with an invisible hinge, applied to the same part of the door and jamb as other butts. It is only visible on the inside when the door is open, and when standing open does not show a space between hanging stile and

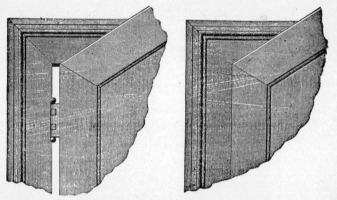

FIGS. 3,175 and 3,176.—Door mounted with butt hinges (fig. 3,175) and with "Soss" hinges, fig. 3,176.

door, unless purposely to swing door clear of architrave, a wider hinge is used.

Loose pin butts possess a feature that has not been improved upon, in that by removing the pin the door is readily removed for any purpose of fitting, moving furniture through, etc., or should the door be locked and the key lost, by removing the pins.

Frequently it is desirable to swing a door so that it opens from you passing through from either direction, and as it is desirable that the door be always closed, for this purpose three styles of invisible, double swing spring hinges have been perfected: one that attaches to the rail and jamb as do ordinary butts; one that is mortised into the bottom rail of door with a floor plate: and one that is mortised into the floor flush. For all purposes this last one is the best. By its use the bottom of the door is not weakened. They are so made as to hold the door open at right angles at will if so desired by simply stopping it at that angle.

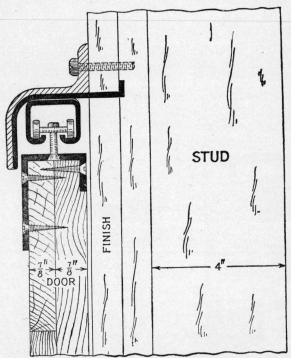

Fig. 3,177.—Outside weather proof barn or garage door trolley hanger

Setting Door Frames.—This work is usually done by two men. Door frames are set in outer walls as follows:

1. The rough floor, etc., must be cut away so that the top o

the sill may rest on a level with the finished floor when that is in place.

2. Carefully level sill, inserting shingle points under the sill where needed to give support.

3. Nail casing close to the sill at each side of the frame.

4. Plumb side jambs, and nail casings with finishing nails.

To set a door frame economically, the opening left in the studs should be plumb on both sides, both ways, and 1 in. wider, and ½ in. higher than the outside of the door frame.

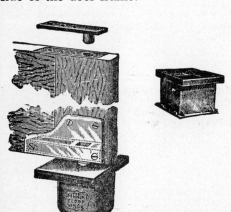

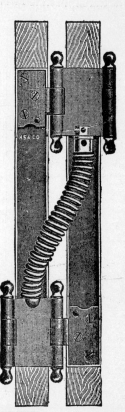

FIGS. 3,178 to 3,180.—Floor mortise spring hinge (figs. 3,178 and 3,179), and cast iron box for setting same and pivots into tile or cement floors. The hinge supports the weight of the door on tool steel ball bearings set upon a raised centerpost, giving an easy movement to the door. The ball bearings are protected from water and dirt. No hanging strip is required. The back edge of the door is slightly rounded. The tension of the spring is adjustable. These floor hinges are double acting; but by using a stop-head, they work equally well single acting.

FIG. 3,181.—Spring butts for screen door. It has a removable pintle, avoiding the necessity of taking out screws when taking down the door.

If the door frame be not set plumb, the door will swing of itself unless fastened. Wedges or stems should be placed between the frame and studs to allow the frame to be nailed straight.

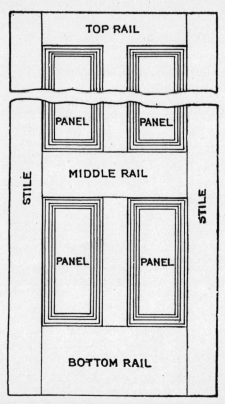

Fig. 3,182.—View of house door with names of parts.

Hanging Doors.—This work requires to be done with considerable precision to make a satisfactory job. If the hinge stile of the door be not true sideways the rounding side should be placed next the rabbet as a good joint between the door and the back of the rabbet can be more easily made than if the hollow side of the stile were to be fitted. Figs. 3,183 to 3,185 show the method of hanging the door. The work is briefly as follows:

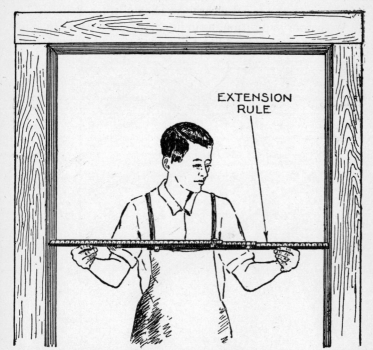

EXTENSION RULE

FIG. 3,183.—Measuring opening for door with extension rule.

1. Fit door to frame, allowing a scant $\frac{1}{16}$ at top and on each side (fig. 3,183).

The bottom of the door is often not touched except to saw away the lugs of the stiles after the door is hung.

2. When a threshold is provided the door is scribed to fit

the thickness of the threshold, allowing ⅛″ clearance at bottom of door.

3. After marking as in fig. 3,184, indicate the amount of stock to be removed, plane door until it fits the side of frame against which it is to be hung; plane top and bottom till door fits frame with the usual clearances shown in fig. 3,185.

4. With door in position, as in fig. 3,185, scribe line M, 8 ins. from the top of door, and line S, at elevation of top of bottom

FIG. 3,184.—Transferring measurement of door opening (as taken in fig. 3,183) to door.

rail of the door; these lines M and S, indicate position of top edges of upper and lower hinges.

5. Having removed door and stood it up edgeways on the floor, lay upper hinge carefully in place with the upper edge of top hinge registering with line M.

6. With scriber or knife, mark carefully on edge of door outline of hinge as in fig. 3,186.

7. Make a similar layout on door jamb.

8. Locate in similar way outline of lower hinge at S, on both door and jamb.

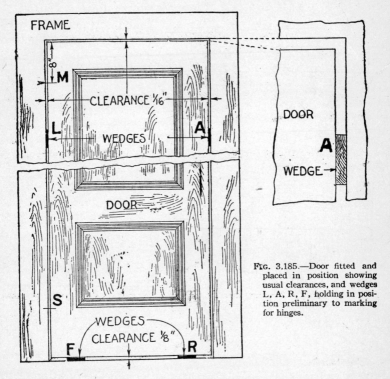

FIG. 3,185.—Door fitted and placed in position showing usual clearances, and wedges L, A, R, F, holding in position preliminary to marking for hinges.

9. Scribe a line LF, fig. 3,187, to denote the depth of gain or section to be cut away in which hinge is to rest.

10. Mark depth of gain on frame.

11. Chisel out gain on door and frame.

12. If loose pin butts be used, separate the parts and fasten them in place.

Use spiral drill for screw holes, and to insure hinges pulling tight against the side of the gain, make the holes a trifle

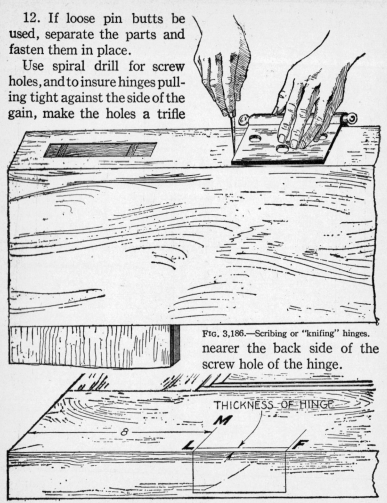

Fig. 3,186.—Scribing or "knifing" hinges.

nearer the back side of the screw hole of the hinge.

Fig. 3,187.—Complete lay out for cutting gain.

NOTE.—The term *right* and *left* as applied to hinges and locks refers to the direction in which the door swings when it is *pushed* open.

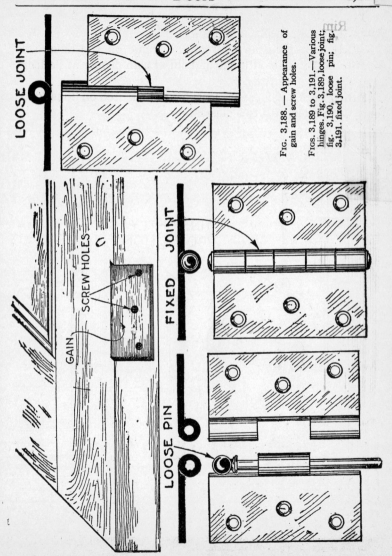

LOOSE JOINT

FIXED JOINT

LOOSE PIN

SCREW HOLES

GAIN

Fig. 3,188. — Appearance of gain and screw holes.

Figs. 3,189 to 3,191.—Various hinges. Fig. 3,189, loose joint; fig. 3,190, loose pin; fig. 3,191, fixed joint.

13. Put door in place and insert pins.

14. If door hang away from the frame on the hinge side, remove door; take off hinge and chisel gain deeper at its front

Fitting Locks.—The various types of lock used on house doors may be divided into two classes:

1. Rim
2. Mortise

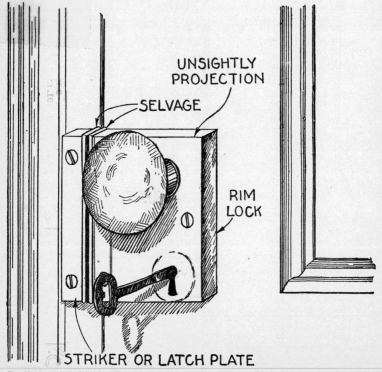

FIG. 3,192.—Rim lock fitted to door. Note how the door may be opened by simply removing the two screws which hold the latch plate.

FIGS. 3,193 to 3,197.—How to fit a mortise lock. First, locate the knob spindle and key holes as in fig. 3,193. In placing the lock, keep the selvage back from the edge of the door a scant ⅟₁₆″ so that the selvage may be sunk below the edge of the door by that amount when mortised in. This will permit the door to be trimmed without the removal of the lock in case the door should swell after being fitted and locked. 2. Bore the holes for knob spindle and key. 3. Locate a center line on the edge of the stile and bore for the mortise which shall receive the box of the lock. 4. Place the box and then mark about the protruding selvage using a sharp knife, fig. 3,195. 5. Remove the lock and "gain in" the selvage, as in fig. 3,196. 6. Fasten the lock by means of the screws through the selvage and attach the escutcheons, knob spindle and knobs as in fig. 3,197. 7. Close the door and mark the vertical position of the latch upon the jamb. 8. Open the door and place the latch or strike plate, locating its vertical position by means of the knife marks just made upon the jamb, and its horizontal position by a measurement taken from the latch to the face of the door; transfer to the jamb by rule or gage. 9. Scribe about the plate and then gain it into the jamb. On a door with a rabbeted jamb instead of an adjustable stop, the essential measurement will be from the back arris of the stile to the front of the latch. 10. Attach the plate, then chisel out the openings for latch and bolt.

Since no cutting is necessary with rim locks they are more easily put on than mortise locks. However, because of their unsightliness, and the fact that they can be removed from the inside by simply taking out the screws, they are used only on cheap work, as shown in fig. 3,192.

If in fitting a rim lock, the door rattle, the striker or latch plate may be set back into the frame, or lock itself may be set out by means of pasteboard or thin piece of wood between it and the door.

The mortise lock is housed in a mortise cut in the door.

To fit a mortise lock, locate the knob spindle and key hole.

In placing the lock, keep the selvage back from the edge of the door a scant $\frac{1}{16}$ in. so that the selvage may be sunk below the edge of the door by that amount when mortised in. This will permit the door to be trimmed without the removal of the lock in case the door should swell after being fitted and locked.

Next bore holes for knob spindle and key. The mortise may now be laid out and accurately cut. First locate a center line on edge of stile and bore for the mortise, cutting mortise to fit box of lock.

Place the box and then mark about the protruding selvage, using a precision scriber or sharp knife. Remove the lock and cut a counter mortise for the selvage. The lock is then fastened by means of screws through the selvage.

Put in place knob and spindle, inserting enough washers to prevent lost motion.

With lock attached to door, close door and mark vertical position of the latch plate upon the jamb. Open door and locate the latch plate in position, scribing the correct position.

Cut mortise so that latch plate will lie flush in jamb. Attach plate and mortise out opening for latch and bolt.

CHAPTER 51

Windows

The term windows as here used includes broadly the window frame, sash and blinds. The construction of window frames is very similar to that of door frames, with provision for pulleys and sash weights. The size of a window frame is governed by the size of the sash it is to accommodate.

The essential parts of a window frame are shown in fig. 3,198.

As here seen, it consists of a sill, side pieces or *stiles*, and a top piece or jamb. Let into the stile is a parting strip where sides form a guide for each of the sashes; stop beads form the outer guides, thus providing two runways for the sash.

Near the top of each runway there is an opening for the sash pulley over which runs the cord connecting sash to weight, thus making the sash work easy.

The finish consists of casing at top and on sides, and a drop cap as shown. Where weights are used there must be a pocket or runway large enough to accommodate the weight. The width of a window frame is between the stiles and the height is measured from the point where the outside of the lower sash strikes the sill or stool, or at the inside of the parting strip to the jamb, as shown in figs. 3,199 and 3,200.

There are various types of frames. Ordinarily they are made after one of two styles. The simpler of these has no sub-sill and no blind stop, the blinds being hung upon the outside of the casing; the other has a sub-sill and a blind stop.

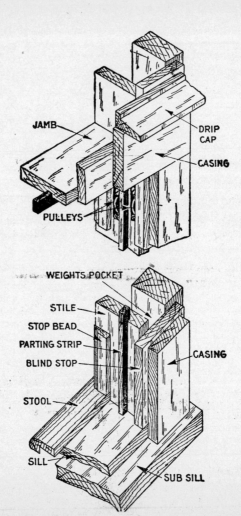

Fɪɢ 3.198.—Detail of window frame showing construction.

'These two types are shown in figs. 3,201 and 3,202.

When the single sill type (fig. 3,201) is used it is customary to sheath the house upon the studding and let the back of the outside casing rest upon the sheathing, cutting the siding against it; this is shown in detail in fig. 3,203.

With the usual thickness of siding a ⅞ in. outside casing is all that is

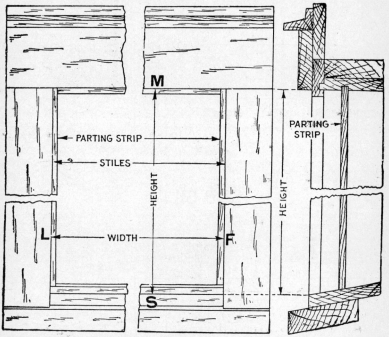

FIGS. 3,199 and 3,200.—Front view and cross section of window frame illustrating bases of measurement for size. The size of frame is stated the same as size of opening for sash which it accommodates, thus MS, height; LF, width.

necessary to give sufficient sinkage to the siding.

Window frame construction is further shown in figs. 3,204 to 3,208, as set in building and with sash in position. The views show frames for brick, stone and wooden or frame walls. The brick frames are usually measured, both in height and width, by the height and width of the brick opening

For the height: from the outside bottom corner of the sill to the upper edge of the head hanging stile; and for the width: from the outside edge of the right to the outside edge of the left hanging stile. These dimensions are also followed for all stone frames. If the frames have circular heads, the

CASING

SASH RUN

PARTING STRIP

SINGLE SILL

CASING

BLIND STOP

PARTING STRIP

SILL

SUB SILL

Figs. 3,201 and 3,202.—The two general styles of window frame. Fig. 3,201, single sill frame; fig. 3,202, frame with sub-sill and blind stop.

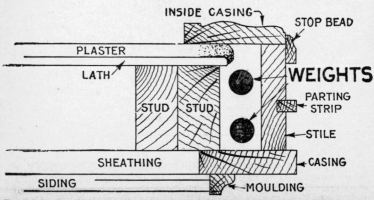

INSIDE CASING

STOP BEAD

PLASTER

LATH

WEIGHTS

STUD   STUD

PARTING STRIP

STILE

SHEATHING

CASING

SIDING

MOULDING

Fig. 3,203.—Detail of single sill frame setting showing construction.

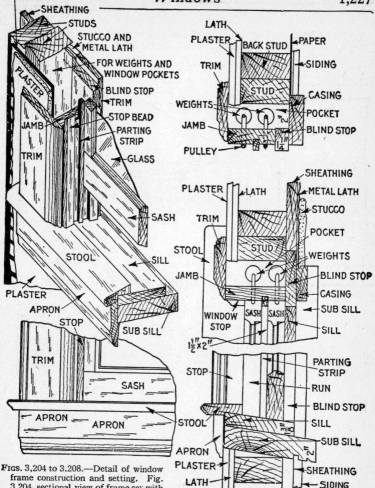

LATHS
SHEATHING
STUDS
STUCCO AND METAL LATH
FOR WEIGHTS AND WINDOW POCKETS
BLIND STOP
PLASTER
TRIM
STOP BEAD
JAMB
PARTING STRIP
TRIM
GLASS
SASH
STOOL
SILL
PLASTER
APRON
SUB SILL
STOP
TRIM
SASH
APRON   APRON

LATH
PLASTER
BACK STUD
PAPER
TRIM
SIDING
STUD
WEIGHTS
CASING
JAMB
POCKET
PULLEY
BLIND STOP

SHEATHING
METAL LATH
PLASTER
LATH
STUCCO
TRIM
POCKET
STOOL
STUD
WEIGHTS
JAMB
BLIND STOP
CASING
SUB SILL
WINDOW STOP
SASH SASH
SILL
$1\frac{1}{2}'' \times 2''$

STOP
PARTING STRIP
RUN
BLIND STOP
STOOL
SILL
SUB SILL
APRON
PLASTER
LATH
SHEATHING
SIDING

Figs. 3,204 to 3,208.—Detail of window frame construction and setting. Fig. 3,204, sectional view of frame set with reinforced stucco siding; fig. 3,205, construction of frame for setting without sheathing; fig. 3,206, plan showing construction of frame for sheathing and stucco. The blind stop joining sheathing on stud so that it is lapped by the cement, which, to further guard against leaks, fill in a core on back of casing. It shows the studs doubled at window opening, and it is tbe best thing to do, but can be omitted when the frame is sheathed: fig. 3,207, elevation side view at sill, of fig. 3,204; fig. 3,208, section of fig. 3,207.

height to the spring line should be obtained, and the radius, if the head be not semi-circular but segmental. If an elliptic head, it must have a wood

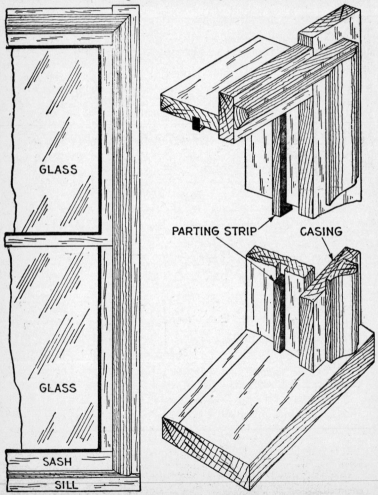

GLASS

GLASS

SASH

SILL

PARTING STRIP

CASING

FIGS. 3,209 and 3,210.—Window frame construction for brick veneer buildings.

pattern made the exact shape to fit the wood head to the brick or stone opening.

In measuring up window frames for framed or wood walls, the sizes are usually taken from the sill to the head, two cross studs top and bottom and an inch allowed for clearance between the studs.

For example: if the frame be 6' 6", then the framer will keep the distance between his head and sill piece about 6' 7 to 8" inches distant, remembering always that they must not change the distance of sill from floor.

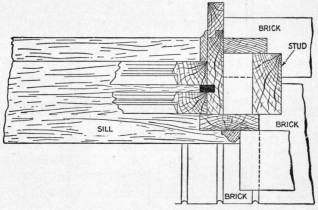

FIG. 3,211.—Plan detail of fig. 3,210, showing setting with brick in place.

The width is taken between studs, and 2½" is allowed for a sash weight-box, each side (5") providing free weight action. Examination of these details will help greatly in measuring, planning and making.

Figs. 3,209 and 3,210 show a window frame for brick veneer buildings.

It is built for frame construction and an outside moulding for abutting brick.

In the box frame for brick houses the sash weights run in a box which is enclosed back of the pulley stile. The outside casing usually projects beyond the back of the pulley stile ½ in., around which bricks are laid, holding the frame firmly in place, as shown in fig. 3,212.

Window Sash.—The essential parts of window sash are

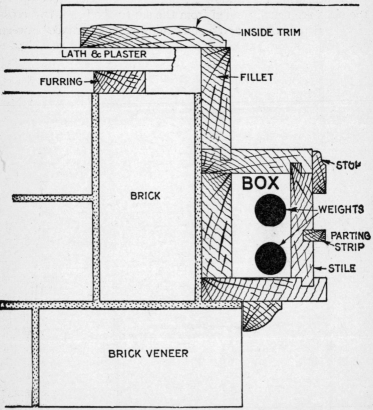

FIG. 3,212.—Section through box frame showing construction for brick building.

shown in figs. 3,213 and 3,214. It is well to note the names of the different parts and become familiar with the general construction. The requirements for sash are severe, as they should be made very light, yet have considerable strength. This is secured by special joints at the corners, as shown in figs. 3,215

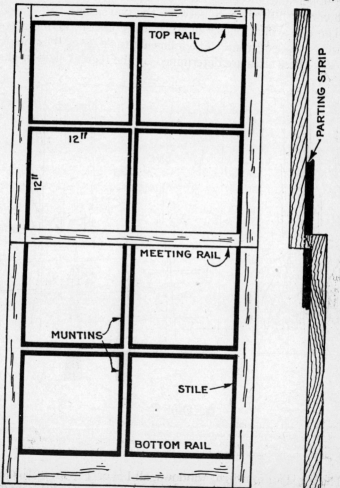

Figs. 3,213 and 3,214.—Side view and section of sash showing essential parts.

The edges of the meeting rails which form the joint between the upper and lower sash are beveled or joggled so that they will closely fill the space between the two sashes.

There is a multiplicity of stock sizes of sash, giving a great variety to select from. The following table gives these various sizes. These sizes are determined by the regular sizes of glass.

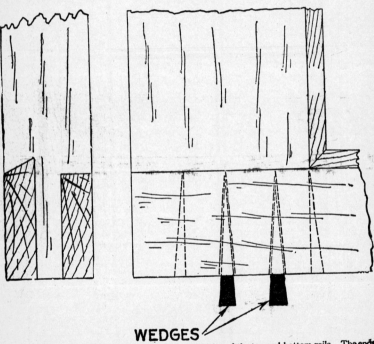

WEDGES

FIGS. 3,215 and 3,216.—Mortised and coped sash joint of the top and bottom rails. The ends of the mortises are fastened to the rail by the same method. The tenon is split in two places near the edge and wedges driven in as shown, thus expanding the tenon and forming a dovetail; the mortise being cut larger toward the ends to allow the tenon to spread out.

The list is for four light windows, all $1\frac{3}{8}$ or $1\times$ in. in thickness. An allowance of 5 ins. in width and 6 in. in height is made for the outside sizes of the sash, which is the size of frame (between stiles, and between jamb and sill).

Sizes of Four Light Sash

Size of Glass	Size of Window	Size of Glass	Size of Window
10″ × 20″	2′ 1″ × 3′ 10″	14″ × 26″	2′ 9″ × 4′ 10″
10″ × 22″	2′ 1″ × 4′ 2″	14″ × 28″	2′ 9″ × 5′ 2″
10″ × 24″	2′ 1″ × 4′ 6″	14″ × 30″	2′ 9″ × 5′ 6″
10″ × 26″	2′ 1″ × 4′ 10″	14″ × 32″	2′ 9″ × 5′ 10″
10″ × 28″	2′ 1″ × 5′ 2″	14″ × 34″	2′ 9″ × 6′ 2″
10″ × 30″	2′ 1″ × 5′ 6″	14″ × 36″	2′ 9″ × 6′ 6″
10″ × 32″	2′ 1″ × 5′ 10″	14″ × 38″	2′ 9″ × 6′ 10″
10″ × 34″	2′ 1″ × 6′ 2″	14″ × 40″	2′ 9″ × 7′ 2″
10″ × 36″	2′ 1″ × 6′ 6″	14″ × 42″	2′ 9″ × 7′ 6″
12″ × 20″	2′ 5″ × 3′ 10″	14″ × 44″	2′ 9″ × 7′ 10″
12″ × 22″	2′ 5″ × 4′ 2″	14″ × 46″	2′ 9″ × 8′ 2″
12″ × 24″	2′ 5″ × 4′ 6″	14″ × 48″	2′ 9″ × 8′ 6″
12″ × 26″	2′ 5″ × 4′ 10″	15″ × 24″	2′ 11″ × 4′ 6″
12″ × 28″	2′ 5″ × 5′ 2″	15″ × 26″	2′ 11″ × 4′ 10″
12″ × 30″	2′ 5″ × 5′ 6″	15″ × 28″	2′ 11″ × 5′ 2″
12″ × 32″	2′ 5″ × 5′ 10″	15″ × 30″	2′ 11″ × 5′ 6″
12″ × 34″	2′ 5″ × 6′ 2″	15″ × 32″	2′ 11″ × 5′ 10″
12″ × 36″	2′ 5″ × 6′ 6″	15″ × 34″	2′ 11″ × 6′ 2″
12″ × 38″	2′ 5″ × 6′ 10″	15″ × 36″	2′ 11″ × 6′ 6″
12″ × 40″	2′ 5″ × 7′ 2″	15″ × 38″	2′ 11″ × 6′ 10″
12″ × 42″	2′ 5″ × 7′ 6″	15″ × 40″	2′ 11″ × 7′ 2″
12″ × 44″	2′ 5″ × 7′ 10″	15″ × 42″	2′ 11″ × 7′ 6″
12″ × 46″	2′ 5″ × 8′ 2″	15″ × 44″	2′ 11″ × 7′ 10″
12″ × 48″	2′ 5″ × 8′ 6″	15″ × 46″	2′ 11″ × 8′ 2″
14″ × 24″	2′ 9″ × 4′ 6″	15′ × 48″	2′ 11″ × 8′ 6″

It should be noted that sash are listed as "2, 4, 8 or more light" as for instance, a 10×20, four light window.

The list here given is for four light windows, all 1⅜, or 1¾ in. in thickness; an allowance of 5 ins. in width and 6 ins. in height is made for the outside sizes of the sash, or the size of the frame between the pulley stiles in width and the stool and header in height.

Fitting Sash to Frame.—This is an operation requiring some precision. The requirements are:

1. That the tops of meeting rails should be parallel and flush.

2. That the lower edge of bottom rail should make a tight joint with the sill.

To accomplish this, the upper sash should be fitted first, being jointed so that the meeting rail will be level.

Joint the lower sash so that the tops of the meeting rails are parallel.

Next close sash and measure with dividers, as in fig. 3,219, amount MS, to be taken off bottom rail to bring top rail flush. Transfer the measurement, as in fig. 3,220, by holding one point of divider on lower edge of sash and describing two arcs LF, at ends of lower rail as seen in fig. 3,221.

With straight edge scribe line tangent to these arcs, as in fig. 3,221.

Set bevel to angle of sill and parting piece, as in fig. 3,222, and in jointing to the scribed line, plane lower edge to this bevel as indicated by dotted

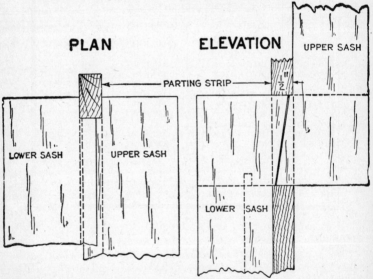

FIGS. 3,217 and 3,218.—Construction of joint between meeting rail and parting strip showing angularity of the joint.

line in fig. 3,223, varying the bevel a trifle from the setting, so that the sash will bear a little harder upon the outside than upon the inside, as indicated in fig. 3,224.

When the work is properly done the tops of the meeting rails will be flush and the upper and lower rails in firm contact with the jamb and sill respectively, when the window is closed.

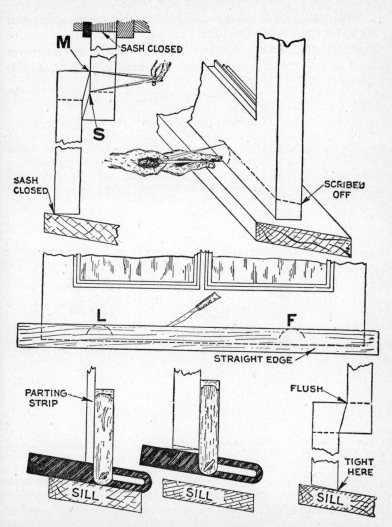

FIGS. 3,219 to 3,224.—Method of fitting sash to window frame.

Sash should be fitted and hung before the house is plastered to protect the latter from the weather. Cover with muslin to protect them from lime spatter. In warm weather the apertures may be covered with muslin and sash hung after plastering is done.

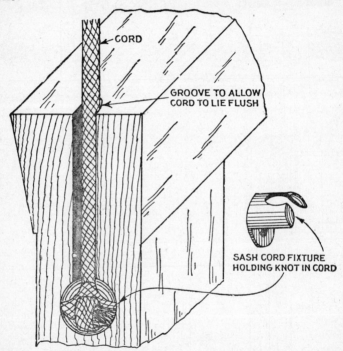

CORD

GROOVE TO ALLOW CORD TO LIE FLUSH

SASH CORD FIXTURE HOLDING KNOT IN CORD

Figs. 3,225 and 3,226.—Method of attaching cord to sash, and view of cord fixture, fitting flush in a hole bored in sash into which a knot in cord is firmly held.

Sash are usually hung by cords which pass over pulleys near the top of the stiles and fastened to weights, thereby supporting most of the weight of the sash and rendering them easy to operate.

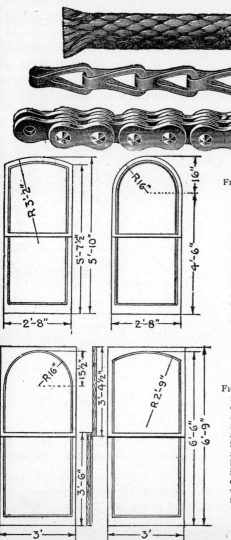

FIGS. 3,227 to 3,229.—Sash cord and sash chains. For light sash, cord is used varying in size from ⅛ in. to ⅜ in. diameter. The various sizes of cord are suitable for weights as follows: ⅛ in., 5 to 12 lbs.; ¼ in., 12 to 20 lbs.; ⁹⁄₃₂ in., 20 to 30 lbs.; ⁵⁄₁₆ in., 30 to 40 lbs.; ⅜ in., 40 to 50 lbs. For above 250 lbs. cable chain should be used. It does not pay to use cheap rough wheel pulleys as they work havoc with the cord, nor cheap cord as it soon strands and has to be replaced.

FIGS. 3,230 to 3,233.—Various segmental and circular sashes. The outisde dimensions of these are always given or determined by the radius, *which must be taken from the frame and be absolutely accurate.* Should these sashes be ordered from a mill, state the size of glass, number of lights per window, thickness, if plain or check rail, glazed or open. For segment or circle corner windows always give the radius of the segment.

The cords are fastened on each edge of the sash by passing them through a sash cord fixture and tying a knot, the edge of the sash being grooved to permit the cord to lie flush. The fixture is an iron socket, let into the sash, as shown in figs. 3,225 and 3,226.

Glazing Sash.—The glass or "lights" as they are called, are generally cut ⅛ in. smaller each way than the rabbet to allow

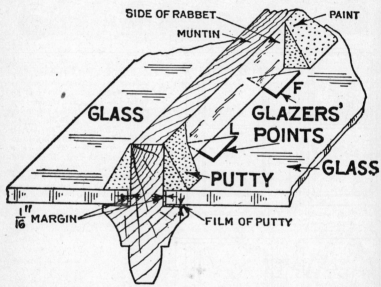

FIG. 3,234.—Detail of muntin showing two lights in position.   Side of mortise rabbet to be painted or oiled before glazing, putty painted after set.

for irregularities in cutting and in the sash. This leaves a margin of ¹⁄₁₆ in. all around between the edges of the glass and sides of the rabbet.

Fig. 3,234 shows two lights or panes of glass in position. In glazing, on best work, first a film of putty is placed on the glass supporting side of the window as shown, although this is frequently neglected.

To do this properly have **the putty** very soft, because the glass must be pressed into it until it bears evenly.

The glass is held in place by glazier's points or small triangular pieces of tin, as LF; these are driven or pressed into the sash with a chisel as shown in fig. 3,234.

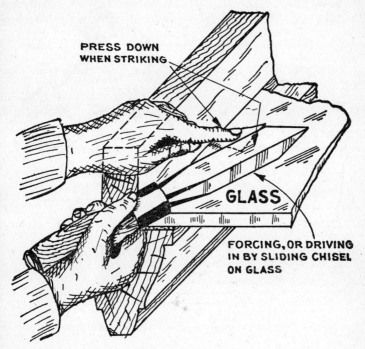

**PRESS DOWN
WHEN STRIKING**

GLASS

**FORCING, OR DRIVING
IN BY SLIDING CHISEL
ON GLASS**

FIGS. 3,235.—Glazing sash *1*. Inserting the glazier's point.

After the glass is firmly secured with the point, the putty, **as soft as can** be handled, is put on with a putty knife, as in fig. 3,326, being careful that the putty does not project beyond the edge of the rabbet so that it will not be visible from the other side.

Storm Sash.—These are made quite similar to ordinary

window sash except that they are mostly in one piece and, like casement windows, open out, being usually hung at the top and fitting into outside casings against blind stop or hanging stiles as they are sometimes called.

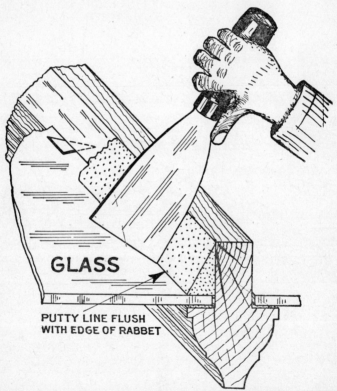

GLASS

PUTTY LINE FLUSH WITH EDGE OF RABBET

Fig. 3,236.—. Glazing sash 2. Applying the putty with putty knife.

To provide for convenient adjustment for ventilation they are fitted with one of the several kinds of adjustment fasteners, two of which are here shown, in figs. 3,237 to 3,239, but the

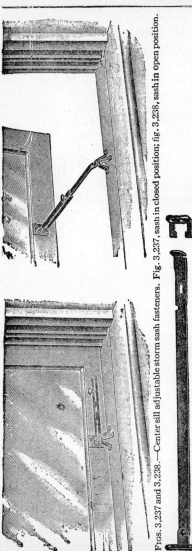

FIGS. 3,237 and 3,238.—Center sill adjustable storm sash fasteners. Fig. 3,237, sash in closed position; fig. 3,238, sash in open position.

FIGS. 3,239 and 3,241.—Adjustable side sash fastener and view of sash showing fastener applied and in close position.

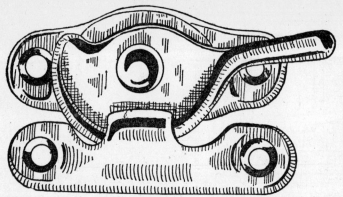

Fig. 3,242.—A desirable type of sash lock.

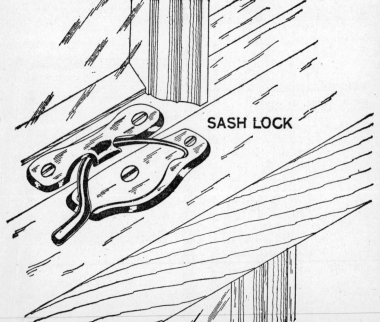

SASH LOCK

Fig. 3,243.—View of sash lock on sash in locked position.

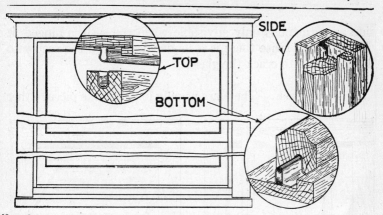

FIGS. 3,244 and 3,245.—Application of metal weather strip to a sliding sash. When meeting rails close the metal strips engage to make an air tight joint.

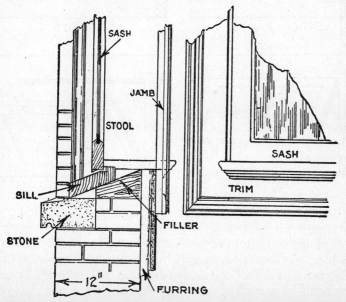

FIGS. 3,246 and 3,247.—Design for casement window opening out.

side adjustment is only advisable when the sash is hinged **at** the side; otherwise there is a tendency to warp the sash **into** ill fitting and to crack the glass.

Transom Sash.—These are usually made in one piece, either

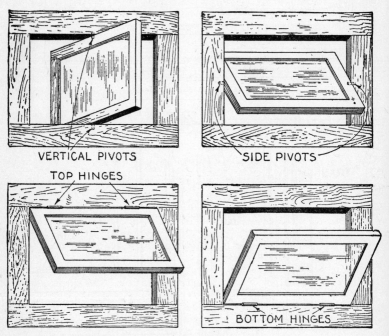

VERTICAL PIVOTS   SIDE PIVOTS

TOP HINGES

BOTTOM HINGES

Figs. 3,248 to 3,251.—Methods of hanging transoms.

hung at top or bottom or pivoted at centers vertically or horizontally. As they are ordinarily built in over doors opening into hall-ways or adjacent rooms, it makes no difference which way they open, in or out, so far as the elements are concerned, but light reflection and air have to do with how they are placed.

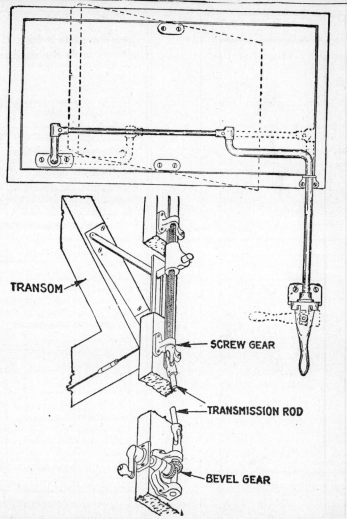

TRANSOM

SCREW GEAR

TRANSMISSION ROD

BEVEL GEAR

Fig. 3,252.—Horizontally pivoted "transom" with adjuster that may be locked in any position.

Fig. 3,253.—Bevel gear transom adjuster for bottom hinged transom.

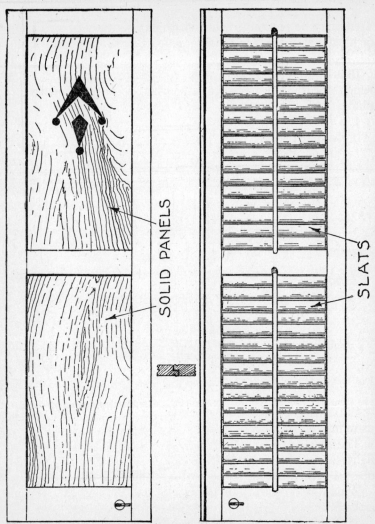

Figs. 3,254 and 3,256.—Solid and slat blinds, sometimes with a design cut in top solid pane, and section showing lap joint.

They may be pivoted to turn either horizontally or vertically, or hinged at the top or bottom, as best suits the conditions.

Blinds.—These are factory made in a variety of types, all of which come under two general classes, according as they are placed:

1. Outside, or
2. Inside

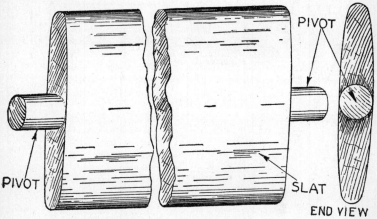

FIGS. 3,257 and 3,258.—Form of slat.

Outside blinds are made with solid panels, or with slat panels, as in figs. 3,254 and 3,255.

The slat blind is generally used owing to the ventilation and light secured by the adjustable slats. The construction and operation of these slats is shown in figs. 3,259 to 3,261.

Blinds are ordered generally by the size of the glass, the same as sash.

They are usually hung upon gravity hinges which are so made that when the blind is swung past the center in either direction it will swing the rest of the way itself. Upon window frames which have blind stops the blinds are hung between the outside casings, but if the frame has nothing but the casing outside of the pulley stile, the blinds are hung with special hinges.

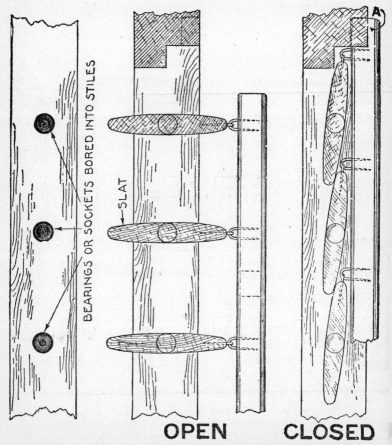

OPEN   **CLOSED**

Figs. 3,259 to 3,261.—Method of pivoting and adjusting slats showing slats in open and closed position.

Where a window has a pair of blinds the ends are lap jointed as shown in fig. 3,263, so that the blind A, is held closed by blind B. Fig. 3,264 shows the hinges and familiar spring fas-

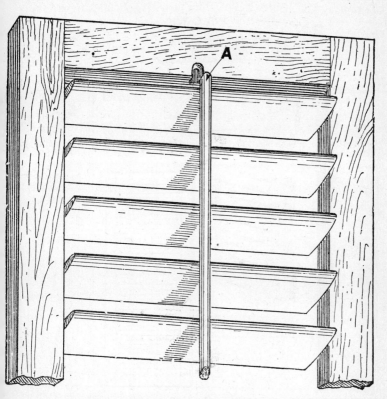

FIG. 3,262.—Portion of slat blind showing slats assembled.

FIG. 3,263.—Plan of pair of blinds showing lap joint at the center.

fastening which engages with a staple in either closed or open position, thus securing blind in either of these positions.

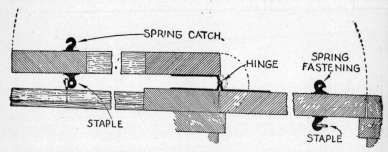

FIG. 3,264.—Plan of single blind showing hinge and spring fastening for locking blind in open or closed position.

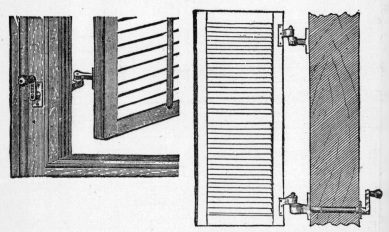

FIGS. 3,265 and 3,266.—Application of inside control to outside blind. Fig. 3,265, perspective view; fig. 3,266, side view.

Inside Blinds.—These are made in several varieties. Two general types are the folding slat blinds and the Venetian blinds shown in the accompanying cuts.

The Venetian blinds are so improved as to be used for blind and awning combined either in a portable frame hung against blind stop, or without the frame. They are as readily removed

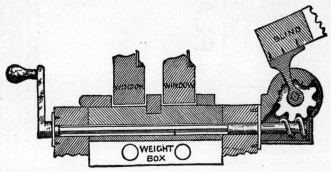

FIG. 3,267.—Inside control for outside blind. *It operates* the shutter from within without raising sash or screen, and holds it in any position. It can only be moved by the handle. The blind is lifted from the hinges the same as from any blind hinge. The sectional view clearly shows its construction, and that the only cutting required is to bore a half inch hole through the casing which does not interfere with weights. The continuous cog gear admits of attaching shutter with it in any psoition. There are a number of such appliances now in use

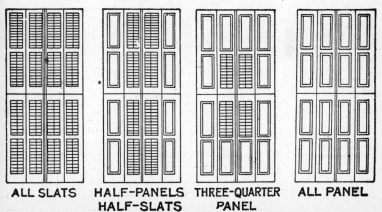

ALL SLATS   **HALF-PANELS HALF-SLATS**   **THREE-QUARTER PANEL**   **ALL PANEL**

FIGS. 3,268 to 3,271 —Various types of folding blinds. Fig. 3,268, all slats; fig. 3,269, half panel and half slats; fig. 3,270, three quarters panel; fig. 3,271, all panel.

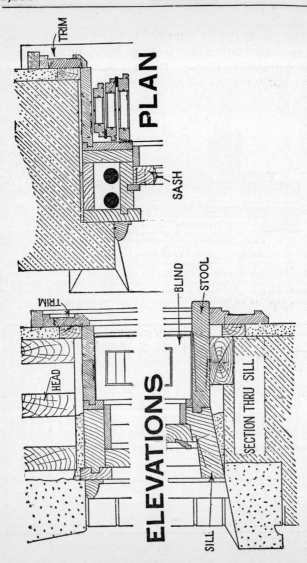

FIGS. 3,272 to 3,274.—Construction details of folding blinds. The detail shows a three section shutter or blind folded back against the jamb entirely out of the way. Sometimes, when the masonry is thicker a box or panel is formed between the casing and trim, and only the face of one blind shows when folded back. As shown the blinds are hinged together by specially made hinges for that purpose. As shown by the small elevations, the panels may be all rolling slats, partly so, or all solid panels. As these are working details, same as doors and sash, care must be exercised in giving exact measurements when ordering, more so because they are made up of two or three different widths. They are ordinarily 1⅛in. to 1¼ in. in thickness.

ANGLE
ADJUSTMENT

FIG. 3,275.—Venetian blind partly drawn. Automatically controlled fixtures hold these blinds at any position open or entirely closed. They do not in any way interfere with curtains. In winter they may be substituted with storm sash. The ordinary inside shade is then sufficient to control the light. These blinds may be fitted in any size, in sleeping porches, piazzas or wherever an awning is required, and are at once awning or enclosure against the element without shutting out all the air.

from the brackets as an ordinary window shade roller, and the latest fixtures do away with all unevenness of run or cord entanglements and when made from correct measurements can be put up by any mechanic.

CHAPTER 52

Sheathing and Siding

In the better class of work, buildings are generally covered with two layers of boards with building paper between. The inner layer is called the *sheathing* and the outer layer the *siding*. This makes a good weather tight covering and should always be provided in cold climates.

Some forms of siding with the lap joint makes a tight covering without sheathing and suffices in some sections not subject to low temperatures.

For the sheathing ordinary lumber is used; common boards, usually 1×6 or 1×8 ins. This sheathing may be put on either horizontal or diagonal, as shown in figs. 3,276 and 3,277.

There are numerous kinds of siding, as:

1. Colonial
2. Clap board
3. Plain novelty
4. Figured novelty
5. False joint
6. Vertical batten joint
7. Shingle
8. Metal

The distinguishing feature of these various forms of siding being in most cases the cross sectional shape of the boards and type of joint, as shown in the cross section figs. 3,282 to 3,287.

Colonial Siding.—The simplest form of siding known as *colonial* consists of plain boards of rectangular section. as in

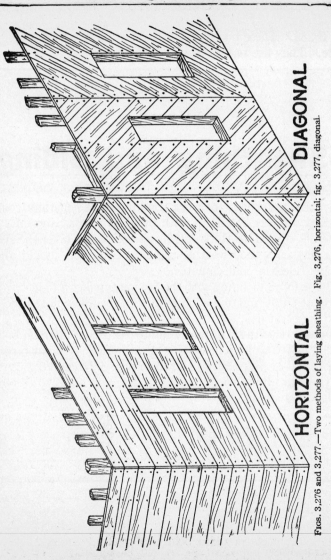

DIAGONAL

HORIZONTAL

Figs. 3,276 and 3,277.—Two methods of laying sheathing. Fig. 3,276, horizontal; fig. 3,277, diagonal.

fig. 3,282. These boards are 1 in. thick and from **9 to 12 ins.** wide. They are put on as shown in figs. 3,288 to 3,290.

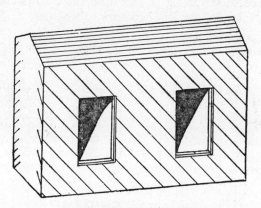

WRONG WAY

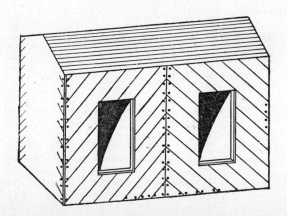

RIGHT WAY

Figs. 3,278 and 3,279.—Wrong and right ways to lay diagonal siding.

*Clap Board Siding or Clap Boards.—This form of siding differs from the Colonial in that the sides are tapered instead of parallel, as shown in fig. 3,283; also the boards are not so wide, being intended for less exposure to weather.

The reason for the tapered sides is to secure a perfect lap joint with narrow boards, as shown in figs. 3,291 and 3,292.

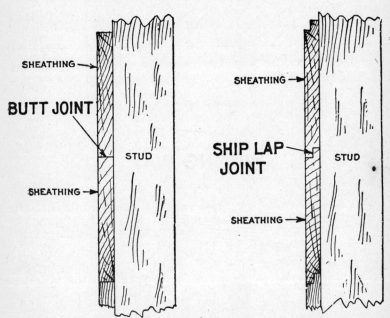

Figs. 3,280 and 3,281.—Sheathing joints. Fig. 3,280, plain butt joint; fig. 3,281, ship lap joint

Evidently, in fig. 3,291, showing two clapboards laid, the distance MS, from edge of board A, to stud is the same as the distance LF, from edge of board B, to stud, and with this nclination, the boards when assembled will come firmly together at the outer edges, as at L, thus giving a good joint instead of being open the length of the lap as with boards B and B' in fig. 3,292.

Nailing into stud as at B', is likely to set up a bulging strain at H, causing board to check at H.

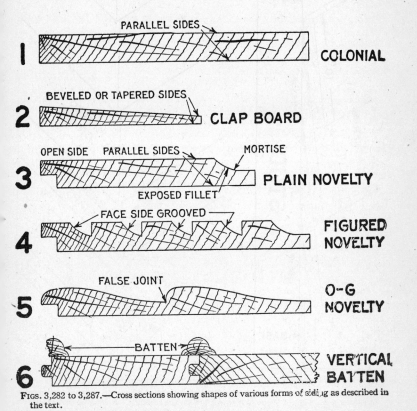

1 PARALLEL SIDES COLONIAL

2 BEVELED OR TAPERED SIDES CLAP BOARD

3 OPEN SIDE   PARALLEL SIDES   MORTISE   PLAIN NOVELTY   EXPOSED FILLET

4 FACE SIDE GROOVED   FIGURED NOVELTY

5 FALSE JOINT   O-G NOVELTY

6 BATTEN   VERTICAL BATTEN

FIGS. 3,282 to 3,287.—Cross sections showing shapes of various forms of siding as described in the text.

To save lumber and labor, the bevel is obtained by taking a diagonal saw cut through a board, as in fig. 3,293, thus each board is sawed into two clap boards, there being no waste except that due to the saw cut and dressing.

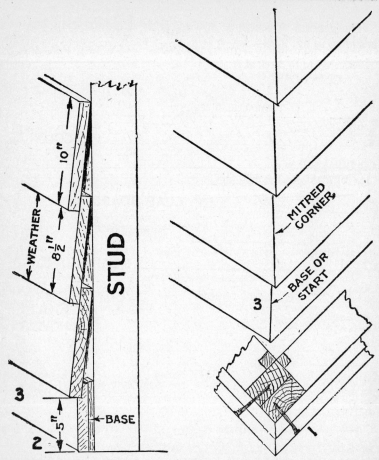

Figs. 3,288 to 3,290.—Colonial siding as put on without sheathing. The boards are 1 × 10 ins. dressed lumber, or may be left rough in rustic work, nailed directly to the studs and mitred at the corners. Fig. 3,288 shows how it is laid on the studding. It can also just as well be set on sheathing. It is readily understood that the casings will need to be at least 1⅛ in. and will better protect against leaks of 1⅜ in. Some architects and owners prefer a corner board instead of mitred corner and there is no objection to it, indeed the bottom half of end wood of siding extending ⅝ in. to ¾ in. beyond the corner board can be made an attractive feature of the whole design. Narrow corners and casings are advocated. The less wood there is to shrink away from the boards the less danger of leaks until painted again.

The general appearance and method of nailing clap boards is shown in fig. 3,294.

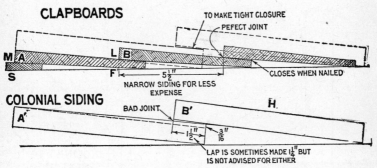

CLAPBOARDS

TO MAKE TIGHT CLOSURE
PEFECT JOINT

M A   L B
S   F

CLOSES WHEN NAILED

5½″
NARROW SIDING FOR LESS
EXPENSE

COLONIAL SIDING

A′

BAD JOINT.   B′   H.

1½″   3/16″

LAP IS SOMETIMES MADE 1¼″ BUT
IS NOT ADVISED FOR EITHER

FIGS. 3,291 and 3,292.—Comparison of clap boards and Colonial siding laid with small exposure to weather, showing faulty joint of the Colonial siding and why tapered planks or clap boards are used to secure a perfect joint. Nailing into stud at B′ will close joint but is likely by a bulging strain to cause board to check at H. At A, is seen by dotted line what bevel in a 1 × 10″ board lapped 1½″ will make a perfect closure, or how at A, by right taper it may be done.

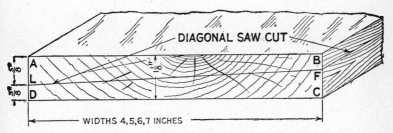

DIAGONAL SAW CUT

A   B
L   F
D   C

⅛″

WIDTHS 4,5,6,7 INCHES

FIG. 3,293.—Method of sawing clap boards two from a plank by diagonal cut.

Clap boards are cut in lengths of 4 feet, this is so that the cut will center every fourth stud the same as lath.

They are 6″ wide, ½″ thick at the butt or bottom edge and ¼″ at the top. This is done for quick handling and the joints ready fitted except where it joins trim.

Care must be used in breaking joints.

It sometimes occurs that bevel siding must be used on a circle or curve on a "clap boarded" house where nothing else would do.

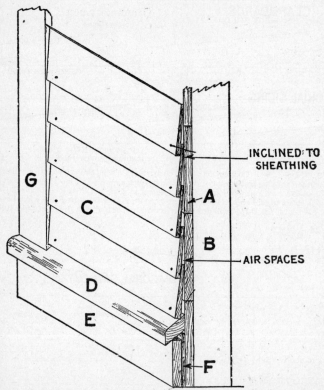

INCLINED TO
SHEATHING

AIR SPACES

Fɪɢ. 3,294.—Method of laying clapboard siding. Before putting on the siding, the sheathing should be covered with a layer of *sheathing* paper especially manufactured for this purpose, one to four ply in thickness, carefully lapping joints and extending it under all casings, being careful not to tear it, sometimes it is rosin sized and sometimes of tar or asphalt. Sometimes in warm or near tropical climates it is done to keep out insects. **B**, indicates a 4″ stud or joint. **A**, ⅞″ sheathing boards. **C**, the clapboards. **D**, the drip of water table. **E**, the band of water table, made of ⅞″ lumber and furred off with a ¼″ strip indicated by **F**. **G**, shows the 3 or 3½″ × 1⅛″ corner board in place and how the siding **C**, is squared against it.

It may be well said just here that more times the architect will, if possible to his design, employ some other method of siding, usually shingles especially if the radius be short. When this cannot be done even by dressing, beveling the edges and setting close so that when painted it will look quite the same, then the boards must be bent.

As bevel siding is a quarter inch thicker at the bottom than at the top, it

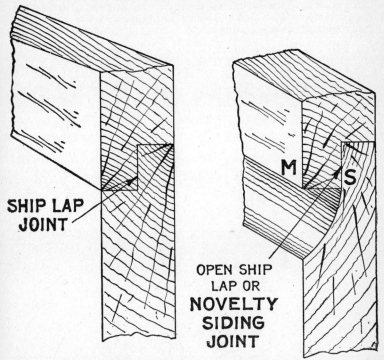

SHIP LAP JOINT

M **S**

OPEN SHIP LAP OR NOVELTY SIDING JOINT

FIGS. 3,295 and 3,296.—Ship lap joint and open ship lap or novelty siding joint. By comparing the two joints it is seen that the novelty siding joint is equivalent to a ship lap joint with one side removed as along **MS**, fig. 3,296.

is at once apparent that it will not spring around level in a horizontal plane unless something is done to make it.

Probably the second best way to determine the amount of curvature to give the edges is to first plot a curve as in fig. 3,297 and draw a line as at **A**, perpendicular indefinitely, set or measure for a piece of siding with its **back** plumb against the circle (wall) and protract a line as at C, on a plane with its level face until it intersects the perpendicular line at B, from which intersection describe an arc with the radius, A, long enough to cut a pattern as long as you require from which all the rest may be cut. However, it is probably the simplest and best to tack a ¼″ strip on the back of the bottom of **a** piece of siding, spring it against the circle with both ends touching **the** base or water table, if level and with a pencil compass scribe the bottom, and thus secure a perfect pattern.

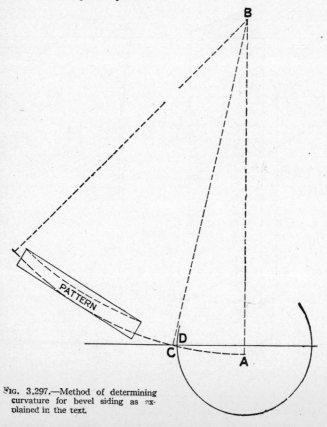

FIG. 3,297.—Method of determining curvature for bevel siding as explained in the text.

A good method is to use a ⅝ in. board rabbetted and face beveled to imitate the siding, showing the bottom edge ⅜ in. instead of ½ in. (almost unnoticeable), and springing it around on ¼ in. furring. If very short radius, steaming is advantageously resorted to.

Plain "Novelty" Siding.—The distinguishing feature of all kinds of novelty siding is the form of joint used which permits laying the siding flush with the sheathing instead of inclined, as

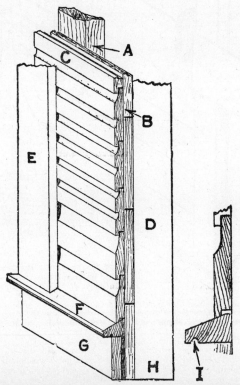

FIGS. 3,298 and 3,299.—Sectional view of novelty siding, and enlarged section of drip of water table. This style siding lies flush against the sheathing.

in the case of Colonial siding and clap boards. This joint is virtually a modification of the ship lap joint as shown in figs. 3,295 and 3,296, and may be further defined as an open side mortised joint.

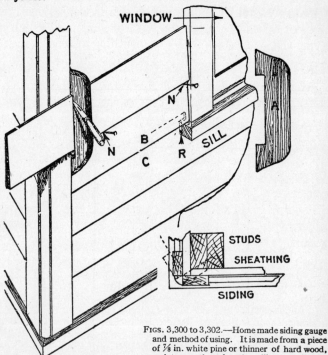

FIGS. 3,300 to 3,302.—Home made siding gauge and method of using. It is made from a piece of ⅞ in. white pine or thinner of hard wood, and two or three lengths will serve all purposes. This one is for marking the end cut against trim after one end has been fitted, to insure a tight joint. This method is quicker than using the square for the reason that the trim is not always perfectly plumb and that it is often desirable to vary the level of the piece to be cut to improve its position or relation to other work or the whole when finished. It is seen that two nails **N N** hold the board in place while being fitted, and that a knife is used, cutting a deep kerf to be sawed to. It makes a cleaner joint than if sawed to a pencil mark. Board **C** is notched to enter rabbet **R**, and extends behind sill 1¼ in—at least above the bottom of board **B**, so that **B** lines with top of sill. Sometimes it might be better to have the bottom of **B** line with the bottom of the window sill which would most probably require different spacing. Then the top of board **C** would line with top of sill, and the spacing from sill to water table, floor or as the case may be, will be of uniform widths.

Figs. 3,298 and 3,299 show detail of novelty siding as laid on top of sheathing. Frequently it is used without sheathing as a matter of economy, the paper, when used being carefully tacked to the studding and the ⅞″ siding nailed directly to the stud, stiffening the building equal to sheathing.

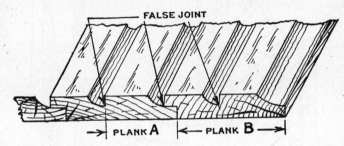

Fig. 3,303.—False joint novelty siding.

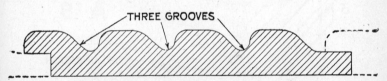

Fig. 3,304.—False joist novelty siding with three groves.

In figs. 3,298 and 3,299 A and D, are studs. B, sheathing, C, novelty siding E, corner board, F, drip of water table, G, band (F and G, together being the water table) H, vertical ¼″ strips allows use of ⅞″ lumber for G, and leaves a desirable air-space that dries out lumber resting upon foundation. I, is F, enlarged to show a groove on the under side which prevents water returning to G, and discoloring or streaking paint, as well as to keep water out of the joint between F and G.

In this illustration it is seen that the corner board is nailed on outside of siding, thereby leaving apertures back of it caused by the grooves in the boards that are not only unsightly, but allow of water getting behind and rotting the wood, for it can be readily understood that where such work would be done, no paint would be put on back of it.

Stud A, is shown to indicate how siding may be put on at random and sawn off after it is put on, thus saving the time of fitting it to the corner board. The object is to save labor, but the method is not to be recommended, except in case of cheap shacks or temporary buildings. Note how line of E, overhangs outside corner of G.

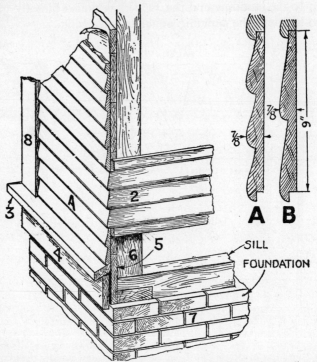

Figs. 3,305 to 3,307.—Corner detail of false joint novelty siding corresponding to design shown in fig. 3,306. In fig. 3,305, where A, joins 8, shows the rich appearance of squaring it against the trim. 3 and 4, is the water table; 5, the sheathing; 6, the studding; and 7, the foundation. Fig. 3,306 shows a three mould and fig. 3,307 a two mould design.

Figured Novelty Siding.—Instead of simply cutting away the siding at the joint, as in the plain type it may be obtained with various ornamental grooves, such as shown in fig. 3,303, giving a more or less rich effect.

False Joint Novelty Siding.—To save labor in laying the siding it may be obtained in double width, so that each piece will appear as two planks, as planks A and B, in fig. 3,303. Evidently such arrangement having half the joints requires less time to lay than the narrow planks.

Vertical Batten Joint Siding.—This type of siding **has been**

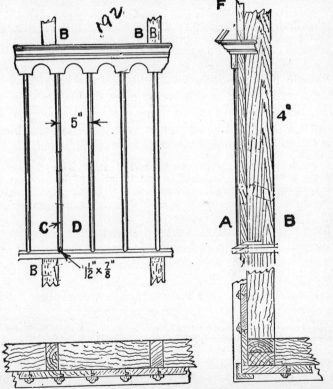

FIGS. 3,308 and 3,311.—Vertical batten joint siding. Fig. 3,308, side view; fig. 3,309, end or sectional view. A, section of siding; B, stud; C, batten; D, face of siding; E, how band course of evecast may be ornamented; F, start of shingles on evecast.

used considerably in some localities where economical construction is necessary and where warmth is not very important.

It consists of ⅞″ pine, or other suitable lumber, from 5 to 8 ins. in width, set vertically and the joint covered with an astragal batten, plain or moulded, ending at the top against a suitable finish, and fitted to water table finish or band course as the case may be. Five-eighths ×1 inch special elliptic pattern is preferable to stock ½×⅞″. Where boards more than 5 ins. wide are used 1⅛ in. width is best

When sheathing paper is used between studding and siding its value is much depreciated unless 1×2″ purlins are set between studs behind the laps on the paper hung vertically and lapping on a stud, otherwise the laps open between the studs and let the air through.

Shingle Siding.—Sometimes buildings are entirely or partially shingled on the side walls, more frequently, the latter siding being used on the first story to a belt line over which a bel-cast is formed and the upper or remaining part shingled. The design determining how the shingles shall be laid.

It is done in a variety of ways with wood and artificial shingles, sometimes a long 24″ shingle is used, laid 10 and 12 inches to the weather. Again the standard 18 in. shingle, laid as much as 6″ to the weather, preferably less.

Metal Siding.—Metal is sometimes used for siding stamped in various designs to represent clapboards, brick and stone. The only excuse for using this kind of siding is when there is great fire hazard.

If not to protect an old building, the new one is best of brick, tile or other monolithic fire proof materials.

CHAPTER 53

Stairs

All carpenters who have tried to build stairs have found it (like boat building) to be an art in itself. This dismal introduction is not intended to discourage the carpenter, but to impress him with the fact that unless he first master the principles of stair layout, he would have as many difficulties to cope with as he would encounter in trying to frame a roof without understanding how to use the steel square.

Although stair building is properly a branch of mill work, the carpenter should know the principles of simple stair layout and construction for he is often called upon to construct porch steps, basement and attic stairs and sometimes the main stairs where the design is not too complicated. In order to follow the instructions intelligently the carpenter should be familiar with the terms and names of parts used in stair buildings. Accordingly these are here given in the glossary which follows.

Definitions

Baluster.—A small column or post forming an ornamental enclosure and supporting the hand rail; usually two to a step.

Balustrade.—A series or row of balusters joined by a hand rail.

Bearers.—Supports for winders wedged into the walls and secured by the strings.

Carriage.—The timber work which supports the steps of a wooden stair.

Close String.—In dog stairs, a staircase without an open newel.

Cockel Stairs.—A winding staircase.

Circular Stairs.—A staircase with steps planned in a circle, all the steps being *winders*.

Curve Out.—A concave curve on the face of a front string at its starting.

Curtail Step.—The first step by which a stair is ascended, finishing at the end in a form of a scroll following the plan of the hand rail.

Dog-legged Stairs.—Such as are solid between the upper flights, or those that have no well hole, the rail and balusters of both the progressive and retrogressive flights falling in the same vertical plane.

The steps are fixed to strings, newels and carraiges, and the ends of the steps of the inferior kind terminate only on the side of the string.

Elliptic Stairs.—Those elliptic in plan, each tread converging so that the assembly forms an elliptic ring in plan.

Face Mould.—A section produced on any inclined plane vertically over a curved plan of hand rail.

Flight of Stairs.—The series of steps leading from one landing to another.

Front String.—The *string* on that side of the stair over which the hand rail is placed.

Fillet.—A band nailed to the face of a front string below the curve and extending the width of a tread.

Flyers.—Steps in a flight that are parallel to each other.

Geometrical Stair.—A flight of stairs supported only by the wall at the end of the steps.

Half-space.—The interval between two flights of steps in a staircase.

Hand Rail.—A rail running parallel to the inclination of the stairs for holding the balusters.

Hollow Newel.—An opening or *well hole* in the middle of the staircase, as distinguished from *solid newel* into which the ends of the steps are built.

Housing.—The notches in the string board of a stair for the reception of steps.

Knee.—A convex bend in the back of a hand rail.

Landing.—Horizontal resting place in a flight.

Newel.—The central column around which the steps of a circular staircase wind; the principal part at the angles and foot of a staircase.

Nosing.—The outer or front edge of the step that projects beyond the riser.

Pitching Piece.—A horizontal timber with one of its ends wedged into the wall at the top of a flight of stairs to support the upper end of the rough strings.

Pitch.—Angle or inclination to the horizontal of the stairs.

Ramp.—A concave or convex curve or casement of an angle, sometimes required at the end of a wreath or an adjoining straight rail.

Rise.—The vertical distance between the treads or for the entire stairs.

Riser.—The board forming the vertical portion of the front of a step.

Run.—The horizontal distance from the first to the last riser of a flight of stairs.

Squaring a Hand Rail.—The method of cutting a blank to the form of a rail for a staircase so that all the vertical sections may be right angles.

Spandril.—The angle formed by a stairway.

Stairs.—The steps whereby to ascend and descend from one story to another.

Staircase.—The whole set of stairs with the side members supporting the steps.

Straight Flight of Stairs.—One having the steps parallel and at right angles to the strings.

Steps.—The assembly consisting of a *tread* and a *riser.*

Scroll or Curtail Step.—The bottom step with the front end shaped to receive.

String or String Piece—The part of a flight of stairs which forms its ceiling or soffit.

String Board.—The board next the well hole which receives the ends of the steps.

Step.—The horizontal board stepped upon in ascending or descending.

Soffit.—The under side of an arch or moulding.

Tread or Run.—The horizontal distance between the risers.

Wall String.—The board placed against the wall to receive the ends of the step.

Well.—The place occupied by the flight of stairs.

Well Hole.—The opening in floor at the top of a flight of stairs.

Well Staircase.—A winding staircase enclosed by walls resembling **a** well.

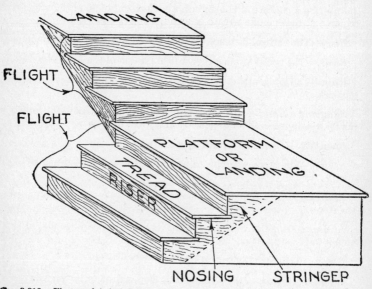

Fig. 3,312.—Illustrated stair definition *1*.

Winders.—Steps not parallel to each other.

Wreath.—The whole of a heliacally curved hand rail.

Wreath Piece.—A portion of a wreath.

The most important of the definitions are illustrated in figs.

3,312 to 3,314, and the student should become thoroughly familiar with the terms before proceeding further.

Laying Out Stairs.—Although the design of stairs is properly

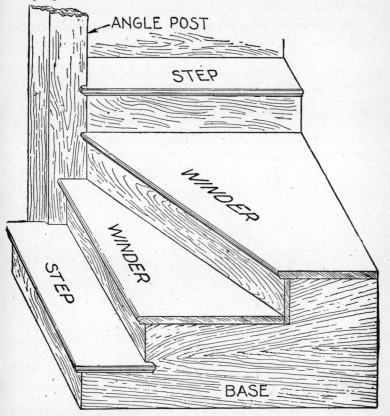

Fig. 3,313.—Illustrated stair definition 2.

the work of the architect, yet the carpenter is frequently called upon to take measurements and work out the problem, especially in the cheaper class of buildings, where it is a comparatively simple job. The principal dimensions to be ascertained are:

1. Rise; 2. Run

The run will be governed not only by the rise but also by the head room. These items being settled, the proportions of tread

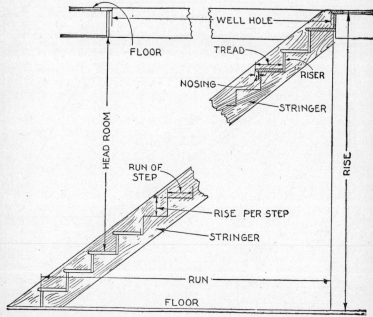

FIG. 3,314.—Illustrated stair definition 3.

and riser must be determined. The following example will serve to illustrate the method of laying out a simple or straight flight of stairs without landings.

Example.—The distance between floors or rise for a straight flight of stairs is 9 ft. Lay out the stairs so that the head room will not be less than 7'-2", the length of opening in upper floor being 9'-6", allowing ¾ in. for plaster and laths, 8 ins. for floor joists, and ⅞ in. for single matched floor.

Run.—In fig. 3,315, draw line LF, to represent elevation of lower floor and MS, parallel and at a distance of 9 ft. (the given rise) to represent floor level. The distance between upper floor and plaster is:

$$¾ + 8 + ⅞ = 9⅝ \text{ ins}$$

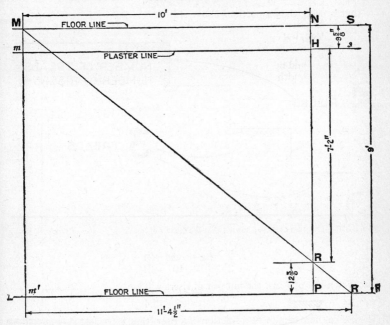

Fɪɢ 3,315.—Preliminary layout for stairs showing method of obtaining approximate run for a given headroom.

Measure down from MS, 9⅝ ins. and draw line *ms*, elevation of plaster.

Now since the head room must not be less than 7 ft. 2 ins., draw vertical line through H, and mark off distance HR = 7'-2" = head room. From M, drop perpendicular M*m'* to LF, and draw through points M and R line MR'. then *m'R'*, is the *approximate* run for head room HR.

Risers and Treads.—For an ordinary building the rise per step or risers should be 7 ins. for a tread of 10 ins. Variation will of course have to be made in both riser and tread to meet the conditions of any particular installation, but the proportions of 7 and 10 may be taken as trial dimensions.

Steps should not be either too steep, due to excessive rise or "slow" due to extreme width of step. An ordinary rule giving good proportions is:

Twice the rise per step plus the tread should equal 24

that is using the proportions above stated.

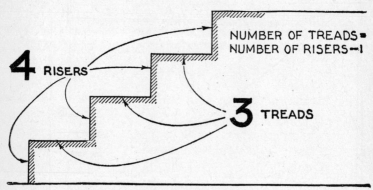

Fig. 3,316.—Diagram of steps showing that *the number of treads = number of risers — 1.*

$$2 \times \text{rise} + \text{tread} = 24$$
$$2 \times 7 + 10 = 24$$

For a rise of 7 ins. the number of risers will be:

$$(9 \times 12) \div 7 = 15.4$$

Since there cannot be a fraction of a riser (that is the last riser should be full size), assume the number of risers to be 15. Take a "story pole" and lay off on it the *rise* or 9 ft.

Set dividers a little over 7 ins. and step off the 9 ft. distance marked on the story pole. If there be a remainder adjust the setting until the 9 ft. distance is divided into 15 parts.

The riser or rise per step is found by measuring one of these spaces. Call the trial run m′R′ or 11 ft. 4½ ins. (as found in fig. 3,315).

The run per step or

width of tread = run ÷ number of steps.........(1)

Substituting the trial values in this equation (1),

width of tread = 11'-4½" ÷ (15−1)
= 136.5 ÷ 14 = 9.75 ins.

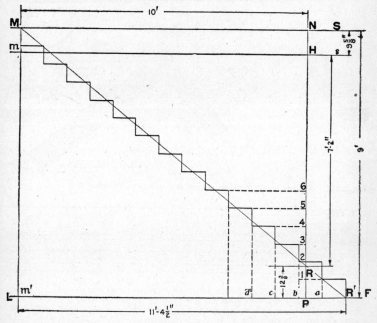

FIG. 3,317.—Completion of layout for stairs. The lines MS, *ms*, LF, etc., are the same as was obtained in fig. 3,315. Divide line *m*'R' or run into 14 equal parts = number of steps as at points *a*, *b*, *c*, etc., and similarly (remembering that the number of risers is always 1 + number of steps) divide the line NP, into 15 parts = number of risers. From these points *a*, *b*, *c*, etc., and 1, 2, 3, etc., draw lines parallel to NP, and *m*'R' respectively, each pair of lines thus drawn giving the riser and tread of each step.

This is near enough the desired 10-in. tread to be satisfactory. Now test for head room by comparing with fig. 3,315. In fig. 3,315, distance PR'=11'-4½"−10'=1'-4½"=16½ ins. Then for 9.75-in. tread there would be 16½ ÷ 9.75 = 1+, or two steps between P and R'.

The height of the second step is 2 $(9 \times 12 \div 15) = 14.4$ ins., or approximately 14 $^7/_{16}$ ins.

For 7′ 2″ head room the allowable height of the second step is 12⅜ ins., but in the trial lay out it is 14⅐/₁₆ − 12⅜ = 2¹/₁₆ in. too high. This is, however, near enough. The complete lay out for the dimensions just obtained is shown in fig. 3,317.

In ordinary carpentry such as common stairs for attic, porch, etc., heads and risers are nailed to place, first risers, then treads. In mill work better construction methods are employed.

FIG. 3,318.—Application of the steel square in laying out stringers.

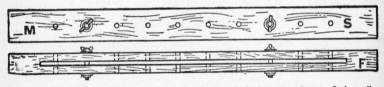

FIGS. 3,319 and 3,320.—Fence for use with steel square in laying out stringers. It is easily made from a piece of oak or other suitable wood by boring a series of holes for wing nut bolts on one side from M to S, and sawing a slot LF on the other side. It is attached to the square as shown in fig. 3,321.

Laying Out the Stringers.

—To transfer the stair layout of fig. 3,317 to stringers full size, must be done with care. Ordinarily the stringers are marked for sawing with a steel square, or a pitch board, but for greater precision a different method is used.

Fig. 3,318 shows the ordinary method of laying out by taking the rise per step on one leg of the square and the tread on the other. To secure accuracy in laying out this way the work should be done with great care.

It is better to use a fence as shown in figs. 3,319 to 3,321, or a pitch board, as in figs. 3,322 and 3,323. While these devices insure a constant setting, they do not give the entire length of the flight with accuracy.

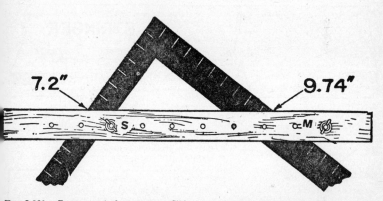

7.2"   **9.74"**

Fig. 3,321.—Fence attached to square. Slide square through the groove to desired setting 7.2 and 9.74; adjust wing nut **MS**, till the bolts are near the square and clamp in position by tightening the wing nuts.

On fine work where precision is required it is better to divide the entire distance into the required number of divisions with dividers and then apply the square or pitch board to these points. This entire distance along the edge of the stringer or "step length of stringer" corresponds to the hypothenuse of a triangle of which one leg is the rise and the other the run of the stairs, as in fig. 3,324. Hence. since the triangle is a right triangle

$$\text{step length of stringer} = \sqrt{\text{rise} + \text{run}^2} \ldots \ldots (1)$$

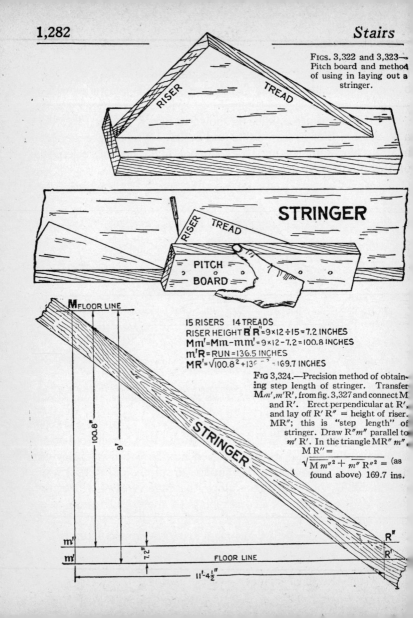

Figs. 3,322 and 3,323—Pitch board and method of using in laying out a stringer.

STRINGER

RISER TREAD

PITCH
BOARD

15 RISERS   14 TREADS
RISER HEIGHT **R'R"** = 9×12 ÷ 15 = 7.2 INCHES
Mm' = Mm − mm' = 9×12 − 7.2 = 100.8 INCHES
m'R = RUN = 136.5 INCHES
MR' = √100.8² + 13⁶·⁵² = 169.7 INCHES

Fig 3,324.—Precision method of obtaining step length of stringer. Transfer Mm', m'R', from fig. 3,327 and connect M and R'. Erect perpendicular at R', and lay off R' R" = height of riser. MR"; this is "step length" of stringer. Draw R"m'' parallel to m' R'. In the triangle MR" m'',

$$M R'' = \sqrt{\overline{M m''^2} + \overline{m'' R''^2}}$$ (as found above) 169.7 ins.

M FLOOR LINE

STRINGER

100.8"

9'

m'

m'

7.2"

FLOOR LINE

11'-4½"

R"

R'

FIG. 3 325.—Precision method of dividing step length of stringer into the required number of divisions. For 14 divisions set dividers as near as possible to the distance MR" ÷ 14, and step off on edge of stringer 14 divisions. If the divider leg register with R" for the last division mark the points stepped off; if not, change setting with mechrometer screw and try again or until the exact setting is obtained.

FIG. 3,326—Operation of marking riser and treads with pitch board from the points obtained in fig. 3,325.

Substituting the values of the example as given in fig. 3,324, step length of stringer, or

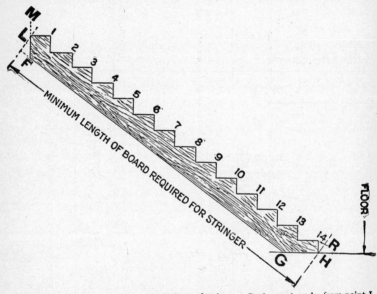

FIG. 3,327.—Complete layout for simple form of stringer. *To lay out ends,* from point L, continue line ML to the edge of board giving LF, top end of stringer. Draw with pitch board line RH, riser to first step *making RH, shorter than riser height by an amount equal to thickness of tread.* From H, draw HG, parallel to tread, RHG being the shape of lower end. Evidently the length of board required for stringer is equal to distance between L and H.

$$MR'' = \sqrt{(9'\text{-}7.2)^2 + (11'\text{-}4\tfrac{1}{2}'')^2}$$

reducing to inches

$$= \sqrt{100.8^2 + 136.5^2} = 169.7 \text{ ins.}$$

Lay off **169.7 ins.** on the edge of the stringer, leaving enough stock at the ends as may be required, and with dividers. divide the distance 169.7 ins. into the same number of parts as there are treads, as in fig. 3,325. From the points thus found lay out the risers and treads with the steel square of pitch board as in fig. 3,326.   The ends of the stringer are laid out as in fig. 3,327, which shows the complete layout.   Where the steps are too wide for two stringers a third or center stringer is provided.

An economical way of constructing the center stringer is shown in fig. 3,328, where use is made of the blocks cut from the side stringers.

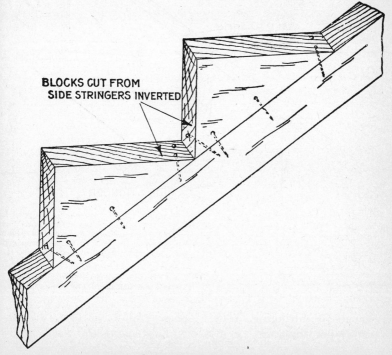

BLOCKS CUT FROM
SIDE STRINGERS INVERTED

Fɪɢ. 3,328.—Economical built up center stringer using blocks cut from the side stringers.

On enclosed or semi-enclosed stringers a combination of stringer and wall board is commonly used as shown in fig. ,3,329 especially upon attic stairs. Such construction is not suited for fine work where the effects of shrinkage would show to disadvantage.

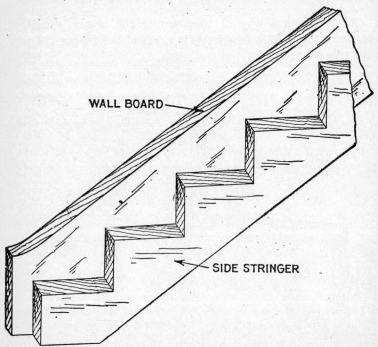

WALL BOARD

SIDE STRINGER

Fig. 3,329.—Combination side stringer and wall board as used in ordinary construction as on attic stairs. One inch stock is used for both stringer and wall board, the stringer being nailed to the wall board.

Types of Stringers.—There are several forms of stringers classed according to the method of attaching the risers and treads, as:

1. Cleated

2. Cut
3. Built up
4. Rabbetted (housed)

   a. Rectangular grooves
   b. Tapered grooves (wedge type)

The distinction between these various types is shown in figs.

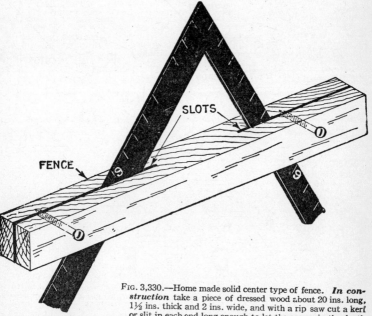

SLOTS

FENCE

Fig. 3,330.—Home made solid center type of fence. ***In construction*** take a piece of dressed wood about 20 ins. long, 1½ ins. thick and 2 ins. wide, and with a rip saw cut a kerf or slit in each end long enough to let the square in the depth required. In the absence of a thumb screw an ordinary or round head screw may be used for binding it to the square as shown. It is obvious that the convenient size given for the fence may be varied so long as it will serve the purpose and have a true contact face.

3,331 to 3,335. The cleated stringer is for very rough work, as for basement stairs. Cut stringers are largely used in ordinary carpentry, as for porch steps or ordinary stairs.

The built up type is used where the stairs are wide enough to require a center stringer, the waste blocks cut from the outside stringer, being used in building up the center stringer, as shown.

These blocks L,R,F, in fig. 3,332 are the same as L,R,F, in fig. 3,333 cut from the outside stringer inverted and nailed on. The rabbetted or

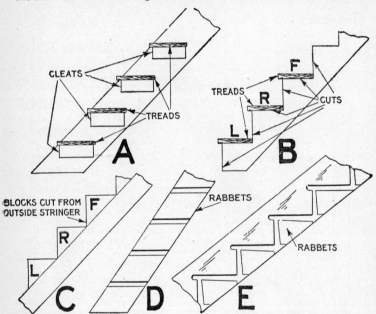

FIGS. 3,331 to 3,335.—Various stringers. **A**, cleated; **B**, cut; **C**, built up; **D**, rabbetted or housed, the sides of the rabbet being parallel; **E**, rabbetted with tapered grooves for wedges.

housed type of stringer is the kind used on fine work and should be made at the mill. In this type the risers and tread are held in the rabbets by wedges set in glue.

These various types of stringer and methods of securing the risers and treads will be described more in detail in the examples following:

Simple Basement Stairs.—The example here given in figs. 3,336 and 3,337 serves to illustrate two types of stringer, the simple cleated type and the rabbetted form with sides of rabbet

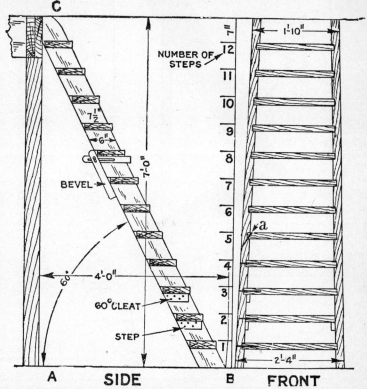

FIGS. 3,336 and 3,337.—Simple basement stairs illustrating cleat and rabbet (straight grooves) type of stringer construction.

parallel. As shown in the figures the run is 4 ft. and rise 7 ft. By finding the corresponding angle the bevel may be set to that angle and the treads laid out at the proper inclination. Thus:

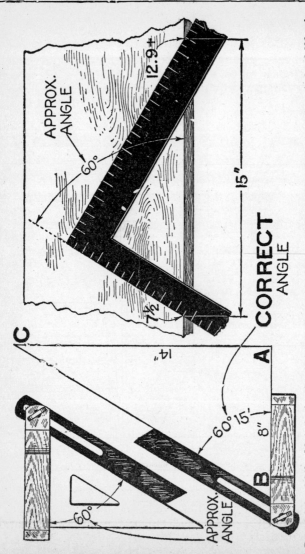

FIGS. 3,338 to 3,340.—Methods of setting the bevel in laying out stringers for the simple basement stairs shown in figs. 3,336 and 3,337. It should be noted that the correct angle is *60° 15'*, and accordingly the draughtsman's triangle and steel square methods are only *approximate*, but in practice are near enough. The progressive carpenter however who is interested in precision methods especially where no extra time is required will set his bevel to the exact angle *60° 15'* by the method of fig. 3,339.

In the triangle ABC,

$$\tan ABC = \frac{AC}{AB} = \frac{7}{4} = 1.75$$

from the table of natural trigonometrical functions (page 522), this corresponds to an angle of 60º15'.

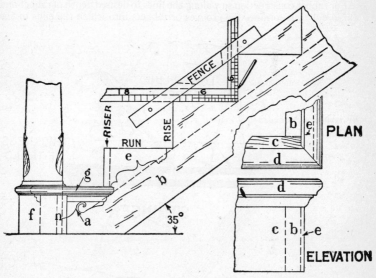

FIGS. 3,341 to 3,343.—Application of home made fence and details of stair construction, showing how stringer intersects newel at *h*. The first tread in place with the nosing *g* returned across end and a mould nosing of the same shape, intersecting and mitred around newel on top of newel base *f*. *e*, shows a bracket of thin material planted on face of string to cover end of riser. On plan it is seen how that e, mitres to riser *c*, and on elevation how riser *c* faces rise of stringer b, mitred to e. *d* is tread nosed and returned as at *g*, on section.

If a draughtsman triangle be at hand, the bevel may be very easily set to this angle. Otherwise draw the triangle ABC, to any scale or apply the steel square with the setting 7½ applied to a 15 in. line. These methods are shown in figs. 3,338 to 3,340. In laying out, first the spacing of the treads on the edge of the stringer is marked and then the bevel is applied to these points and lines drawn. These lines represent the level of the upper surface of the treads.

Now set compass to radius equal to thickness of tread, with one point of compass on each line just drawn, describe arcs and with bevel draw lines tangent to these arcs, as in fig. 3,344.

These lines will be parallel to the tread lines and the distance between the pair will equal thickness of tread.

If cleats are to be used nail cleats flush with lower of each pair of lines.

For rabbet construction saw along the lines to desired depth of rabbet and chisel out thus forming the grooves or rabbets into which the ends of the

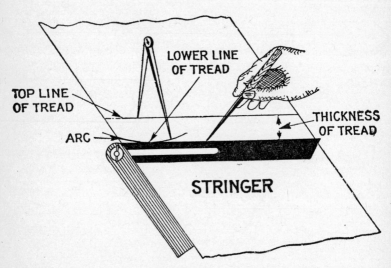

Fig. 3,344.—Method of laying out lower tread line parallel to upper tread line and at distance apart equal to thickness of tread, with aid of compass and bevel.

grooves should fit tightly. Hence to make a good job the tread lines should be laid out accurately to thickness of treads, and accordingly, in applying the bevel, use a precision scriber rather than a dull carpenters' pencil with an acre of lead on the end of it.

When the grooves have been cut and stringers sawed off accurately to length the parts are ready to assemble. Fig. 3,346 shows the assembly and method of nailing, both for the cleat and rabbet construction.

Ordinarily the stringers may be built of 1¼ in. spruce or equally tough wood

The length required for these stringers will be a little over 8 ft. Figs. 3,345 and 3,346, show methods of using steel square and bevel in laying out the stringers.

The setting for the steel square as shown in 7 and 12¾. It is seen (in fig. 3,346), that the bevel set to the angle and the rule is much faster **and**

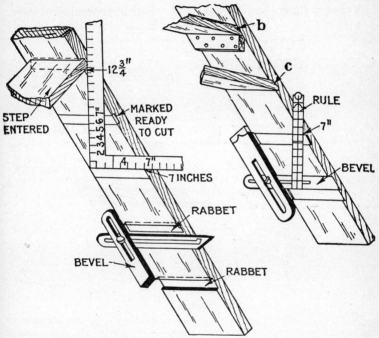

FIGS. 3,345 and 3,346.—Method of using the steel square, bevel and rule in laying out stringers for simple basement stairs.

the method possesses less danger of error in this class of stair building where the stairs approach the angle of a ladder and has open rise. These sketches show the rise between steps to be 7″, but they may be placed at any distance that best suits the requirements. As at *b* and *c* a little added refinement may be had by chamfering and beveling top edge of step and raw end of wood exposed by reason of the stringer being on an angle and face of step square.

By cutting this square corner off with a sharp chisel takes off the saw-cut, looks and paints better.

Instead of solid stringers, they may be of the built up, cleated type, as shown in fig. 3,347.

Types of Risers and Treads.—There are in general two classes

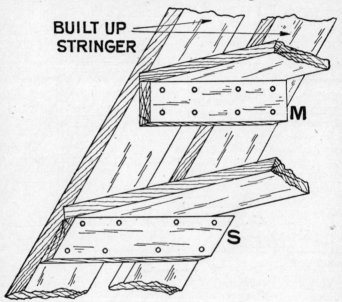

BUILT UP STRINGER

M

S

Fig. 3,347.—Built up cleated type of stringer with treads in position showing construction. Can be used to advantage where small stuff is on hand and no wide boards available.

of risers and treads, classified according to the method of jointing, as:

1. Plain
2. Tongue and groove

For ordinary work the plain class is used, the tongue and groove for finer installations.

There are two types of plain risers and treads, as shown in figs. 3,348 and 3,349 representing American and English practice, the effect of shrinkage on these types being shown in figs. 3,350 and 3,351.

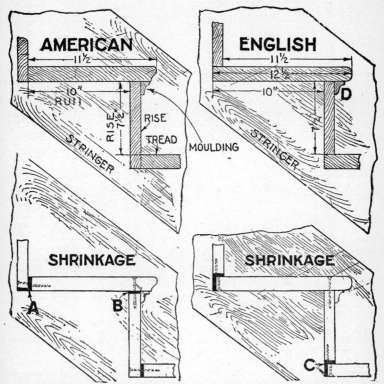

FIGS. 3,348 to 3,351.—American and English types of plain treads and risers, showing effect of shrinkage as described in the text.

When constructed of materials that are not thoroughly seasoned, or when the rise and tread is not as well seasoned as the string shrinkage is sure to occur as seen in figs. 3,350 and 3,351. The nailing in fig. 3,350 is best arranged for the least showing of shrinkage.

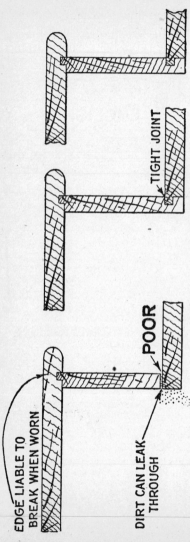

FIGS. 3,352 to 3,354.—Various forms of tongue and groove construction for treads and risers.

In the riser it will be greatest at and hidden by moulding D, which is nailed to tread and cannot pull down with rise. Instead of the tread receding from riser at A, it will remain as in fig. 3,348.

If nailed, as in fig. 3,351, the shrinkage will occur as at C. A good plan is to wedge the treads and risers and leave the gluing and nailing or setting of nails until all is well seasoned, perhaps artificially, then the finished stairs will remain as in figs. 3,348 and 3,349. Remember that the most conspicuous joint is the one you see ascending the stairs. The American method affords the most practical opportunity for this.

It is clearly seen that if all the materials be of the same kind and seasoned, either method will show no material defects. The disadvantage of the English method is, if the desired tread be 11½", a 14" board must be used. It is overcome by using a 9" run.

On fine work to minimize the effect of shrinkage and prevent dirt sifting through the joints between treads and risers, the tongue and groove construction, as shown in figs. 3,353 and 3,354, is used. There are several forms of this construction, the riser being tongued at the top, or bottom, or both top and bottom.

A tongue at the top of the riser, while making a good joint, is objectionable in that it weakens the nosing of the tread, especially after the latter has become worn by long use. Accordingly, when this construction is used, the tread should be amply thick or the width of nosing reduced, to prevent abnormal stress coming on the reduced section of tread along the groove.

The tongue or lip is usually about ⅜ in. deep and ⅜ or ½ in. thick. This

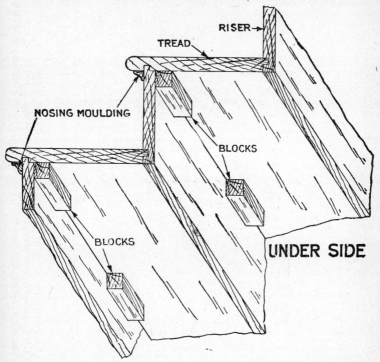

FIG. 3,355.—View of underside of steps showing retaining blocks glued in the angles of the steps to hold them together, and nosing moulding.

construction should be done at the mill but if the carpenter be called upon to do the work he should be careful not to get the risers too narrow.

The tongue should fit snugly in the groove: the risers and treads are held together by a series of blocks, as shown in fig. 3,355 These blocks should be from four to six inches long and made of dry wood. They are usually about 2 in. square. On a step three feet long. Three of these blocks should be used, spaced equal distances apart.

Housed, Wedge Type Stringers.—Generally in finish stair construction the treads and risers are housed into the wall stringer, the rabbets being of the tapered side or wedge type as

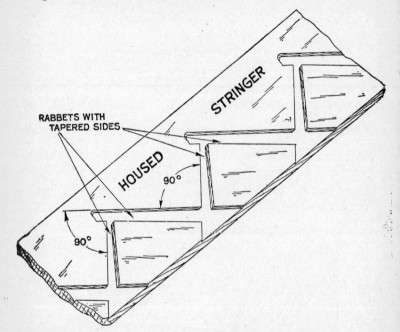

Fig. 3,356.—Detail of housed (tapered rabbet or wedge type) stringer showing appearance of the tapered rabbets.

distinguished from the plain (parallel side) rabbet used on rough basement stairs already described. The general appearance of the rabbets are shown in the detail illustrated in fig. 3,356. This is the wall stringer.

The routing out or rabbeting is one-half to ⅝ in. deep and so shaped as to allow for a wedge from one-half to ¾ in. thick at the butt which is for the purpose of forcing and holding the tread and riser faces tight against the outside cut of rabbet. When this work is accurately done the joint is hardly visible. This represents best stair construction suitable for fine first floor work and is usually done at the mill and the parts brought to the building knocked down, the carpenter having only to assemble the parts.

FIGS. 3,357 and 3,358.—Center housed stringer. The grooves are cut by an electrically operated machine to accurately fit the ends of the treads and risers.

The carpenter will have framed the rough stringers which are to support the ceiling below the stair and placed them so that they may be used as a temporary stair for the workmen.

If the stairway be an open one or semi-open, the plastering under the

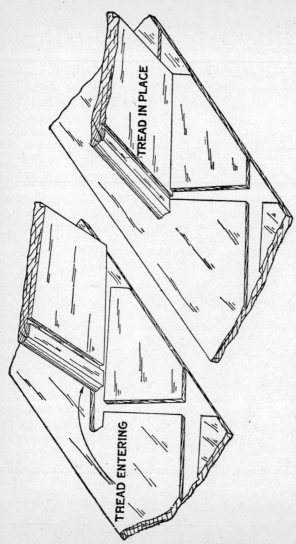

FIGS. 3,359 and 3,360.—Tread *entering*, and *in place* in housed stringer tapered rabbet.

stringers will have been placed, the stair being put together on the floor and then raised to its place.

If the well hole be such, that the stair must be assembled while the strings or wall boards are in place, the lath and plaster must be left off the rough stringers until after the stair has been assembled and the wedges glued and driven in place.

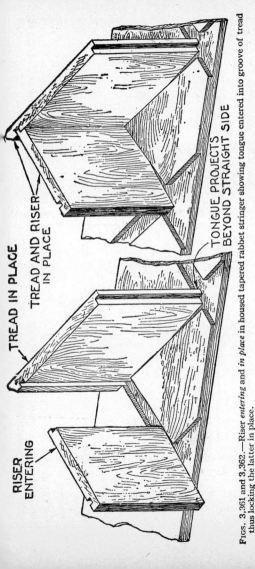

TREAD AND RISER IN PLACE

TREAD IN PLACE

RISER ENTERING

TONGUE PROJECTS BEYOND STRAIGHT SIDE

Figs. 3,361 and 3,362.—Riser *entering* and *in place* in housed tapered rabbet stringer showing tongue entered into groove of tread thus locking the latter in place.

Figs. 3,361 to 3,362 show tread and riser being put in place in the tapered rabbets.

It will be noted that the tread is first put in place, then the riser, and when thus assembled, as in fig. 3,362, are locked in position; that is, the tread cannot be withdrawn without first removing the riser, being held by the tongue on the top edge of the riser.

It remains to further secure these parts by the insertion of wedges cut to the angle of the tapered sides of the rabbets. These wedges, as previously mentioned, are dipped in glue and driven home in the rabbets, thus firmly forcing the treads and risers against the outer side of the rabbets, as shown in fig. 3,363. The treads and risers may be further secured by retaining blocks, as shown in fig. 3,355.

The general appearance of stairs with housed (wedge type rabbets) wall stringer, as seen from the under side, is shown in fig. 3,365.

In laying out a housed (wedge type rabbet) stringer, a tool (which can be easily home made) shown in figs. 3,367 to 3,369, can be used to advantage.

In making a tool of this kind it is necessary to determine the correct shape

FIG. 3,364.—Center treads and risers showing tongue and groove joint.

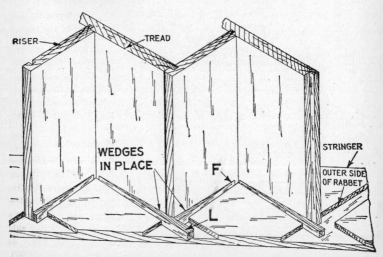

FIG. 3,363.—Wedges driven home in tapered rabbets of housed stringer. When the tread wedge L is cut long to project beyond riser rabbet, the riser rabbet wedge F is driven in first, then the long wedge L. Since the wedge F is vertical when the stairs are in place, the long wedge L will hold F in place against any tendency of the latter to fall out because of poor glue and vibration. However, both the wedges are sometimes made short.

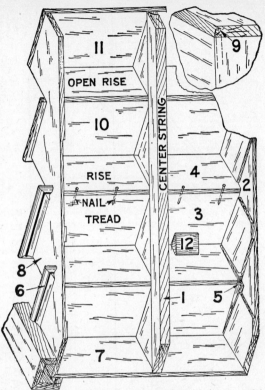

FIGS. 3,365 and 3,366.—General appearance of stairs with center stringer and housed (wedge rabbet type) wall stringer, and detail showing mitre cut tread. As mentioned elsewhere, the center stringer is built up using waste triangular blocks cut from outside stringer. They are seen nailed to the top of a piece of joist center string 1. It may be any size that will not fall below lath or finishing line. It shows how the wall string is rabbetted 2, as previously described, to receive the tread 3, and riser 4, and the final wedging 5. The bottom tread, 6, is shown return nosed on a plain stringer. The bottom rise is shown mitred. This is not necessary when the newel is placed half on the first step and the base is a continuation of wall string, but would be necessary on the succeeding risers on outside stringer unless as at 8, the square end of riser should be covered by such finish as shown, then the tread must be as much longer as the thickness of this finish. If the mitre be cut as at 9 (fig. 3,366), it insures easy nailing without danger of driving it out of place or the need of securing backing for it on the string. 10 shows a tread with the end cut off square overhanging the string about 1 in., without other finish. The top step 11 is cut off flush with the string as would be the case if it were for a "boxed in" stairs. Between it and the next step is shown an open rise in which manner cellar stairs are ordinarily built.

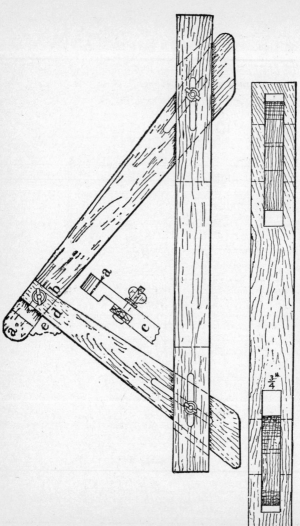

PLAN OF FENCE OR GUIDE

FIGS. 3,367 to 3,369.—Special bevel for laying out tapered rabbet of housed stringers. *It is made* of three pieces of hard wood adjustable at its three extremities by wing nut bolts working in grooves as shown. These bolts may be ⅞ or ¼ in. The slots are readily made with a ¼ or a ⁷⁄₁₆ in. bit and a keen chisel. It can be set to various depths of rise and run. The illustration shows it set for 7½″ rise and 10′ run. Fig. 3,367, shows a section at its right angle *b*, showing that the tongue *d*, can be adjusted for less overhang of nosing when it is desirable to use a smaller or no moulding *e*, under it. It is shown set as most generally applied, to receive a ⅞ × 1½ in. moulding as dotted of the blades—width at narrow end, length and angle between the inclined sides.

Since the tread is placed in its rabbet first, the width of the riser rabbet at the lower end must be such that there will be room enough between the projecting of the tread and side of rabbet to permit the insertion of the riser, that is, at the lower end of riser rabbet.

minimum width = length of tread tongue + thickness of riser

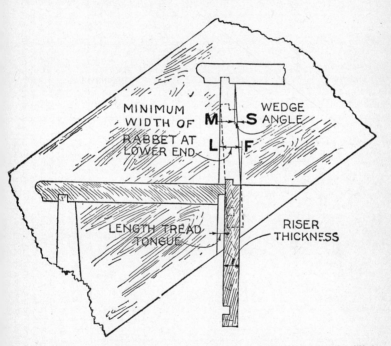

FIG. 3,370.—Condition which governs minimum width of riser rabbet at lower end. *Minimum width LF = length of tread-tongue + thickness of riser.*

This condition is clearly shown in fig. 3,370. Accordingly, following this principle, the layout of riser blade for the bevel tool is made as explained in fig. 3,371, and somewhat similarly the tread blade layout is obtained as explained in fig. 3,372.

Skirting Board.—By definition a skirting board is a dressed board placed and fitted at either side of the steps to form a finish or "skirt" over the rough work. Instead of housed

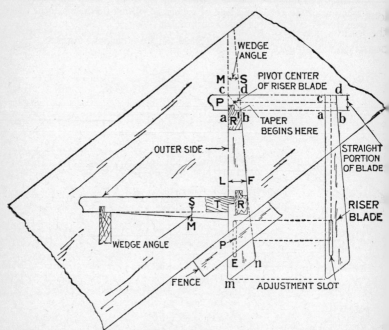

Fɪɢ. 3,371.—Layout of riser blade for home made special bevel. First draw outline of outer side of tread and riser rabbets and edges of stringer. Sketch in end of tread T, in position, and show upper end of riser just entering rabbet at R, and in position at R'. Draw line from *b* to *b'*, giving wedge side of rabbet. Draw perpenticulars *ac* and *bd*, then the intersection P, of the diagonals *ad* and *bc*, is position of pivot for riser blade. Sketch in portion of *fence* and continue sides of rabbet down past fence and connect as indicated by dotted lines, giving outline *camnbd* of riser blade. Make length of fence slot, say, twice width of fence, or to suit the desired range of tool. The riser blade, made according to the layout, is shown more clearly at the right, the letters corresponding to those in the lay out.

stringers, the steps may be supported by open stringers and skirting boards used for the finish at the sides.

On cheap work the skirting board will be cut to fit over the treads and risers with *butt joints,* as in fig. 3,373, and for fine work with *rabbetted joints,* as in fig. 3,381.

No matter how fine a fit be made with butt joints the work will look very bad in a few months, as shown in fig. 3,378, because the joints open up on account of shrinkage. In fitting a skirting board the nosing of the treads is cut off at the joint so as to

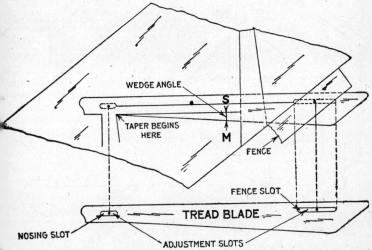

Fig. 3,372.—Lay out of tread blade for home made special bevel. The outline for the tread blade is obtained in exactly the same manner as for the riser blade explained in fig. 3,375, except that the wedge angle **MS,** is made the same as for the riser blade. There will be in addition to the fence slot a short slot at the other end of the blade making the tool adjustable for nosing.

simplify making the joint. This is clearly shown for the butt joint skirting board in fig. 3,375, the shape of the board being shown in fig. 3,374.

Cut and Mitred Stringer.—This is a form of open stringer in which the ends of the risers are mitred against the vertical

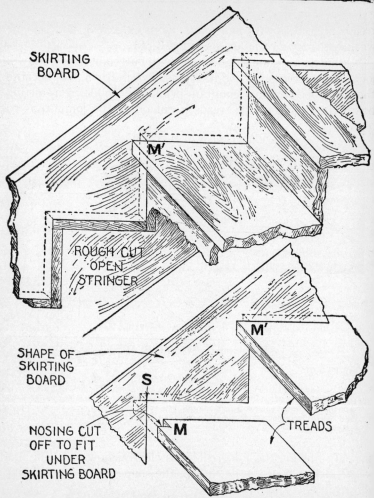

SKIRTING BOARD

M'

ROUGH CUT OPEN STRINGER

SHAPE OF SKIRTING BOARD

M'

S

M

NOSING CUT OFF TO FIT UNDER SKIRTING BOARD

TREADS

Figs. 3,373 to 3,375.—Butt joint skirting board and detail of joint. To simplify fitting the board the nosing of the treads are cut off as at M (fig. 3,374). When the board is in place the cut away part M, fits under S, of the board (fig. 3,373), indicated in position by the tread in dotted lines at M'. Here note how the skirting board fits on top the tread and against the riser.

FIGS. 3,376 and 3,377.—Two examples of Curtis center cut and mitred stringer stairs, colonial design.

JOINTS OPENED UP

SHRINKAGE
THIS WAY

BUTT JOINT SKIRTING BOARD

M

S

CUT STRINGER

SHRINKAGE
THIS WAY

Fɪɢ. 3,378.—Appearance of butt joint skirting board after the wood shrinks. It should be noted that the large cracks opened up are due both to the shrinkage of the skirting board away from the steps and the shrinkage of the rough cut stringer away from the skirting board. As indicated by the arrows these shrinkages are in opposite directions.

Fɪɢ. 3,379. Curtis center open stringer colonial stairs, straight run first to second floors. There are 16 risers and 14 treads, 1 starting and 1 landing newel, 1 lasting, 1 gooseneck and 27 balusters. Note effect of white open stringer and mahoganized treads and rail.

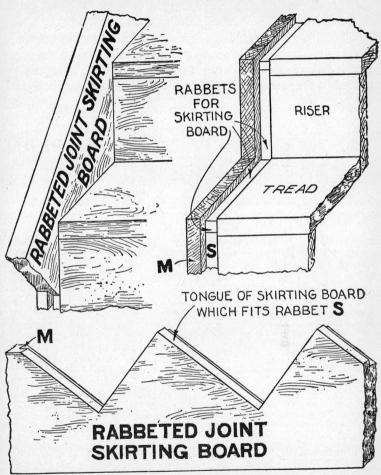

RABBETS
FOR
SKIRTING
BOARD

RISER

TREAD

M

S

RABBETED JOINT SKIRTING BOARD

TONGUE OF SKIRTING BOARD
WHICH FITS RABBET **S**

M

RABBETED JOINT
SKIRTING BOARD

Figs. 3,380 to 3,382.—Rabbetted skirting board and views of groove cut in steps and tongue cut in the board. For clearness the size of the groove is exaggerated in fig. 3,381. Evidently shrinkage will not cause visible opening of the joint because of the tongue projecting beneath the surface of the steps.

notch and a moulding is carried around the two exposed edges of the tread. This construction is shown in figs. 3,383 and 3,384 and is used when the outside stringer is to be of the same wood as the finish of the house and is intended to take the place of the face casing or skirting board. All the risers should be mitred to the stringer, as shown in the illustrations at MS, and LF.

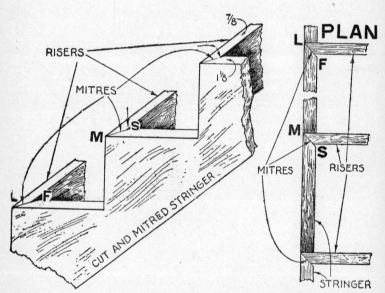

FIGS. 3,383 and 3,384.—Cut and mitred stringer and view showing mitres in place. The mitres MS and LF. are lettered the same in both views.

Treatment of the Stringer Ends.—In order that the stairs may be firm and rigid they should be well fastened at the ends.

Figs. 3,385 to 3,387 show some methods of fastening the stringers at the top to the header for different relative positions of the top step and header. These methods are satisfactory and may be used where the stairs are not supported by section posts.

Fig. 3,391 shows method of support at lower end.

The illustration shows part of the outside stringer broken away making

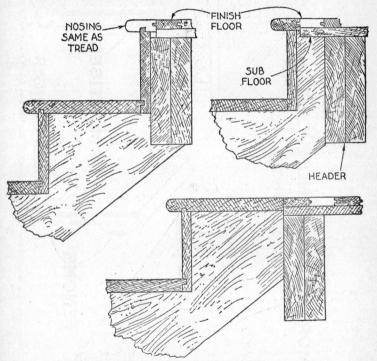

FIGS. 3,385 to 3,387.—Some methods of fastening stringers at the top to headers.

visible the carriage or rough piece of lumber to which the finished stringer is nailed or otherwise secured.

Fig. 3,388 shows method of fastening end of a housed stringer to the end posts or *newels*.

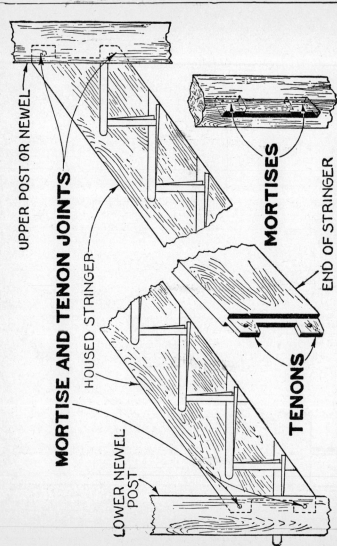

UPPER POST OR NEWEL

MORTISE AND TENON JOINTS

HOUSED STRINGER

LOWER NEWEL POST

MORTISES

END OF STRINGER

TENONS

Figs. 3,388 to 3,390.—Housed stringer fastened to end posts or *newels* by mortise and tenon joints and detail of the joint.

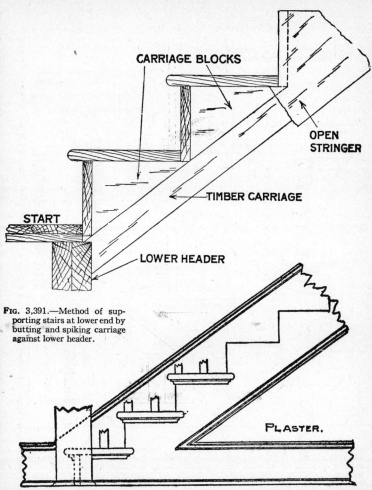

CARRIAGE BLOCKS

OPEN STRINGER

TIMBER CARRIAGE

START

LOWER HEADER

FIG. 3,391.—Method of supporting stairs at lower end by butting and spiking carriage against lower header.

PLASTER.

FIG. 3,392.—Stairs with cut and mitered stringers. The ends of the risers are mitered against the vertical or riser line of the string, which prevent the end wood of the risers being seen. The other end of each riser is in the wall stringer. The outer end of the tread is also mitered at the nosing and a piece marked like the nosing is mitered against, or returned at the end of the head. The end of this returned piece is again returned on itself back to the stringer.

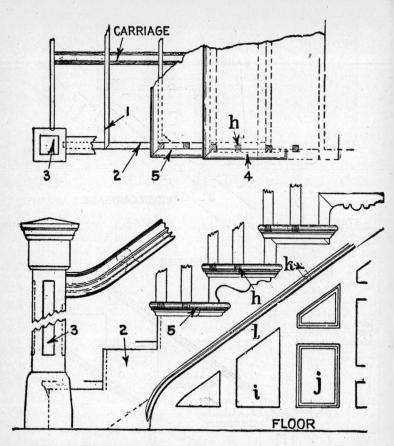

FIGS. 3,393 and 3,394.—Stairs with open outside mortised stringer and steps *return nosed.* The riser 1 is mitred to stringer at 2. At *h,* is shown a dovetail mortise into which the tenon of baluster is stepped before the return 4 is nailed on, which is mitred at the corner. When ready to brad, it should be coated with hot glue. 3, shows location of newel; 2, the face of string on which is first shown two treads and risers without finish. The next three show the treads in place and the equal division of balusters. In this instance, two to a step. It will be seen that but one side of mortise and tenon *h,* is beveled instead of both. The first tread shows its return with its inside flush with string and the necessity of the rise being mitred to the stringer. *k,* shows how string with a bead worked on the bottom sets over jib panel rail *l.*

FIGS. 3,395 and 3,396.—Treatment of center stringer ends. Face stringers as shown in fig. 3,395 are tenoned to fit into a mortise in the corner or landing newels, and as shown in fig. 3,396 are secured on the inside by means of cleats screwed to the stringer and newel.

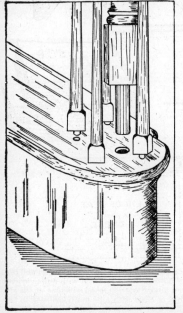 

FIG. 3,397.—Center round starting newel and balusters showing dowel pin joint with starting tread.

FIG. 3,398.—Center square newel showing mortise and tenon joint with tread.

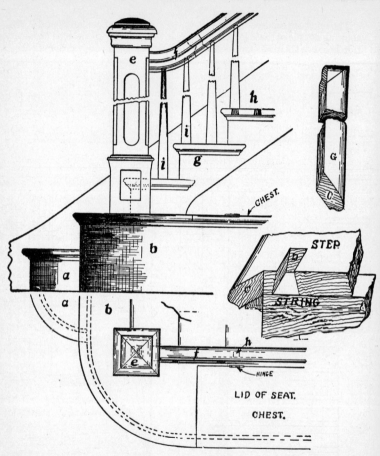

Figs. 3,399 to 3,402.—Placement of newel half on the third step with open stringer, and construction details. As shown the outside end of bottom step is returned with a rounded end into the riser to step *b*, which in turn continues around outside newel widening at the side of stairs forming a seat into which is built a box or chest with a lid cut out of seat in proportion to the size of box. This seat may finish either against the wall or with a pew end. *C*, is the cut on step to fit nosing G, and D, is the dovetail mortise to receive dovetail tenon of baluster. *h* is beveled both sides. The newel *e* is of simple construction; *f* is the rail; G, nosing. The *balusters i*, *i'* suggest a square at bottom graduating, the top half tapering to a round, and square the whole length.

The ends are secured by mortise and tenon joints, figs. 3,389 and 3,390, showing details of these joints. This method makes a substantial construction because the posts can be securely fastened to the floor timbers.

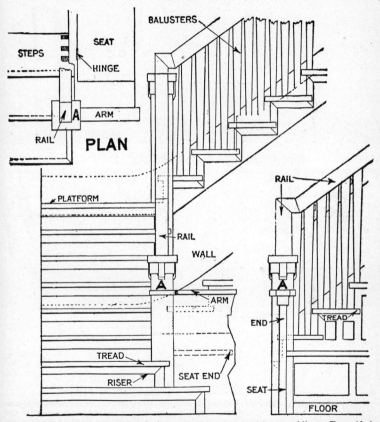

FIGS. 3,403 to 3,405.—Example of platform stairs mission style with no mouldings. Turned balusters with square ends may be used. Fig. 3,403, plan; figs. 3,404 and 3,405, elevation. The only mitering necessary is that for returning the tread nosing across the outside end. Other joints being covered with the ½ × 2 strip shown on stringer and riser where it shows a panel. The best way to place this finish is to mitre at corner and at angles on string, though it may be done, if the material be thoroughly seasoned, with a butt joint and make a reasonably fair job if properly bradded and glued. Fig. 3,403 shows spandrel.

The newel should run down beneath the floor by the side of a joist to which it may be very securely fastened by spiking or bolting.

Figs. 3,406 and 3,407 show two examples of this construction. If the joist runs the other way try to get the newel post against it if possible, either by furring out the joist, or cutting a portion off the thickness of the newel, as in fig. 3,407.

In ordinary work the usual method is to let the newel rest on the floor, but this arrangement is less substantial. A method of doing this is shown

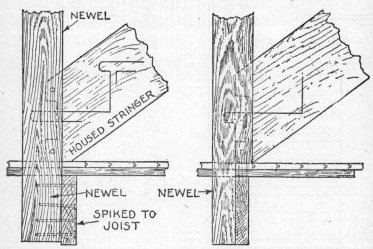

NEWEL

HOUSED STRINGER

NEWEL   NEWEL→

SPIKED TO JOIST

Figs. 3,406 and 3,407.—Newel attached to joist. Fig. 3,406, flush; fig. 3,407, partly cut **away.**

in fig. 3,408, where the floor is reinforced by a block and the newel secured by a long lag screw; another and better method is by bridging between joists, as in fig. 3,409.

When the position of the newel comes between joists it may be firmly secured by bridging across the joists, as in fig. 3,410.

The treatment of the finish between housed stringer and base board at the ends is shown in figs. 3,411 and 3,412.

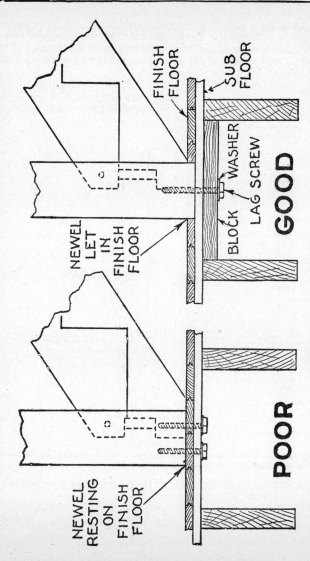

FINISH
FLOOR

SUB
FLOOR

NEWEL LET
IN
FINISH
FLOOR

BLOCK

WASHER

LAG SCREW

GOOD

NEWEL
RESTING
ON
FINISH
FLOOR

POOR

Figs. 3,048 and 3,409.—Methods of securing newel between joists. Fig. 3,408, cheap and inferior method of placing newel on finished floor and fastening with screws or spikes; fig. 3,409, more substantial method of letting in newel through finish floor, reinforcing from below by a block and securing newel by a long lag screw. The block may run across to the joist as shown, giving extra rigidity.

In fig. 3,411, there will be a little triangular section LAF, (shown shaded) at the junction of the stringer and baseboard. The stringer may be broadened in width, the outer edge being an arc tangent to the top edge of the baseboard; it may be worked out of one piece or built up according to the width of lumber used for the stringer.

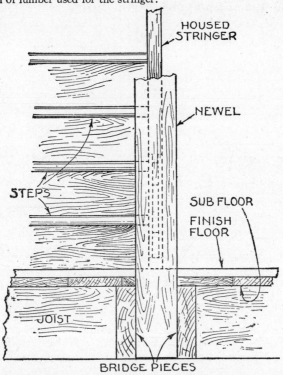

HOUSED STRINGER

NEWEL

STEPS

SUB FLOOR

FINISH FLOOR

JOIST

BRIDGE PIECES

Fig. 3,410.—Method of fastening newel by bridging across between joists. The illustration shows a bridge on each side but ordinarily one bridge will be ample.

Fig. 3,412 shows similar treatment at the top end.

Numerous details of construction are shown in the accompanying cuts, illustrating treatment of approach end of stairs, placement of newel, etc.

Hand Rails and Balusters.—The hand rail which is made in various design runs parallel to the inclination of the stairs and serves the purpose of holding the balusters, the assembly forming a sort of fence, giving protection against falling over

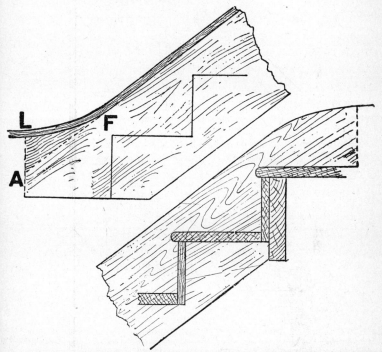

Figs. 3,411 and 3,412.—Method of joining the wall stringer ends with the base board. Fig. 3,411, lower end; fig. 3,412, top end.

the side of the stairs. As mentioned, there are a multiplicity of forms of hand rail, of which a few are shown in figs. 3,414 to 3,418.

The particular part of hand rails which presents difficulty to the carpenter is the curved portion usually required at the ends.

In former times when labor was cheap these curves were very elaborate, but the present tendency is toward straight lines, some examples of curved portions of hand rails being shown in figs. 3,420 to 3,425. In this con-

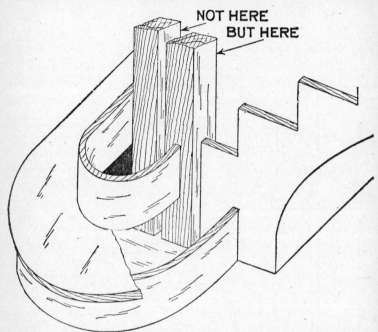

NOT HERE
BUT HERE

FIGS. 3,413.—Right and wrong methods of locating bottom newel starting from the floor.

nection the student should understand the meaning of the terms *wreath* and *ramp* as given in the definitions.

The methods of shaping the wood to these curves, which is one of the difficult branches of carpentry, is later described.

Sometimes, because of length, it is necessary to splice the

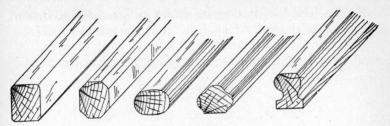

FIGS. 3,414 to 3,418.—Various forms of hand rail.

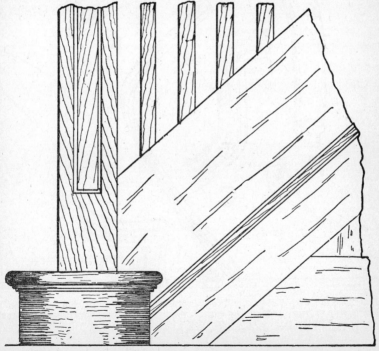

FIG. 3,419.—Only construction that admits of placing newel in center of tread.

hand rail. This may be done as shown in figs. 3,426 to 3,428. The material from which hand rails are made should be straight grained and thoroughly seasoned. Weak hand rails of small cross section are sometimes strengthened in the middle

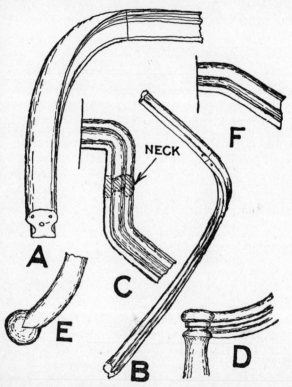

FIGS. 3,420 to 3,425.—Various curved portions of hand rails. **A**, wreath with quarter turn from pitch of stairs to second floor level; **B**, wreath following from one flight around the cylinder to the pitch of the next flight; **C**, "goose neck," so called from its head being raised up to newel position by a *neck*, the length (height) of which is determined by the number of risers to where it must start on the next angle; **D**, and **E**, is plan and elevation of rail intersecting cap turned to same design; **F**, ramp, turned from pitch line to intersect newel on a level. It requires but one joint to make the turn.

by a cast iron baluster of the same design as the other, this baluster being firmly secured at the bottom.

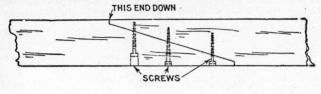

ELEVATION

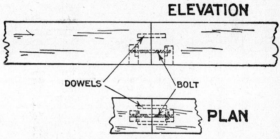

FIGS. 3,426 and 3,428.—Hand rail splice joint. Fig. 3,426, lap joint secured by screws; figs. 3,427 and 3,428, butt joint secured by dowel and bolt.

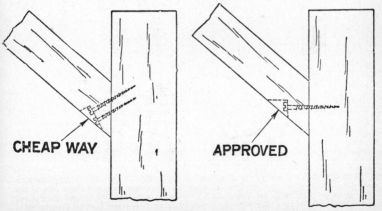

FIGS. 3,429 and 3,430.—Methods of fastening hand rail to newel. Fig. 3,429, with nails (cheap); fig. 3,430. with bolt.

Two methods of securing the hand rail to newel are shown in figs. 3,429 and 3,430. The lap-joint with lap pointed dowel is used on the best work. If the butt joint be used the rail should be handled carefully until it is in place.

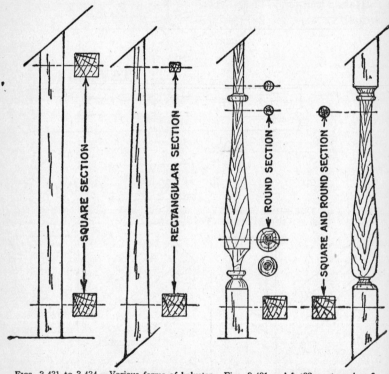

FIGS. 3,431 to 3,434.—Various forms of baluster. Figs. 3,431 and 3,432, rectangular; fig. 3,433 and 3,434, turned. The cross section at various points are shown.

There are numerous forms of balusters, in both the rectangular and turned or circular types, the turned type being the cheapest, except the rectangular form without tapering cross section.

A few forms of baluster are shown in figs. 3,431 to 3,434 and some methods of fastening the ends to hand rail and treads, in figs. 3,435 to 3,443.

Hand Railing.—The process of laying out and making a wreath or ease off is known as *hand railing*. In mills where

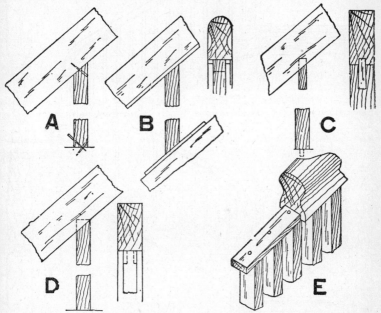

FIGS. 3,435 to 3,443.—Treatment of the baluster ends showing various methods of fastening balusters to hand rail and treads. **A,** shows a cheap method of simply nailing the ends; **B,** balusters fitted in channels both top and bottom; **C,** dowel method of putting in round balusters; **D,** mortised into underside of the rail and dove tailed into the tread before the return or end nosing of the tread is put on; **E,** method of placing balusters before hand rail is set concealing the nailing.

there is a band saw, the piece from which the wreath is to be worked is held at the correct pitch by a jig and the four sides of the wreath sawed. Upon the ordinary work it is rarely

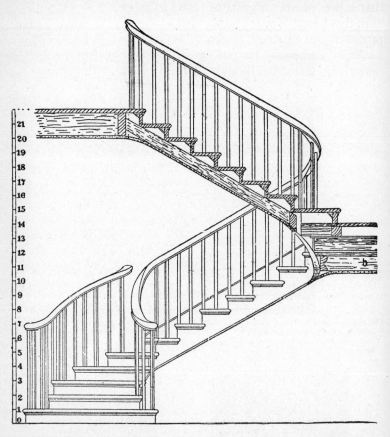

Fig. 3,444.—Geometrical stairs having a cut stringer, quarter space of winders with two commode steps at bottom, and a quarter-space landing and quarter space of winders at the half height, the stairs finishing at a half-space landing. This is a suitable stair to place in a wide hall or shop. The curved portion of the first wall string is treated as a cut string to correspond with the outer strings. The winders in each space are made to "dance"— that is, to radiate from varying centers. This, by increasing the going of the steps, produces a better falling line in the strings and handrail, and makes the stair safer to use than they would be if the steps did radiate from a common center.

necessary to work out a hand rail to special dimensions, as all that is needed may usually be found in stock.

In the theory of hand railing figs. 3,447 to 3,452 illustrate the production of a pattern or *face mould* as shown in fig. 3,451.

FIG. 3,445.—Center colonial open stringer platform stairs. As *shown,* there are 6 risers to landing and 9 risers to second flow. The assembly comprises: 15 risers, 13 treads, including bull nose, tread and riser, 2 noseup, 1 starting newel, 1 volute, 1 easing, 2 goosenecks, 10 ft. hand rail, 28 balusters.

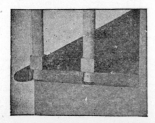 

FIGS. 3,446 and 3,447.—Center baluster joints. The balusters are dovetailed into the treads as shown in fig. 3,446, and the dovetailing is concealed by strips of nosing and moulding mitred to fit the treads. This allows no end grain to show.

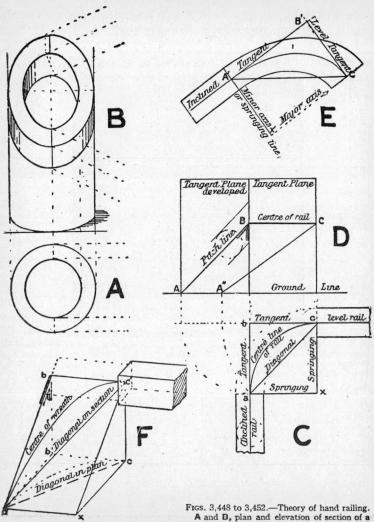

FIGS. 3,448 to 3,452.—Theory of hand railing. **A** and **B**, plan and elevation of section of a cylinder; **C**, plan diagram of a wreath enclosed by tangents; **D**, development of tangent planes in elevation; **E**, face mould diagram; **F**, sketch of the prism shown in **C**.

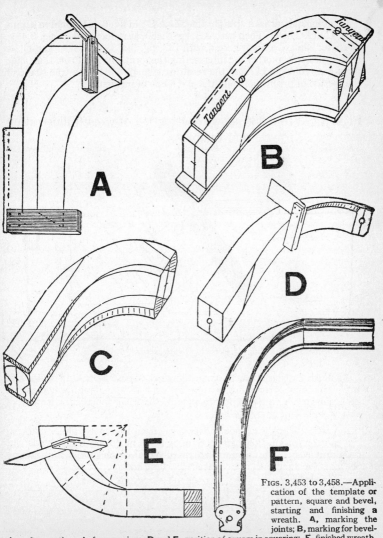

FIGS. 3,453 to 3,458.—Application of the template or pattern, square and bevel, starting and finishing a wreath. **A**, marking the joints; **B**, marking for beveling; **C** wreath ready for squaring; **D** and **E**, position of square in squaring; **F**, finished wreath.

In laying out, draw a straight line, as A'C', in fig. 3,451, equal in length to A''C, fig. 3,450. Then with AB, fig. 3,450, as radius, and A', fig. 3,451, as center, describe an arc; and with BC, fig. 3,450, as radius, and C' as center, describe another arc intersecting the former at B'. From this point draw lines to A' and C' and the resulting triangle will be the true shape of the section of prism *abc*, upon the given line of inclination.

Figs. 3,453 to 3,458 show construction of wreath illustrating use of bevel, square and template.

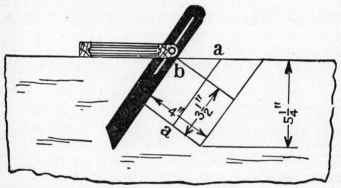

Fig. 3,459.—Method of finding thickness of wreath piece.

As much cutting must be done, the stock should be held in a vice and worked off, first, preferably, with a saw or draw knife and finished with a spokes have before beginning to mould, for which purpose a variety of chisels and planes may be had.

A *template* should be made of some very firm, thin material, for marking the ends or section the shape the rail is to be made so that the ends will meet uniformly. The one universal method of invisible bolting and binding the ends together with draw bolts is the best known.

CHAPTER 54

Flooring

As a rule the laying of floors is done by specialists in this line because they can lay considerably more in a given time than the all round man. The ordinary carpenter however must do the work sometimes and therefore should be familiar with the methods employed.

Floor Lumber.—The boards used for floors should be perfectly free from sap and from large loose or dead knots. As soon as possible in the construction of the building, floor boards should be laid out across the joists bottom upward, so that they may have every opportunity of drying and seasoning without being damaged by being walked upon.

In order to minimize shrinkage floor boards are made in narrow widths, 3 or 4 ins. as the joints can be kept tighter.

The two kinds of boards in most general use are:

1. Plain or square edged
2. Tongue and groove type as shown in figs. 3,460 to 3,462.

In the tongue and groove form of board the board is 3½ ins. wide over all of which ½ in. is required, making net width of board or width of covering surface 3 ins.

Classification of Flooring.—There are numerous kinds of floors to meet the varied requirements and they may be classed:

1. With respect to number of layers, as:

    a. Single
    b. Double

2. With respect to the form of joint as:

    a. Straight or butt
    b. Tongue and groove
    c. Ploughed and tongued
    d. Doweled

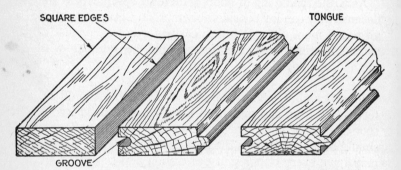

FIGS. 3,460 to 3,462.—Plain square edged, and matched tongue and groove floor boards. *In laying,* the groove of one board is pressed against the tongue of the previously laid board until the edges come together thus making a tight joint.

3. With respect to special features, as:

    a. Sound proof
    b. Fire proof, etc.

Single Floors.—In the cheaper construction it is often that only a single finish board floor is laid when there is a warm cellar under the whole house to keep the cold or dampness out. Then it is imperative that all joints be cut centering a beam.

By carefully sorting for lengths and a uniform distribution of joints about the room, there is no reason why such a floor should not be laid to look as well as one overlaying another.

Moreover, if the sorting of the boards be carefully done there will be little waste in cutting the beams so as to break joints and have them come over the joists; joints of this kind are called *head joints*, as distinguished from the joints made by the abutting sides of adjacent planks. If these head joints be cut between joists the boards will always spring enough to make the joint unsightly, for if not very near the center between beams the longer one will spring more than the other and will sometimes split the

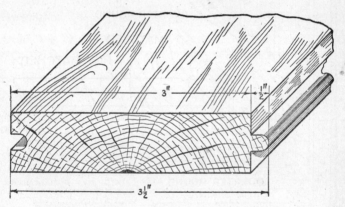

Fig. 3,463.—Tongue and groove board full size showing amount lost in laying by the projecting tongues.

top part of board that forms the groove, and it might be that one of the abutting boards will be more springy than the other because of being sawn further from the heart of the wood.

Just here it is well to mention the value of so matching abutting boards as not to have a striking contrast of the grain of the wood when it is to be finished natural.

This plays an important part in the appearance of the floor as a whole.

Fig. 3,464 shows a single floor with plain square edge or butt joints laid on joists spaced 16 in. centers. As shown it extends between the studs to the outside, sheathing, covering and closing the space between it and the first joist or sill, shutting off draught and easy access of mice from cellar.

A square edge floor should not be laid one board at a time, but a "*bay*" two or three feet wide of boards should be cut to the

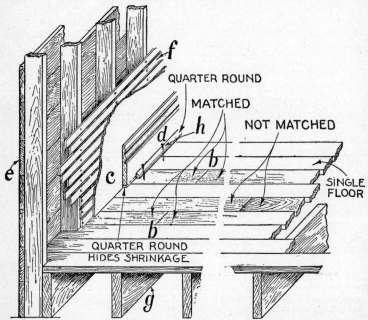

QUARTER ROUND

MATCHED

NOT MATCHED

SINGLE FLOOR

QUARTER ROUND HIDES SHRINKAGE

FIGS. 3,464 and 3,465.—Single floor with square edge or butt joint, showing method of laying. One of the boards joining at A, is flat grain and the other edge grain; this contrast emphasizes the joint and therefore constitutes bad practice. In contrast to this are the matched joints at B and B. At C and F. are shown plaster wall and lath finished to floor, the importance of which is apparent. D, shows the base in place. As this must be nailed to the studding which does not shrink lengthwise more than 4/100 of an inch in 20 feet, and as the floor boards must be nailed to the floor joists which are liable to shrink from 1/16" to 1/16" in depth, according to how much the wood has been seasoned, it at once becomes apparent that the floor will separate likewise from the base. To overcome this and to retain a tight closure the quarter round 5/16 is nailed in the angle where floor and base meet. The base board should be painted or varnished before strip H is set so that as it settles it will not expose an unfinished streak on the base board.

same length and wedged so tightly that each joint will be perfect as shown in fig. 3,466.

Enough nails are driven to hold the board in place and the process repeated until the entire area is covered. When the boards are all cut and laid, marks should be made with a chalk line to indicate the location of the joists as a guide in driving nails.

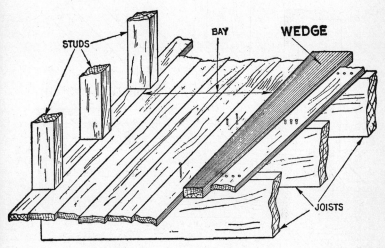

FIG. 3,466.—Single square edge floor showing method of laying in *"bays."* *Of course* a single straight edge floor is subject to leakage through the joints when the boards shrink and should not be used except in special cases or when cheapness of construction is the chief consideration.

The objection of leakage through the cracks of the butt joint single floor is overcome by the tongue and groove joint as shown in fig. 3,467.

This represents approved floor construction and is more expensive than the butt joint because of the reduced covering area per board due to the tongue, and because when the job is properly performed the floor has to be laid one board at a time by the wedging or dogging methods, as shown in fig. 3,466 and 3,467.

An inferior method is the *folding* method, shown in fig. 3,468.

Double Floors.—Usually the floor consists of two layers:

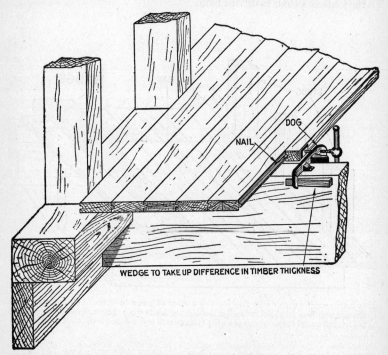

WEDGE TO TAKE UP DIFFERENCE IN TIMBER THICKNESS

FIG. 3,467.—Single tongue and groove floor laid by the dogging method.

1. The rough or sub-floor
2. The finish floor

The first or under layer is of rough boards and on top of this is laid the finish floor. These two layers are generally laid at right angles or at 45° to each other and in the best work a layer of building paper is placed between the rough and finish boards.

An advantage of the double floor is that the rough boards may be laid early in the construction of the building, forming a floor for the workmen to walk on and the finish boards laid afterwards, thus protecting them from rough usage and possible

SPRING
FIRST AND FINAL POSITION OF BOARDS

FIG. 3,468.—Single tongue and groove floor laid by the folding method. Commencing at the studs the starting board MS, is nailed down. Next take from four to six boards and lay them down closely together against MS. Next mark upon the joists the position of the outer board as at *ms* and *lf*. Remove the inner board and nail down the end board LF, about ¼ to ½ inch short of the marks *ms* and *lf* according to the number of boards to be "folded." Replace the inner boards and bring pressure on them by standing or bringing your weight on cross boards RR′, so the flooring will be forced down from the curved or sprung position to the straight position against the joints as indicated by the dotted lines.

injury. The finish boards may be laid after the painters are through and all other work finished.

Figs. 3,469 to 3,472, showing wrong and right methods of laying base board moulding should be carefully noted.

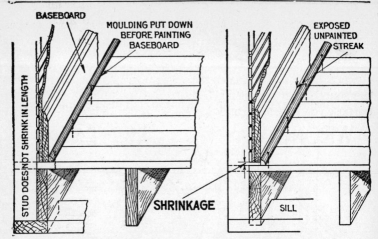

Figs. 3,469 and 3,470.—Result of painting the base board after nailing on moulding. Since the base board is nailed to the studs and the moulding to the floor, the latter will be carried down when shrinkage takes place in the joists, exposing an unpainted streak as shown in fig 3,470.   Accordingly *paint or varnish the base board before nailing on the moulding.*

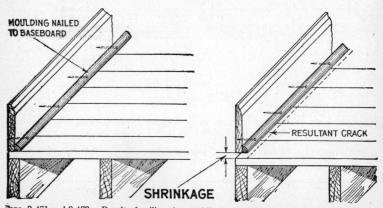

Figs. 3,471 and 3,472.—Result of nailing the moulding to the base board. Since shrinkage of wood takes place principally in a direction across the grain, the joists will contract carrying down with them the flooring, resulting in a space or crack between the floor and lower side of the moulding as shown in fig. 3,472.   Accordingly, *always nail the moulding to the floor.*

In fig. 3,475 is shown a double tongue and groove floor laid on finished joists. This gives economy of air space at the ceiling by not plastering it, and the saving of plaster, especially if the ceiling be low, which is usually the reason for this construction.

Since there is no plastered ceiling it is advisable to deaden the sound, so a deadening felt or quilt manufactured for that purpose, or three-ply building paper is laid smoothly over it,

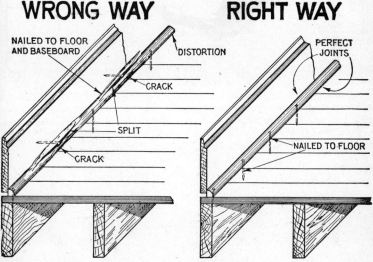

WRONG WAY   **RIGHT WAY**

FIGS. 3,473 and 3,474.—Wrong and right ways of nailing the moulding. When nailed to both floor and base board, shrinkage will bring stresses on the moulding causing distortions and possible splitting as in fig. 3,473. When nailed to the floor, no abnormal stress will be brought on the moulding and the joints will remain perfect regardless of shrinkage. Accordingly, *always nail the moulding to the floor.*

after that the finish floor is laid, preferably at right angles to the first.

If the first be of thin lumber, then, because of insufficient nail hold and strength the second should parallel it. This last way prevents uniform shrinkage and is likely to show greater shrinkage in one joint than in another, thus the value of a thick under floor or top ceiling boards.

Care must always be taken not to allow edges of paper or quilt to become turned over under the floor when nailing it down.

Instead of placing paper between the two layers of floor boards, or, as additional proofing, lay one of the several good makes of fibre boards on top of joists, the under side being the ceiling, as in fig. 3,476. A 4-foot width will center every third joist. This admits of using a cheap lumber in the under flooring boards and makes a pretty ceiling with such clean angles along the beams as not to require mouldings.

If the fibre board cannot be had in lengths to reach, the joint can be so

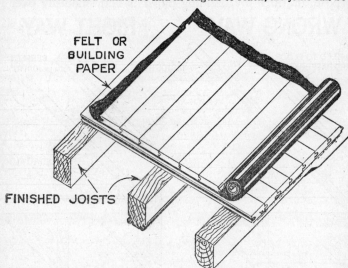

FELT OR
BUILDING
PAPER

FINISHED JOISTS

Fig. 3,475.—Double tongue and groove flooring laid on exposed finished joists. *In construction,* before the joists are put in place they are dressed on three sides, and sometimes, when economy does not prevail over possible dignity and refinement of appearance, the beams may be square faced, chamfered or beaded, or the aris changed to a round. It is seen that there are two thicknesses of boards with a deadening felt between them. The first is laid with the face (that part coming in contact with the top or undressed edge of beam) down, showing as a ceiling. It may have one, two or more beads stuck on the face or be used perfectly plain. If there be any danger of shrinking one bead stuck on tongue edge will save its showing. However, unless the bead be worked very smooth the painter is likely to leave a rough job.

plastered as not to show after decorated or they may be hidden by thin strips forming cross panels, as at L.

Diagonal Sub-Floors.—Whether side walls shall be framed and raised before the rough or sub-floor of the first story of a

COMPO
BOARD

TOP FINISH FLOOR

UNDER DIAGONALLY
LAID FLOOR

FIG. 3,476.—Double tongue and groove flooring laid with fibre board on open or exposed joists, the fibre board serving as a finish and deadener between joists.

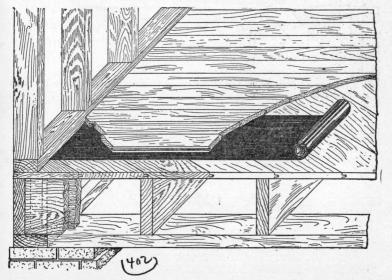

(402)

FIG. 3,477.—Double floor with diagonally laid rough or sub-floor showing type of built up sill suitable for the diagonal method.

building is laid will depend upon the type of sill used. These sub-, or rough floors may be laid either straight across the joists, as already shown, or they may be laid diagonally, as in fig. 3,477. The diagonal method of laying is considered the better.

Sound Proof Floors.—Various expedients are resorted to in

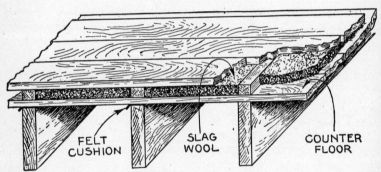

FELT CUSHION   SLAG WOOL   COUNTER FLOOR

Fig. 3,478.—Sound proof double floor having the proofing material laid between the rough and finish floors.

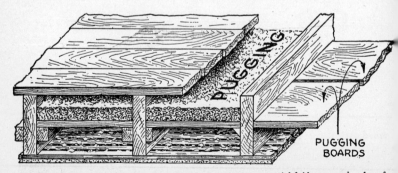

PUGGING

PUGGING BOARDS

Fig. 3,479.—Sound proof single floor having the proofing material laid on pugging boards fastened to the joists between the lath and floor.

order to deaden the sound audible through floors. This is particularly necessary in apartment houses.

Figs. 3,478 and 3,479 illustrate two methods in common use of insulation against sound. These methods are frequently misunderstood.

Of the two, that illustrated in fig. 3,478 is the better and lighter.

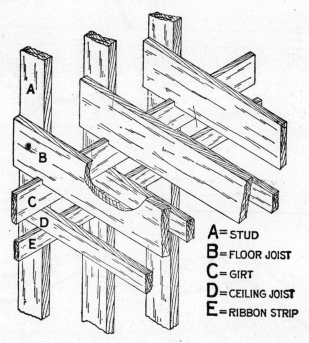

A = STUD
B = FLOOR JOIST
C = GIRT
D = CEILING JOIST
E = RIBBON STRIP

Fig. 3,480.—Hollow method of constructing sound proof floor.

In construction, after the under floor is laid, 1 × 2 strips are laid across it the flat way directly over the beams and a layer of mineral (slag) wool is leveled between them and crowded in as the finish floor is laid.

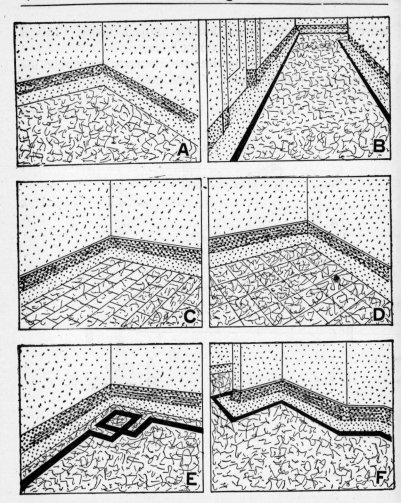

FIGS. 3,481 to 3,486.—Various designs of Asbestone composition flooring. **A,** light red field, black base and border; **B,** light buff field, light red base and border black inlay border; **C,** gray field scored for tile effect, black base and border; **D,** dark red field scored for tile effect, black base and border; **E,** dark buff field, dark red base and border black inlay border; **F,** green field, golden brown base and border black inlay border.

The method shown in fig. 3,479 is resorted to when it is desirable to save the extra 1 in. in height of ceiling and some cost. The plan is to nail 1 in. strips (any old odds and ends) along inside of joists at the height desired to have the pugging lay about half way between ceiling and floor.

These are covered with the short ends of lumber that usually accumulate about a new building such as sheathing boards, and covered with a layer

Fɪɢ. 3,487.—Detail of hollow sound proof floor at girders.

of any kind of weak mortar of cement or lime, sometimes, in order to reduce the weight in floor it is troweled in not much over an inch in thickness, but 2 ins. is better. In wood construction these constitute a fire retardant of considerable extent.

Figs. 3,480 and 3,487 show a hollow method of sound proofing by which there is no contact between the joists upon which the finish floor rests and the ceiling except at wall ends and the girder or girders.

In the detail sketch of girder some labor is represented that can just as well be omitted. The floor joists can be notched over it and spiked sufficiently strong without the notching of girder, and the ceiling beams can be spiked to hold just as securely without the slip mortise and tenon.

Fire Proof Floors.—So called "fire proof" or fire resisting floors are made in various ways. Fig. 3,488 shows a *solid*

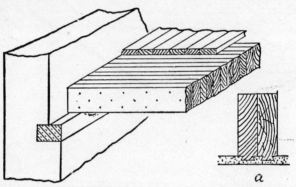

FIGS. 3,488 and 3,489.—Solid fire proof floor and detail of dovetail ends for securing the plaster.

wood floor designed for heavy loads which is fire and sound proof to a great extent.

In construction each board (turned on end) is nailed tight to the next board and dovetailed on the bottom edge to receive the plaster. This makes a solid mass, shutting off all draught and sound and has a great carrying capacity. If care be used in placing together the grain in each can be made to oppose the other and thereby obtain the maximum strength.

Parquet Floors.—These consist of thin layers of wood worked into some geometrical pattern, either extending over the whole room or used only as a border around the sides. The parquet may be laid directly on the joists or on top of an ordinary floor.

This type of floor is kept clean by the use of turpentine and wax and is in every respect a more sanitary finish to a room than ordinary washed floors.

Parquet is made in all thicknesses from ¼ to 1 in. of oak, walnut, teak, etc. Most hard wood flooring, such as oak, maple, birch, cherry, walnut

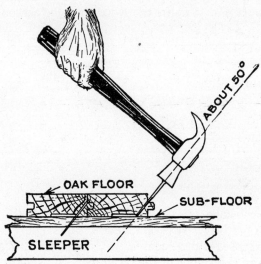

ABOUT 50°

OAK FLOOR   SUB-FLOOR

SLEEPER

Fig. 3,490.—How to blind nail on oak floor.

and sometimes fir is supplied in varying short lengths with the ends matched the same as edges to hold the joint true. Care should be exercised in laying these and to the uniform distribution of joints.

Generally nail holes are drilled in them at the mill so that nailing them will not split off the tongue. In this connection always take the precaution to use a nail set in driving nails home.

As these floors are usually laid over another floor it is not necessary in such case that the nailings come over joists.

The angle of nail in the under floor furnishes sufficient hold. When more than one room is to be laid it makes it possible to select shorter lengths for one and longer for the other, thus making the distance from joints uniform and having the least in the best room.

Any thickness of flooring down to ¾ in. may be laid directly on the joists when the latter are spaced not over 16 ins. centers. Any thinner should be over a core or under floor in dwelling houses.

Laying floors in design requires first class workmanship. If it is to be a mitred joint, the wood must be seasoned beyond

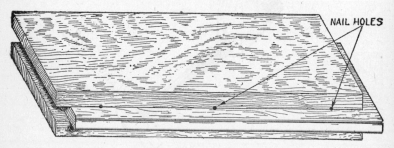

NAIL HOLES

FIG. 3,491.—Quarter sawed tongue and grooved end matched oak flooring.

further shrinkage, else the mitre will open on the inside end and be very unsightly. It is best to generally employ designs that can be executed with a square cut. If a rug pattern is to be laid, finishing in the center of the room a zig-zag square cut can be used effectively, even if various colored woods are to be used.

Fig. 3,492 shows the corner of a room laid with narrow (3 in. face) boards showing several possibilities of design, any of which may be heightened by the use of two colors of wood.

It may all be made by use of a mitre box with four cuts in it, a right angle (square) 45 degrees, 30 degrees and 60 degrees. Many of the pieces are made from one pattern. By this a mechanic of inventive mind will be able

FIG. 3,492.—Inlay corner floor design for large room. *The inlays* for borders or any designed pattern are more or less pronounced according to the color contrast of woods. Often they are selected to harmonize with an interior decoration scheme.

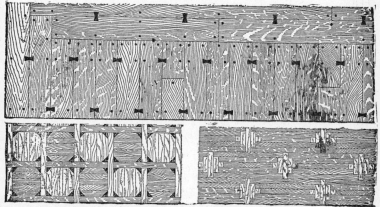

FIG. 3,493.—Old English doweled floor showing method of drawing joints of boards tight and holding them firmly together with a dovetailed key or dowel of hard wood with a color contrast. Surface nails are set deep and plugged with same color. All are set in hot glue.

FIG. 3,494.—Inlay pattern for a whole floor. Squares are formed as if woven. Can be more accentuated by selecting the boards in contrast. Octagonal centers are formed by right angle triangle corner inlays. The centers are laid in alternate directions or not, as desired and may be further emphasized by again selecting light and dark boards.

FIG. 3,495.—One of numerous and varied designs of hardwood floor that may be employed. Here again another color wood may be used for the pattern.

to create many simple and attractive layouts. Whole floors may be covered by use of the squares. If very much is to be laid, it will be economy to have the lumber sawn into the lengths at a mill.

Piazza Floors.—The treatment of piazza floors is illustrated in figs. 3,496 to 3,498, which explains methods of building piazza floor, and shows framing of an end where it is desirable to continue the fascia of its sill level across end to house. To do so properly requires that a hip joist be built in as shown and

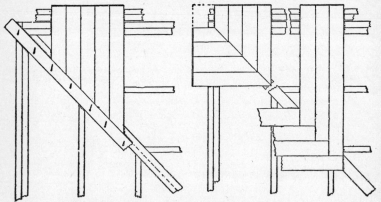

Figs. 3,496 to 3,498.—Piazza flooring, showing various methods of laying along hip joist. The framing should be adequate to prevent a settlement toward the house. *For safe practice* place 2 × 10 cross beam in an 8 ft. wide piazza eight feet apart using 2′ 6″ joists set on 2′ centers. The nailing strip at house end of flooring need not be more than 2 × 4 or 2 × 3″ and must be well spiked through sheathing into studs.

that the other joists be returned from it on a level to house sill. This would not be necessary if the piazza floor were level, but the need of enough fall (pitch) from the house for water to run off is the occasion for it. Too often too much fall is given to it. One inch in ten feet is ample if the house construction be not faulty, causing a settlement toward the house or a sagging of the floor by a too long span between cross beams, more than the size of beam will warrant.

Even with but one inch pitch in the width of floor, if shown **at** the end, gives the whole house an uneven and cheap appear**ance**. The flooring should always extend, at least one inch be**yond** moulding and top nosed only.

The bottom left square causes the water to fall clear of fascia.

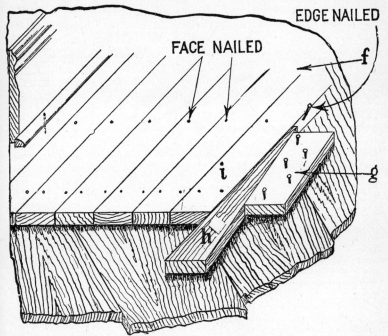

EDGE NAILED

FACE NAILED

f

i

g

h

Fig. 3,499.—Butt joint or square edge finish floor laid over diagonal sub-floor showing **use of** wedge in drawing up joint where the floor is to be face nailed.

If rounded it will run back against paint and stain it with dirt and discolorations.

Figs. 3,496 and 3,497 show two ways of cutting joint at hip, if as at 1, the boards on each angle must be laid alternately; if as at 2, one angle may be laid continuously as at *b*.

A straight edge nailed temporarily on the hip, lining its center, as at 3, facilitates placing the work. To keep it from crowding, the mitred end should always be nailed first.

In fig. 3,498, from L to F, is seen the pitch at house line that makes the face level.

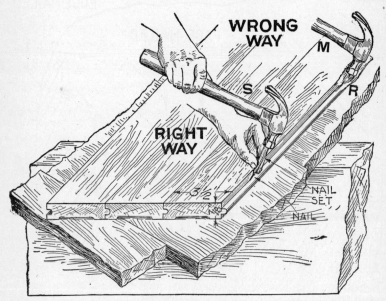

FIG. 3,500.—Right and wrong way to nail tongue and groove flooring. Instead of driving the nail home with direct blows as at M, a nail set should be used as at S, when the nail is driven nearly in. R shows appearance of plank when nail is driven as at M.

Points on Floors

In starting to lay a floor, strike a line exactly paralleling the wall of room, tack the first course of finish flooring the whole length and then prove and establish its accuracy by sighting or possibly drawing the line along it. When certain of its correctness, securely nail and then watch to see that the driving to place of the next one or two courses does not change it. It is well to occasionally measure the width of floor laid for variation, and then, should there be any, correct it as the opposite side of room is approached unless it be that the room is not of uniform width, in which case it will not be necessary or of any importance.

Any thickness of flooring down to ¾ in. may be laid directly on joists.

Floors in commercial houses, factories, etc., need to be stronger, according to the service.

Maple over a ⅞ in. under floor will stand very hard usage.

Some builders think it good enough to nail flooring to every other joist, but it is better practice to nail to every one, otherwise there is a tendency, sometimes not until it has seasoned out, to spring and squeak, especially should there be any unevenness under it. This is particularly important in the use of thin flooring.

Southern yellow pine, especially North Carolina, is extensively manufactured into flooring and is the most used in the East for average building purposes, it being hard and tough and yet easily laid.

Like Arkansas soft pine, red gum and other soft woods, it comes in lengths from 8 to 20 ft. long. Edge (comb) grain yellow pine makes a very handsome and durable floor. It has great wearing qualities.

Red gum is tough, dark and has a very artistic grain.

The selection of flooring is generally based upon the use it is to be put to and the relative cost.

Where hard wood floors are to be finished natural, as in dwellings, offices, etc., it should be dressed and scraped and protected against injury until in the painters' hands.

Many times carpenters spoil or injure a well laid floor by carelessness in dropping tools or allowing square corners of

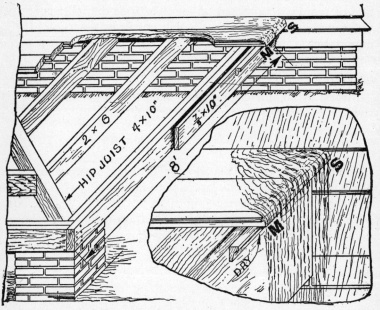

Figs. 3,501 and 3,502.—Details of piazza flooring showing nosing. Fig. 3,501, from **M**, to **S**, shows nosing. In fig. 3,502 on larger scale is shown how nosing should overhang finish with top edge nosed and bottom square so as to cause the water to fall clear of fascia.

boards to fall upon it, denting and marring it, or getting it wet before dressing, causing abrasions; walking or working upon it with nailed shoes, or staining with shoe soles while dressing it, or with tobacco juice; this can be avoided by proper precaution.

There is a patent plastic cement that, if spread thick enough over a rough cement floor, eliminates the use of wood nailing, to which floors can be directly nailed, or after cement slabs have their initial set the wood nailing blocks may be removed (they need not be wider than 2″) and the nailing cement filled in. Can be nailed to after about 18 hours set.

For hardwood fancy floors, birch, oak, fir, yellow pine or almost any light wood border is more to be desired than dark walnut with light body.

If a dark body, such as red gum or cherry is to be used, then a mahogany border is suitable.

In laying any of these floors their stability may be increased by use of fresh, hot glue applied to the back and saw cut joints. Always use a whisk broom or suitable brush to keep under floor free from chips or dirt ahead of you as the work advances.

Flooring boards for piazzas should be of lumber most resisting the elements, and preferably $1\frac{1}{8}$ or $1\frac{1}{4}$ in. thick. White pine, cypress and fir are among the best; spruce is better than hemlock. All should be free from sap. If Carolina pine be used, it should be heart and edge grain.

Beside the floors already mentioned there are patent floors that the carpenter should be sufficiently familiar with as to be able to lay them.

They are manufactured in sections ready to lay, some of them are of very thin material with back laminated to canvas and are laid in strips and joined in place on the floor, others to wood backs in squares on patterns.

The laying of cork and vulcanized rubber tile floorings is usually done by experts and by the manufacturers, but as carpenter or practical man must prepare to perfect levels the under floors, or may want to lay a floor for himself, he can just as well follow manufacturers' instructions and lay them himself.

CHAPTER 55

Interior Walls and Ceilings

The term *interior walls* as here used, means *the interior covering placed over the studding to form a finished surface.*

Usually this consists of the familiar lath and plaster, but numerous substitutes have been introduced and one largely

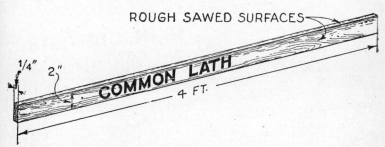

FIG. 3,503.—Proportions of common wood lath.

used, such as the various "wall boards" designed to be nailed direct to the studding, being more durable and installed with less labor than plaster walls.

Lath.—When plaster is used to form the wall surface it is held in place by lath or thin strips nailed to the studding. There are two kinds of lath, classed according to material:

1. Wood
2. Metal

The best wood for laths is white pine, although spruce is used to a great extent. Yellow pine should not be used, on account of the pitch which it contains. Half green laths are best for use, although dry laths may be wet before using.

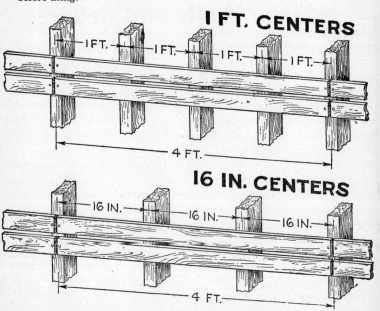

Figs. 3,504 and 3,505.—Why laths are cut to four foot lengths. This length allows the studding to be spaced either 12 ins. or 16 ins. between centers.

Wood laths vary in dimension, the common size being $1\frac{1}{2}'' \times \frac{1}{4}'' \times 4'$, as shown in fig. 3,503. This allows proper nailing to studding spaced either 12 ot 16 ins. on centers, as shown in figs. 3,504 and 3,505.

In nailing, the laths should have a nail to each stud and often two nails are required at the ends of each lath.

The lath should be spaced about ⅜ ins. apart or about ¼ in. for patent or hard plasters, breaking joints about every sixth lath, as shown in fig. 3,506.

When laths have a bearing surface over 2 ins. in width, strips of wood should be placed under the lath so as to allow a space for "keying" the plaster. The sectional view, fig. 3,507, illustrates how the plaster, by spreading out behind the lath, keys itself securely to the lath.

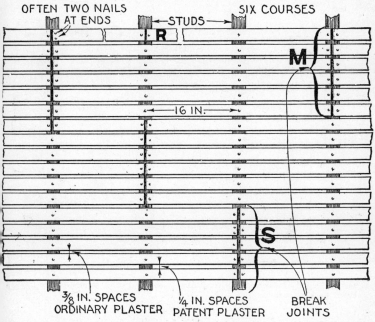

FIG. 3,506.—Section of lathing nailed to studs illustrating the breaking of joint about every sixth course as at M, S, and R, also method of nailing and spacing.

Wood lath are sold by the 1,000, in bundles usually containing 100 lath. Fig. 3,508 illustrates the approximate number of lath required per 100 sq. yds. of wall and the time required by a good lather.

Grounds.—In order that the plasterer may make walls true and of uniform thickness about the doors and window openings and along the floor, "grounds" must be provided.

By definition, *grounds* are *strips of wood for the purpose of assisting the plasterer in making a straight wall and in giving a place to which the finish of the room may be nailed.*

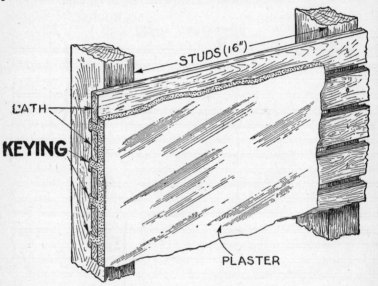

FIG. 3,507.—Section of plastered wall illustrating *keying*, or locking secured by the plaster projecting back of the laths.

Fig. 3,509 illustrates these grounds. For ordinary lime plaster grounds are usually ¾ to ⅞ in. thick by 2 ins. wide.

For hard wall plaster common thickness is ¾ in. with wood lath. Where pulp or fibre plaster is used ⅝ in. should be allowed for both lath and plaster.

It is good practice to set grounds about ⅛ in. narrower than the finished work, so as to allow for the thickness of the finish coat.

Fig. 3,508.—Properties of lath; 100 sq. yd. section lathed illustrating number of lath required, weight, nails required and labor.

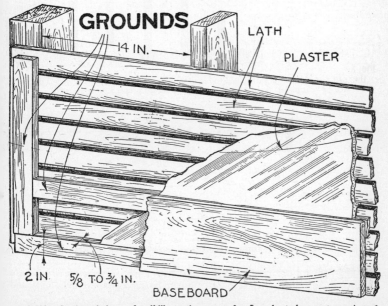

Fig. 3,509.—Section of plastered wall illustrating *grounds*. In order to keep out vermin and cold, grounds for base should be placed so that the wall may be lathed and plastered down to the floor.

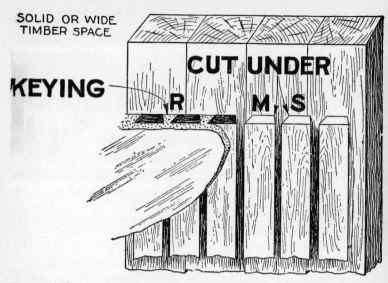

SOLID OR WIDE
TIMBER SPACE

CUT UNDER

KEYING

R   M   S

FIG, 3,510.—Treatment of lath nailed to broad timber. When the timber is over 2 ins. wide, the lath be "cut under" as at M and S; this provides for proper keying as at R.

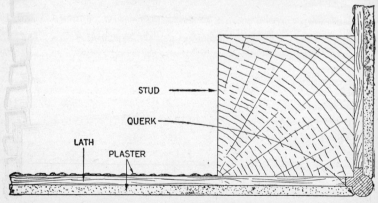

STUD

QUERK

LATH

PLASTER

FIG. 3,511.—Plaster or corner bead. Although this makes more work for the plasterer, as the plastering has to be stopped against it forming a *queck*. yet it is still used to some extent, because, if well done, it makes a good looking and substantial corner.

Metal Lath.—There is a great variety of metal lath now obtainable. These may be classified as

1. Expanded metal lath:

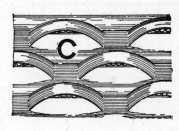

FIGS. 3,512 to 3,514.—Expanded metal lath. **A,** diamond and rectangular mesh; **B,** ribbed and corrugated, **C,** integral combining functions of both lath and studding.

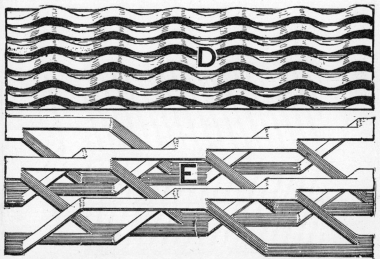

FIGS. 3,515 and 3,516.—Sheet metal lath. **D,** flat perforated; **E,** integral, combining functions of both lath and studding.

    a. Diamond and rectangular mesh
    b. Ribbed and corrugated
    c. Integral, combining functions of both lath and studding

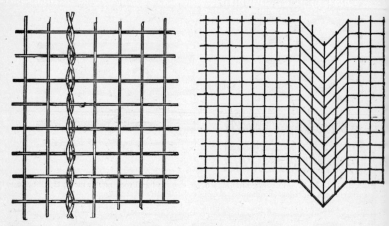

FIGS. 3,517 and 3,518.—Wire woven lath. **A,** flat perforated; **B,** integral combining functions of both lath and studding.

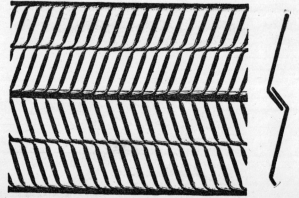

FIGS. 3,519 and 3,520.—Herringbone metal lath. The longitudinal ribs are set at an angle of 45° and the cross strands are flattened. The ribs act as shelves and hold the mortar. The cross strands curl the plaster behind the lath completely covering it.

2. Sheet Lath:

   a. Flat perforated
   b. Integral, combining functions of both lath and studding

3. Wire woven lath:

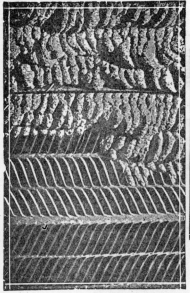

FIGS. 3,521.—Herringbone metal lath, partly plastered as seen from the back showing the effect of the slanted ribs in causing the plaster to "key" itself and embed the lath.

FIG. 3,522.—Herringbone metal lath in position on stud and partly plastered.

   a. Plain
   b. Stiffened

Various metal laths are illustrated in the accompanying cuts.

Plaster.—The subject of plaster and method of applying it to the lath is not a carpenter's job and accordingly is not treated in this volume.

Wall Boards.—These are thin boards made of various materials. They may be divided into two general classes, according to their function as

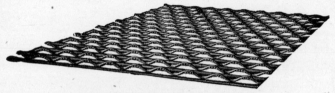

FIG. 3,523.—Bostwick "Truss loop" metal lath. There are 652 metal trusses in a **sq. yd.**

FIG. 3,524.—Bostwick "Truss loop" metal lath in place on studs and partly plastered.

1. Plaster boards
2. Finish boards

Plaster boards are used instead of wood or metal lath and **are** of service as a fire proof covering or for sound deadening.

A common size of plaster board is 32×36 of various thicknesses, ranging from $\frac{1}{4}$ to $\frac{1}{2}$ in.

These boards are light (standard board weighs $1\frac{1}{2}$ lbs. per sq. ft.). They are intended to be nailed directly to the studding and plastered over the same as lath. In nailing, the boards are placed with the plastering side out, and the center of the board nailed first and edges last.

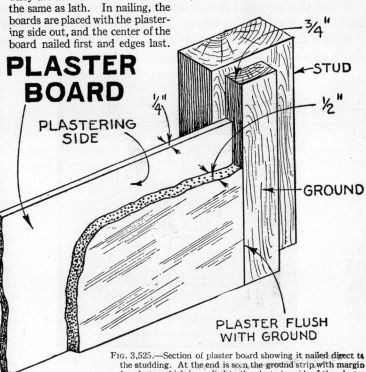

PLASTER BOARD

PLASTERING SIDE

STUD

GROUND

PLASTER FLUSH WITH GROUND

Fig. 3,525.—Section of plaster board showing it nailed direct to the studding. At the end is seen the ground strip with margin for plaster which is applied to the plastering side of the plaster board bringing the finished plaster surface flush with the ground as shown.

The grounds to be provided will vary from $\frac{3}{4}$ in. (for $\frac{1}{4}$ in. boards) to $\frac{7}{8}$ in. (for $\frac{3}{8}$ in. boards). A space of $\frac{1}{4}$ in. is left between boards and each edge of the board must have a bearing on the nailing piece of at least $\frac{3}{4}$ in.

In applying on studding or joists, use $1\frac{1}{2}$ in., $11\frac{1}{2}$ gauge,

$\frac{7}{16}$ head smooth wire nails spaced 4 ins. apart, driving each nail in firmly. These plaster boards require but little plastering material.

When this saving is considered they cost less than metal lath and but little more than wooden lath with three coats of plaster.

Finish boards are primarily intended for use as an interior finish on side walls and ceilings in buildings of all classes. They

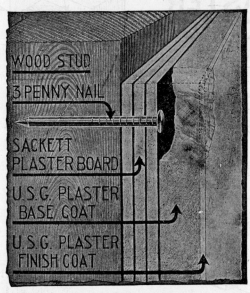

Fig. 3,526.—Sackett plaster board; sectional view showing $\frac{3}{8}$ in. board nailed to studs and covered with plaster. Sackett plaster board is made in two thicknesses, $\frac{1}{4}$ in. and $\frac{3}{8}$ in. and should be plastered with $\frac{1}{2}$ in. of plaster.

may be used in all situations where finishes of lath and plaster may be used, and in many places where the latter finish is not suitable.

One form of wall (finish) board known as the "Best wall" consists of a single layer of fibre calcined gypsum, surfaced on each side with specially prepared water-proofed paper securely bonded to the surface.

It is ⅜ in. in thickness and is furnished in stock sizes 47¾ ins. wide and in lengths of 5, 6, 7, 8, 9 and 10 ft. The finished product presents a smooth surface, which is light cream in color on the face tide and gray on the reverse tide. The edges are slightly beveled to provide for the filling of the joints and are doubly reinforced. Weight about 1,850 lbs. per 1,000 sq. ft. Finish wall boards are applied by nailing direct to the studding, joists or furring and

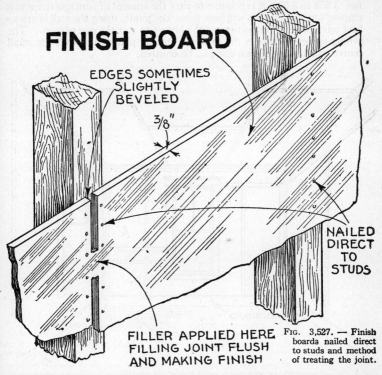

FINISH BOARD

EDGES SOMETIMES SLIGHTLY BEVELED

3/8"

NAILED DIRECT TO STUDS

FILLER APPLIED HERE FILLING JOINT FLUSH AND MAKING FINISH

Fig. 3,527. — Finish boards nailed direct to studs and method of treating the joint.

filling the joints between the boards with a specially prepared filler of the same composition as the core of the board. In nailing 3*d* fine wire nails are used, spaced from 2 to 3 ins. at the edges and from 8 to 12 ins. at the intermediate supports. Filling in the joints consists of two operations: first, *roughing in*, and second, *trowelling out* to a smooth finish flush with the surface of the boards. The boards are cut and fitted either with a saw, or by scoring and breaking over a straight edge.

The boards after being installed may be painted or covered with wall paper if desired. Fig. 3,527 shows detail of finish boards nailed to studs and treatment of the joint.

Another, and decorative method of treating the joints between the boards is by paneling that is by nailing narrow strips over the joints. As shown in figs. 3,528 to 3,530, it is possible to vary the amount of paneling strips and employ any design that will best cover the joints, using the wall board to best advantage in proportioning the layout to suit the size of room. The ceiling in perspective is the same as that on plan except that the small center panel is not shown and can be omitted.

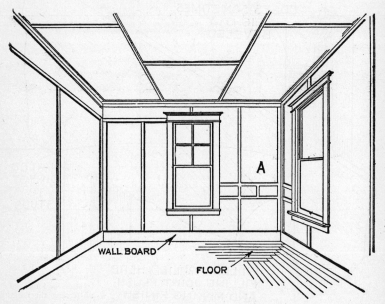

FIG. 3,528.—Room finished with finish panel board and paneled joint, showing treatment of the panel work.

A dado may be carried around over window openings without any strips reaching to the ceiling, or they may extend to ceiling without dado or in corners with dado.

If in a dining room or den, a dado (wainscote) may be suggested by

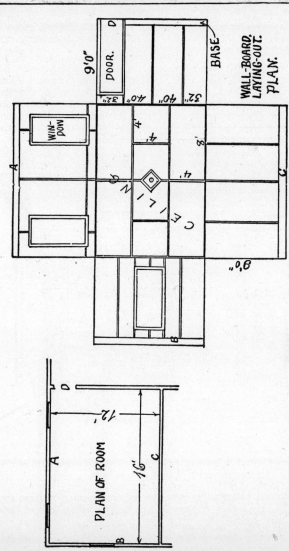

FIGS. 3,529 and 3,530.—Finish wall board lay out for the room shown in fig. 3,528.

FIG. 3,531.—Typical framing construction for Sheetrock finish boards. 1, headers; 2, plate, girt or ribbon; 3, double studs; 4, splice to straighten bowed stud. *Preparation of frame work:* Surfaced 2 × 4s should be used for studding wherever possible. Place all studs and joists 16 ins. centers. Begin by placing a stud in one corner of the room and then space studs out exactly 32 or 48 ins., depending on the width of sheetrock to be used. Set intermediate studs in 16-ins. centers and have them all properly aligned. The face of studs must be in line with face of the plate. In case of a bowed stud, straighten by making a saw cut and splicing as at 4. Double studs should be provided at corners. Use sized 2 × 4s for partitions. To save sawing and fitting, sheetrock should be applied to all bearing walls and ceilings before erecting non-bearing partitions. If partitions be already erected, a backing plate should be placed along the top edge of the partitions to form a nailing surface for the Sheetrock. *Headers:* A solid nailing surface must be provided for all four edges of Sheetrock. Headers should be inserted wherever wall heights and ceiling lengths exceed the length of the boards. Use 2 × 4s for headers with the 4 in. side placed for nailing surface.

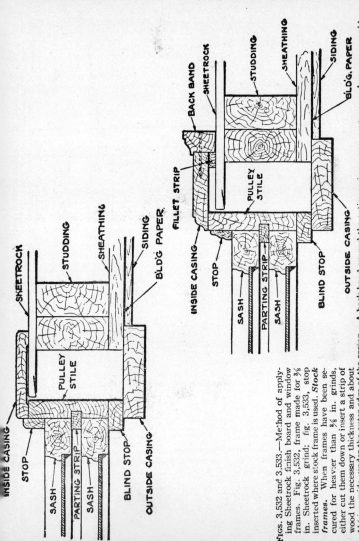

Figs. 3,532 and 3,533.—Method of applying Sheetrock finish board and window frames. Fig. 3,532, frame made for ⅜ in. Sheetrock grind; fig. 3,533, stop inserted where stock frame is used. *Stock frames.* When frames have been secured for heavier than ⅜ in. grinds, either cut them down or insert a strip of wood the necessary thickness and about 1½ ins. wide, under the outer edge of the casing. A back band around the entire casing, or a quarter round or curve moulding at junction of the casing and Sheetrock, will complete the trim.

Fig. 3,534.—Sawing Sheetrock finish boards and applying it to the ceiling. The ceiling is always covered before the walls. 5 shows cheat which to rest end of Sheetrock and 6, a T, for holding board in place while nailing.

stripping, as at A. What the room is used for and its size influences the layout.

A,B,C,D, of fig. 3,530, which represents the sides of the room (shown in plan in fig. 3,529), if turned up to a right angle with the ceiling and the whole layout inverted, would fit the plan at A,B,C, and D.

Correct the mistake of side wall A, so as to cover the joints with the stripping, and note that in side wall D, 8″ have to be cut from two strips, reducing them to 40″. These strips can always be worked into some

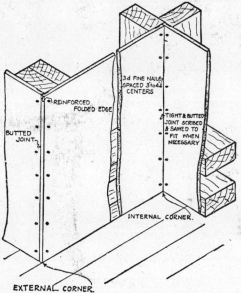

FIG. 3,535.—Method of applying Sheetrock at corner angles. Double studs should be provided at corners as shown.

other design. When desirable, to carry out some special feature where a joint must be made that cannot be covered it is entirely possible to so fit, nail, fill and paint or stain with oil or water color as not to show.

The use of wall board covers a wide range of use. A dilapidated ceiling or side wall may be renewed with it, putting it on over the plaster, or an unfinished attic may be converted into living quarters without the inconvenience of plaster. and can be accomplished much quicker.

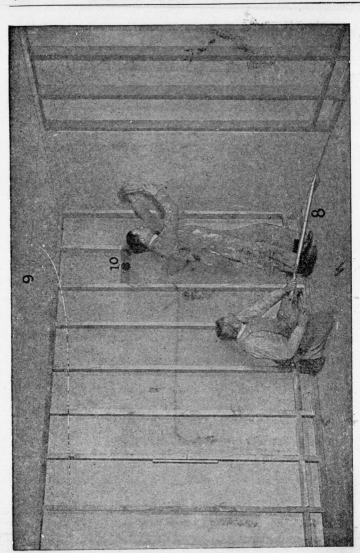

Fɪɢ. 3,536.—Applying Sheetrock finish boards on walls. *In applying,* pry for lifting Sheetrock flush with ceiling as at 8. Note ceiling joints are broken across joints as at 9. Place header back of electrical fixture as at 10.

Panel Strips.—These may be had or made in a great variety of patterns. In stock they are usually plain, $\frac{1}{4}'' \times 1\frac{1}{8}''$ and should not be less than $\frac{4}{16}'' \times 1\frac{1}{2}''$; $\frac{3}{8}'' \times 2''$ is better.

Figs. 3,537 to 3,540 show several practical patterns. No. 1 is most generally used because the square butt joint is much

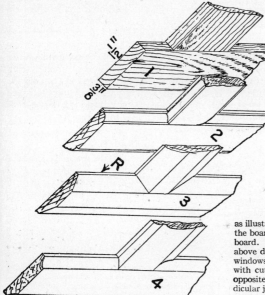

FIGS. 3,537 to 3,540.— Various forms of panel strips.

NOTE.—Application of Sheetrock finish boards on walls. Make sure that the first board is square with the adjacent wall. Use a pry as illustrated in 8, fig. 3,536, to lift the board up flush with the ceiling board. Leave until last the spaces above doors and above and below windows, covering these spaces with cut pieces of Sheetrock. On opposite sides of partitions, perpendicular joints must not come on the same stud. Boards should be butted on all external and internal angles. On external angles, the exposed edge of Sheetrock should be a folded edge, as illustrated in fig. 3,535. Proper construction of internal angles is also illustrated in fig. 3,535. In applying Sheetrock, all edges of sheetrock should be butted tightly together; they should never be spaced apart. Where boards do not fit tightly, scribe with a pair of dividers and saw to fit. Folded edges should be placed against folded edges; sawed edges against sawed edges. Never butt a folded edge against a sawed edge. It is good practice to snap a chalk mark as a guide for intermediate nailings. Sheetrock should be applied to ceilings before walls. Apply sheets parallel with the joists. Saw horses should be of the proper height to allow 2 or 3 inches of head room. With the trade mark side of the board upward, place one end of the board upon the cleat, and then raise the other end into position by means of the T, (6, fig. 3,534) which should be about one-third the distance from this end of the board. It is important that the first board be fitted square with the adjacent walls. Recut the ends of any boards that have been made imperfect by handling. Do not butt cut ends of boards too tightly. Simply make a snug fit, if necessary leaving $\frac{1}{8}$ inch space at the wall junction. When cross joints are necessary on the ceiling they should be broken, except when the joints are to be paneled.

easier and quicker to erect and admits of some slight variation either way from its point of intersection and remain a perfect joint, whereas Nos. 2, 3 and 4 would have to be coped to admit of such variance. If mitred, then great care must be exercised in locating all cuts.

Mitring requires less time than coping and is the best job to make when the price will permit. These three patterns show a mould that leaves a narrow square edge between the wall arris and beginning of pattern, as at R, and serve an important purpose when the panels are to be colored different from the stripping. This thin edge may be left the wall color, and forms a line easy to finish. Color on stripping, and make easily a clean angle. For No. 1 panel, the color on strips should finish to wall, and to cut the color in neat without making an irregular line on the wall requires skill and patience. Otherwise the job looks at least, undignified. It may be added that a perfectly coped joint cannot be distinguished from a mitre.

Matched Ceilings.—Matched and beaded boards are regularly stuck in the same widths as flooring. The standard (nominal) thicknesses of yellow pine ceiling are $\frac{3}{8}$, $\frac{1}{2}$, $\frac{5}{8}$ and $\frac{3}{4}$ in., the actual thickness of each being $\frac{1}{16}$ in. less. The $\frac{3}{8}$ in. ceiling is dressed one side only, the other thicknesses being dressed on both sides.

NOTE.—*Nailing Sheetrock* finish boards. When nailing direct to supports, 3d fine flat head or 3d fine countersunk head nails, cement coated, should be used. Nails should not be less than $1\frac{1}{8}$ in. in length. 6d cement coated box nails should be used for attaching Sheetrock to old plastered walls which have not been furred. One lb. of 3d fine flathead nails will be sufficient for 200 square feet of Sheetrock. One pound of 3d fine countersunk-head nails will be required to apply about 150 sq. ft. of Sheetrock. On old plastered walls, not furred, about one lb. of 6d common nails will suffice for 50 ft. of Sheetrock. Use a bell faced hammer. Drive the nails straight into Sheetrock, heads slightly below the surface but do not use a nail set. Draw all Sheetrock edges firmly and evenly against supports. First drive a few nails at the edge of Sheetrock where it joins the board last applied; nail the first intermediate stud or joist; nail the second intermediate stud or joist; then nail the edges; finally nail the ends. If the board be slightly bowed, set several nails along the support, push the board tightly against the support and drive the nails "home." This will prevent loosening of nails which have been driven already. On intermediate supports, nails should be spaced six inches apart on ceilings and nine inches apart on walls. On all sides and ends of boards, nails should be spaced 3 ins. apart and about $\frac{3}{8}$ in. from the edge on both walls and ceilings. All edges must be nailed. At internal corners where it is difficult to drive nails, use a nail set, but do not let the nail head cut through the paper. When a nail does not hit a support, it must be removed or it will work through the decoration.

Metal Ceilings.—For the ceiling of stores, stables, etc., corrugated metal sheets are much used and this construction is an

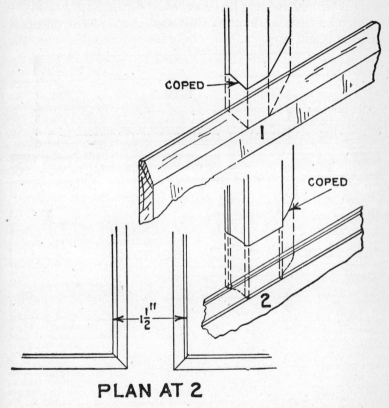

PLAN AT 2

Figs. 3,541 and 3,542.—Method of coping joints. The figures show how one piece of moulding or shaped wood such as bevels shown are fitted against another as if mitred. Its great value is in that the piece fitted may be moved along that to which it is joined and remain a tight joint. It is especially valuable where mouldings are nailed in an angle where a mitre will be forced apart. Usually the work is cut in a mitre box, reversed, and with a suitable tool cut to the shape shown on the face.

excellent one for such installations. The nature of the material is such as to readily lend itself to ornate effects and therefore a variety of designs may be produced.

Metal ceilings are durable, easily applied and more economical than lath and plaster. When once erected and decorated the

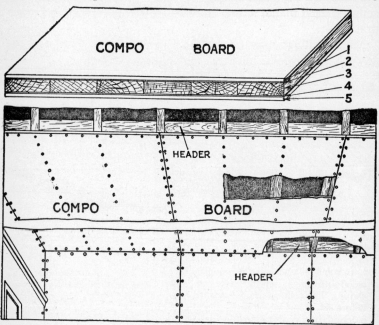

Fig. 3,543.—Sectional view of Compo-board showing its construction comprising a core made of wooden boards embedded in cement and covered with heavy paper. *The parts are:* 1 and 5, heavy paper; 3 wooden slats; 2 and 4, airtight cement. All boards 4 ft. wide, and from 1 to 16 ft. in length.

Fig. 3,544.—Compo-board (finish board) as applied to walls and ceilings.

metal ceiling will require little or no attention except occasional cleaning.

The deadening of sound and insulation of ceilings to prevent radiation of heat may be accomplished by the use of any good deadening or insulating felt, the process being to nail the insulating material into place before putting on the ceiling.

Where moisture is present rust may be prevented by using galvanized or copper plates.

There are various methods of forming the joints of metal ceilings, each manufacturer having his own ideas as to the best practice.

Metal ceilings may be applied directly over old plaster or any other form of ceiling in the case of remodeling jobs.

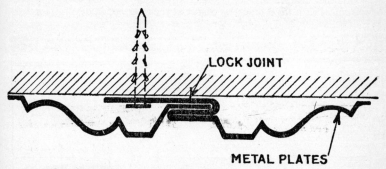

LOCK JOINT

METAL PLATES

Fig. 3,545.—Form of lock joint used on metal ceilings.

In some instances metal ceilings may be applied direct to the joists and wood sheathing but in the majority of cases it is better to make use of furring strips. The ceilings are given a good coat of special gray factory primer before shipment, which protects them from rust in transit and gives them a foundation coat for further decoration.

The use of a gray primer is regarded as an advantage due to the fact that it can be covered over when decorated at less cost than where a dark primer is utilized.

In designing a metal ceiling it may be interesting to state that the desired patterns are modeled in clay and plaster of paris casts made of them from which are produced the heavy steel dies used in the press for stamping the metal.

Consideration of course must be given in the designing to the depth of the panel of the "draw" and to see that the strain or stretch is equal in all directions so as not to fracture the metal or force it into some undesired shape. The stock must be of the right analysis properly rolled and tempered and in this connection it is well to note that for the production of deep panels a very different stock is necessary than that which is used for flat designs or embossed plates. The gauges used from 23 to 30, depending upon the depth of the panel of the design to be produced.

The joints of the plates are made in various ways, a form of lock joint being shown in fig. 3,545. This interlocking slip joint or quad lock joint, as it is called, insures safety of construction, the arrangement being such that the ceiling can readily be applied directly over old cracked plastering if desired with the confident assurance that it will not fall down.

Another feature of this ceiling construction is doing away in many instances with wood brackets, except at the intersection of cornice mitres.

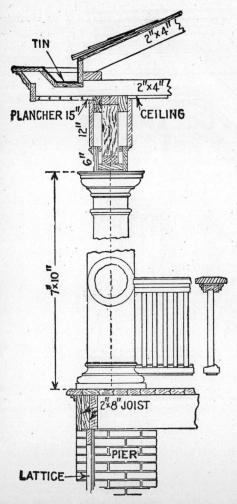

CHAPTER 56

Piazza Finish

Important details that are too often overlooked in designing exteriors are those of ill-proportioning columns supporting roofs, balconies, etc.

This result of carelessness or ignorance is too often seen.

Columns supporting a piazza roof or cornice, that are too large and numerous suggesting over abundance, no matter how beautifully or expensively done, will pull

Figs. 3,546 and 3,547.—Sectional view of piazza floor, balustrade, column and cornice framing, and (fig. 3,547), section of hand rail.

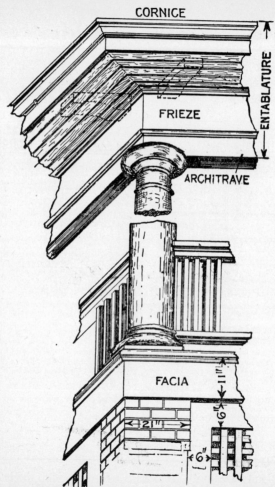

CORNICE

ENTABLATURE

FRIEZE

ARCHITRAVE

FACIA

11″

6″

2″

6″

FIG. 3,548.—General appearance of finished piazza, showing fascia, column, balustrade, and parts of the entablature. If a considerable mass of the roof show above cornice, its overhang may be narrowed 5 to 6″ and the frieze about 2″. In either case, its suggestion of massiveness may be increased by adding false brackets, as shown by dotted lines under plancher, set on about 24″ centers or to such distances and in such proportion as to unify the whole mass.

out of harmony, indeed, may distort the whole facade, or even the whole house or that part of it seen in perspective with the piazza.

There must be a suggestion of massiveness and weight in proportion to the size and number of columns used, of whatever style of architecture.

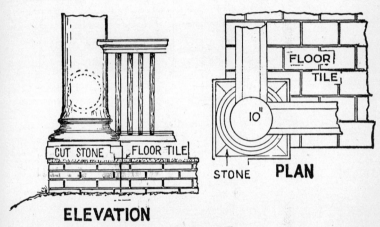

FLOOR TILE

CUT STONE   FLOOR TILE

10"

STONE   **PLAN**

ELEVATION

FIGS. 3,549 and 3,550.—Piazza construction with tile or cement floor. *The plan* shows the pier set out beyond the line of wall, by it the piers stand out in greater relief, defining the column. If the wall of piazza floor foundation were extended out to face of pier, the pier effect would be lost and the additional floor space, requiring more tile would be valueless except for flower boxes. If the grade be brought up to floor level, then there will be no need of defining piers and the roof extension will be the difference in placing the column on line (one inch inside) of edge of floor, less than otherwise as the center of top of column should meet the center of the under side (plancher) of the architrave of cornice.

In figs. 3,546 to 3,547, notice that the piers show a slightly wider face than the width of base as should be.

The pier may be built so that its face is flush with fascia or so that the fascia extends its thickness beyond it. Also notice that the lattice is set so as to reveal about 2½" of the side of pier.

The whole entablature is in proportion to suggest the need of strength in column.

Sometimes a different construction is necessary in order to

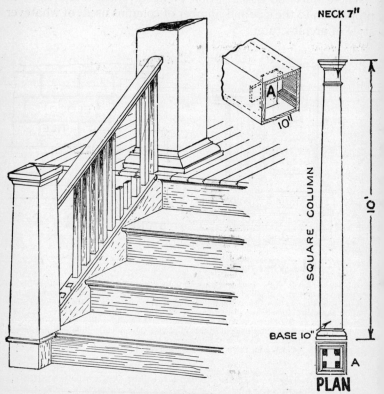

FIGS. 3,551 to 3,553.—Plain wood piazza step construction.

make the floor of tile. In such cases the whole foundation is monolithic, brick, cement or stone, as shown in figs. 3,549 and 3,550.

The accompanying illustration, fig. 3,551, shows some practical suggestions for the erection of piazza steps.

In fig. 3,553, showing square piazza columns, the four sides are tapered to produce the spring.

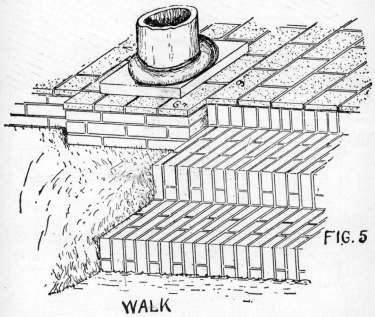

FIG. 5

WALK

Fig. 3,554.—General appearance of the tile floor shown in plan in fig. 3,550. *As shown* the steps may be built of brick nestling down into the terrace that reaches up to within 8 to 10 inches, more or less of the floor level, avoiding use of cheeks or quoins. The floor tiles may be any size. They are here shown to be 6 × 9, which is a very popular size. The tile should never be laid on a grouting of concrete with earth filling under. Either fill from the natural—undisturbed—earth with stone, cinders, gravel or other monolithic material, else put in supports and reinforce the concrete base so there may be no settlement. Even a few inches in depth of earth filling will settle some for months after, no matter how well tamped. A white joint always looks well, though any color mortar may be used. Notice that the 3 joints in the 4 floor tile under column may be spread (widened) enough to overhang a pier of 3 bricks (25 to 26 inches) in width about ⅝ inch. In other words a whole lot of cutting and fitting may be avoided in all such work by varying the width of joints.

FIG. 3,555 —Wooden piazza construction with floor a little higher from grade than in **fig.** 3,554, and the steps built in between cheeks, the width of which, of course, will be in proportion to suit the design. Here the bottom step is shown of brick set on edge, as are those of fig. 3,554, which not only adds permanence and durability to their appearance, but **keeps** the wood work away from the earth thereby preventing rot. It may continue under **the bulk**head or a little higher pier or brick, as shown, may be built for it. The width of **bulkhead is 11** ins., and its top which intersects the floor level, is 14″ wide, and suggests up **and down** staving of ⅞″ × 4½″ matched boards for the cheeks. The frame should be of at **least** 2 × 4″ stuff so as to afford strong nailing, especially for the top so that it will not **warp.** In erecting, its underside should be painted before fastening in place.

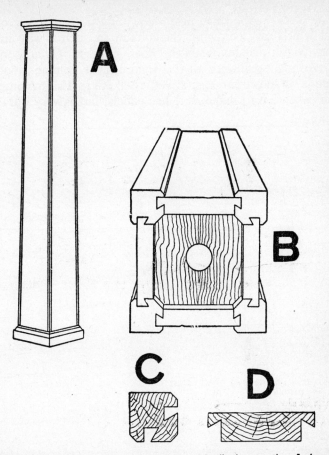

FIGS. 3,556 to 3,559.—Square, paneled porch column and details of construction. **A**, shows general appearance of the column. In **B**, a small brace shelf is shown placed in the bottom and top of column to strengthen the dovetail construction, and the column is ready to be put together. It will be observed that in this type of construction practically no nails are used, except the few used in inside brace itself. Consequently there are none to show, or putty to fall out after the column is on the house, which often given a column of this type a bad appearance. It can be safely claimed for a column thus constructed that it cannot split, pull apart, warp, check or break, and will practically last as long as there is a roof on the house. The sections **C** and **D**, show cut of corner pieces and sides.

The piece A, shown in figs. 3,552 and 3,553, is a reinforcement which may be put in the column in such a way as to prevent joint evening when the wood shrinks.   On account of the growing popularity of the square taper column, another example is shown in figs. 3,556 to 3,559.   This column is more expensive to make as it has panels, but is very durable.

CHAPTER 57

Mill Work

Under the heading *mill work* is included the various wood-working machines found in the mill with explanation of their construction and use.

There are various kinds of mills such as the ordinary saw mill where the cut logs are sawed up into lumber of various sizes; sash and door mills, furniture, stair mills and various other mills specializing in some particular product. Such machines as band and circular saws, lathes, planers, joiners, sanders, etc., are to be found in nearly all mills.

Mill Operations.—The various operations ordinarily performed in mills may be classified as:

1. Sawing.
2. Turning.
3. Planing.
4. Scraping.
5. Shaping.
6. Boring.
7. Mortising.
8. Tenoning.
9. Rabbeting.
10. Polishing.
11. Bending.

In addition to the machines for performing the above operations, there will be found in some mills highly specialized machines such as multiple hand gainers, pencil, skewer and dowel machines, gang dovetailers, etc.

Saws.—There are several kinds of saws used and they **may** be classed according to their principle of operation as:

1. Circular.
2. Band.
3. Scroll.

These various saws have their special uses.

Circular Saws.—Both circular and band saws have been treated at length in Guide No. 1, with respect to simply the

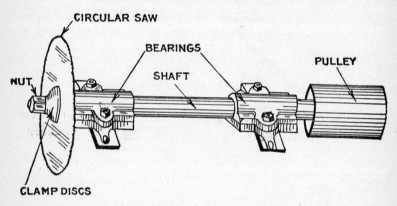

CIRCULAR SAW

BEARINGS

SHAFT

PULLEY

NUT

CLAMP DISCS

Fig. 3,560.—Small circular saw mounted on arbor showing bearings, clamps, pulleys, etc.

saw itself. The saw is here considered as a machine, that is the complete apparatus.

A small circular saw mounted on a frame adapted for light work with hand feed is known as a *saw table* as distinguished from a *saw mill*, or assembly of large heavy duty saw, log carriage with power drive, etc.

Fig. 3,560 shows method of mounting a circular saw on arbor, and fig. 3,561 saw table complete with saw, countershaft, etc. Some of the numerous operations that can be performed with the circular saw are shown in figs. 3,562 to 3,565

FIG. 3,561.—Ordinary circular table, showing position of saw, countershaft, etc. Since the saw must run at a high rate of speed, the step up counter shaft is necessary between the line shaft and saw pulley. Usually a tension idler or equivalent device is provided to take up stretch in the saw belt and keep it tight.

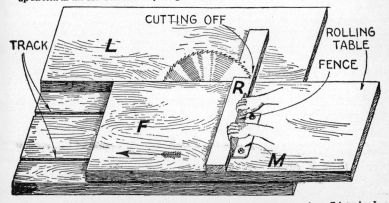

FIG. 3,562.—Circular saw with rolling table and fence showing saw cutting off board. L, stationary part of table; F, rolling table. The arrow indicates the direction of movement of the part F (which is mounted on rollers), in cutting off end of the board R. The board is fed to the saw by pushing on the fence M, which is securely clamped to the table.

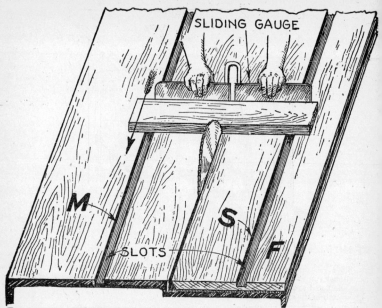

Fig. 3,563.—Method of cutting off a board by aid of the sliding gauge. *In this operation* the rolling section F, of the table remains stationary and the sliding gauge slides in the slots M,S, in feeding board to the saw by pressing forward on the sliding gauge.

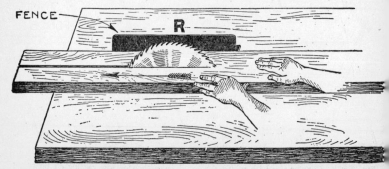

Fig. 3,564.—Method of ripping a board. The fence R, is set parallel to the saw and at a distance to one side equal to the desired width of strip to be cut and camped in position. The board then as it is fed to the saw is kept n contact with the fence by a slight lateral pressure.

An important safety attachment is the *spreader blade*, or splitter, as shown in fig. 3,567. It is placed close to the back edge of the saw, giving protection at the most dangerous point. Accidents are usually caused by pieces catching on the rear of the saw after they have passed through the cut and are about to be brought back again.

When the saw catches the piece, the operator's hand is usually caught at the same time. The use of the spreader greatly reduces this danger

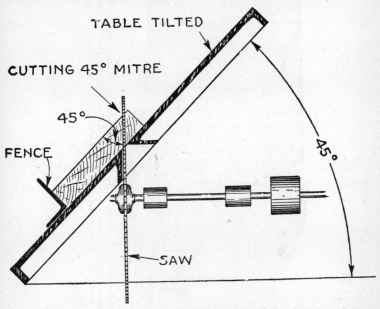

FIG. 3,565.—Section through circular saw table showing table in tilted position for sawing at an angle. The usual range of adjustment is 45°. The illustration shows table tilted 45°, and saw cutting a 45° mitre. *In construction,* a quadrant with scale in degrees, permits easy setting of the table to any angle within range with precision.

An example of circular "saw mill" is shown in fig. 3,566.

The illustration at once indicates heavy duty work, although the mill shown is only one of small size. Note the carriage travelling on rollers and moved by power drive. This type of mill is designed for sawing short logs of medium diameter and for edging light or heavy material.

FIG. 3,566.—Fay and Egan short log "saw mill" and edging saw designed for sawing short logs of medium diameter and for edging light or heavy material. It is adapted to various wood working plants, such as furniture factories, chair, handle and spoke factories, carriage and wagon works, etc, *It consists of* a self-contained circular saw mill outfit, including power driven carriage.

Fig. 3,566.—*Text continued.*

tables for center splitting and quarter sawing. *Capacity:* Will rip 23 ins. between saw and fence and will cut through 9 to 18 ins. thick, or up to 24 ins, with a 60 in. saw. Feed 50 ft. per minute. *Table:* The table on right when made stationary is 29 ins. wide; when movable, 21 ins. The one on left is always made to move and is 17 ins. wide. It returns at the rate of 180 ft. per minute. Right hand is fitted with a fence adjustable from operator's position. Left hand table is fitted with device for dogging the log and for holding in position after it is dogged. Both devices are simple and easy to use, saving a great deal of time. *Counter shaft:* Tight and loose pulleys 12 × 10½; 650 r. p. m.

Fig. 3,567.—Spreader blade or splitter, designed to prevent pieces catching on the rear of the saw, after they have passed through the cut and are about to be brought back again. *In construction,* the blade of the spreader is fastened to the machine under the table so as to keep its proper relative position with the saw at all times, whether the table be level or tilted. As usually constructed it is readily adjusted for various sizes of saws.

Power for Saw Mills.—The heavy duty to which circular saws are put, require considerable power and for a saw to operate properly there must be plenty of reserve power.

According to Dodge the approximate power required for circular rip saws running at from 7,000 to 9,000 ft. per minute is

$$\text{approx. horse power} = \frac{(\text{diam. saw})^2}{40} \quad \dots\dots\dots\dots (1)$$

Example.—What is the approximate horse power required for a 50-in. rip saw running under ordinary conditions?

ᖴIG. 3,568.—Oliver universal saw "bench" or table showing adjustable fences and table tilted to 30°. *In construction,* the table is of metal, one side stationary and the other rolling so as to slide past the saw. An extension bracket at the right supports the fence when ripping stock the maximum width. Table tilts.

Substitutes in the formula (1)

$$\text{approximate horse power} = \frac{50 \times 50}{40} = 62$$

Of course the actual power required will depend largely

upon: thickness of cut, rate of feed, kind of wood and its condition, condition of saw. The above value may be taken as a rough approximation for average conditions. In any case there should be ample reserve power to meet severe conditions frequently encountered, due chiefly to dull saw, hard cutting woods, etc.

Cutting Speeds for Circular Saws

(Speeds given in feet per minute)

Circular rip saws for hard knotting wood......3,000 to	6,000
Circular rip saws for oak...................4,000 to	8,000
Circular rip saws for soft woods.............6,000 to	12,800
Circular cross cut saws.....................3,000 to	6,000

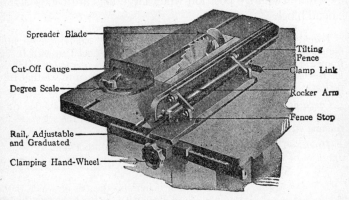

Fig. 3,569.—Crescent saw table. View showing saw, spreader, fences, gauge, etc.

Example.—The size of tight and loose pulleys on countershaft of a circular saw is 10 in. diameter. If the countershaft speed must be 650 *r. p. m.* to give 3,000 *r. p. m.* of the saw, what diameter of line shaft pulley must be used for a line shaft speed of 250 *r. p. m.*?

The relation is expressed in the following proportion:

speed of line shaft: speed of counter shaft = diameter of counter pulley: diameter of line pulley

Substituting, $$250 : 650 = 10 : x$$

solving for x

$$250x = 6,500$$

$$x = \frac{6,500}{250} = 26 \text{ ins.}$$

Foundation of Mill.—In the manufacture of lumber a good mill is essential to good work.

The foundation of the mill must be strong to withstand the shock in turning big logs. The stringers should be of sound heart lumber, at least 8 ins. × 10 ins., few pieces, set perfectly level and parallel with the saw frame, gained into the girders and joists of the mill floor, secured by keys and bolts so that they will not change position when large logs are rolled against the head blocks.

Track.—The track irons, particularly the "V" side, must be firmly bolted to the stringers, absolutely level and in perfect line with the saw frame. Keep gum and sawdust off the tracks. Where a guide rail is used in the center of the carriage, great care should be taken to see that this is perfectly straight and parallel with the saw frame.

Carriage.—The carriage is the movable truck on which the log travels to the saw. It must be substantial, free from side play, the set works firm, running straight and smoothly.

Husk.—The husk is the frame that holds the arbor and the saw. It must be of well-seasoned wood, bolted in place to overcome vibration and strain.

Arbor or Mandrel.—The arbor or mandrel is the axis on which the saw is hung. It must be absolutely level, lined with the track, having $\frac{1}{64}$ in. to $\frac{1}{32}$ in. end play, fitting the boxes easily without heating so that the arbor cannot lift. The stem must be true, receiving the saw and collars freely but snugly. Nearly all arbors run more or less warm, and it is essential that the exact warmth be given as nearly as possible, so that allowance for this can be made in adjusting the saw. This is particularly the case with regard to low speed saws—that is, saws that do not run at a rim speed of more than 50 to 60 per cent of the standard. A saw that runs 400 revolutions per minute is affected by a certain amount of heat—twice as much as it would be if the speed were 800 instead of 400 revolutions per minute. Hence, the importance in low speed mills of having the arbor run cool.

In case it do heat a little, exact amount of heat, as nearly as possible, should be given. No arbor should be allowed to heat to any great extent, never those in low speed mills. Remember that the manufacturer of saws should know all the conditions in order to make a saw that will run successfully.

Collars.—These are the flanges that support the saw. They are 6 ins. to 8 ins. in diameter, the center hole 2 ins. to 2½ ins.

The fast collar on the mandrel is concaved, the outer edge being flat for ¾ in. This collar contains the pin holes.

The loose collar is flat or slightly concaved, holding the pins.

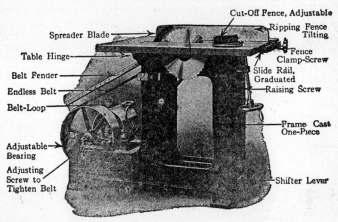

Fig. 3,570.—Crescent saw table. General view showing adjustment, drive, etc.

The collars by being concaved press their rims tightly against the saw, holding it flat and straight on the log side.

If the collar be worn, rings of writing paper, oiled, may be put between the collar and the saw on the dished side.

Relative to large circular saws cracking and breaking over the collar line, we find saws never break in this manner when running straight, but invariably when "laying over" or crowding out of the log.

In mills where there is trouble from saws cracking over the collar, the following rule should be carefully observed. Test the saw to see that it hangs perfectly true and flat on the log side. This can be done by holding a 24 in. to 30 in. straight edge lightly on the face or log side of the saw when in motion. If the saw be found to be correct in this respect, the center should be carefully examined to see that it does not heat above normal degree.

If it be found that the saw heats quite a little at the center, the cause should be located and corrected; it is usually caused by a hot arbor. Where this is the case, the arbor should be made to run cool, but where it is impossible to do so, the tension of the saw should be readjusted so as to leave it a little stiffer toward the center. This will offset the tension produced by the heat of the arbor.

The same adjustment of the tension is advisable where there is not sufficient power to maintain a uniform speed when the saw is in a heavy cut.

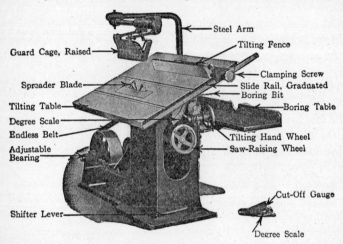

Steel Arm

Tilting Fence

Guard Cage, Raised

Clamping Screw

Spreader Blade

Slide Rail, Graduated

Boring Bit

Tilting Table

Boring Table

Degree Scale

Endless Belt

Adjustable Bearing

Tilting Hand Wheel

Saw-Raising Wheel

Shifter Lever

Cut-Off Gauge

Degree Scale

Figs. 3,571 and 3,572.—Crescent saw table. End view showing table in tilted position, **saw** guard, adjustments, boring table, and (fig. 3,572), cut off gouge.

If a saw be left a little stiffer for a distance of about 10 in. to 12 in. from the center, the tendency will be to prevent it laying over and crowding out should there be a reduction in the speed.

Lug Pins.—These are flat headed bolts to hold the saw in place. They must have good bearing with the burr filed off. Light mills will have 2 holes $\frac{5}{8}$ in. on a 3 in. circle, 6 in. collar. Heavy mills will have 2 holes $\frac{7}{8}$ in. on a 5 in. circle, 8 in. collar.

To get the size and position of the pin holes accurately place a sheet of paper on the collar. or better still, if you have a saw that you have been running, place the paper on the center of the saw so that it will cover both eye and pin holes. Hold the paper firmly in its place over the eye and with some hard smooth object rub the paper over the eye and pin holes until their outlines can be seen plainly on the paper. This will leave an impression on the paper that will guide the sawmaker accurately.

Hanging the Saw.—Hang the saw on the mandrel. After placing on the loose collar, screw up the nut with the fingers just enough to steady the saw. Now try the face of the saw with a straight edge to see that it is straight. Then tighten up the collar with a wrench. Another trial of the straight edge willl make sure that the position of the saw has not changed. If the rim has been thrown over either way, the collars are not right and should be corrected into the proper shape.

The saw should slip freely on the mandrel and close up to the fast collar. In many cases where the stem of the arbor is a trifle large near the collar, the saw, in being forced to its place by the nut, is made full on the log side.

Frequently it will be found that the metal around where the steady pins are driven, will be raised to form a bunch around the pins; if so, file it off.

A six-inch collar should have a perfectly flat bearing of at least three-fourths of an inch on the outer rim, the rest being chambered out, as this will hold tighter than a flat collar.

Where collars are larger than six inches in diameter, this rim should be proportionately larger. The pin holes should be in the fast collar; the pins in the loose collar.

To have a saw run perfectly true, it is absolutely necessary that collars and stem of mandrel be true and well fitted, for any imperfections in these may lead to no end of trouble; they should fit exactly.

To guard against saws breaking over the collar line, great care should be taken to have the saw hang perfectly true on the mandrel. To ascertain whether the collars be defective, place the saw on the mandrel and tighten up the collars by hand. Test the saw with a straight edge, and, if found correct, tighten up the collar with a wrench, and test again with a straight edge to see if the position of the blade has been altered. If any change be noticed, it is safe to assume that the saw is true, and that the trouble lies in the collars, and that they require trueing up before satisfactory results can be obtained.

For large saws it is better to have a collar that has a perfect bearing on the outer rim of at least three-quarters of an inch (in a six inch collar), the other part being chambered out so that it will not come in contact with center of saw, as they hold tighter than a solid flat collar. For a collar larger than six-inch, this rim should be proportionately greater.

If the collars have become worn at the outer edge, so that when tightened with a wrench the saw will be full or convex on the log side, it will heat at the center and become more convex, causing it to lay over from the log. The arbor should be so lined that the saw will lead into the log just enough to clear the center in good shape, so that it will not rub against the log and heat at center. If it heat and become expanded at this point it will dish and run either in or out of the log (usually out), causing the same kind of trouble referred to above.

Another cause for saws cracking over the collar in this manner is that the saw when adjusted for a certain (high) speed, is usually dishing when not in motion, but, when running at the speed for which it is made, is perfectly straight. If the speed be reduced while in the cut, the saw will become dished for want of the necessary speed to straighten it out. In a case where it heats at center, it will run either in or out of the log (generally out) forming a wedge between the saw and head blocks, eventually cracking or breaking the saw at or near the collar line by forcing it over this rigid point. Hence, the importance of maintaining a uniform speed, and having the tension adapted to it.

As stated, large saws for a high speed mill are when properly adjusted, dishing when not in motion, and great care should be taken to see that they are straight when running at their normal speed. In other words, they should dish or drop through a trifle more on the log side than on the board side. To see that they are right in this respect lay the saw on an anvil or board, hold a straight edge across the saw at right angles with the part that rests on the board, and the opposite edge that is being raised to allow the saw to drop through at the center, then take the measurement of the amount it drops through at center, turn the saw over, and repeat the operation, noting if it drop or dish alike on both sides. If it do. it is correct.

In putting the pins into the loose collar, the holes should be drilled clear through the collar, so that in case the pins are broken off, they can be driven out with a punch, and thus avoid having to drill them out. On all saws 48 in. and larger we recommend 8 in. collars with ⅛ in. pin holes on a 5 in. circle are recommended.

Spread Wheel.—Set the spread wheel flush with the saw and about ½ in. behind the teeth.

Guides.—These should be adjusted clear of the teeth and just touching the plate while the saw is in motion.

Lead.—The amount of lead for circular saws should be the least amount that will keep the saw in the cut and prevent it heating at the center. If the lead into the log be too much,

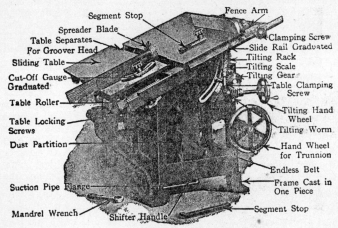

FIG. 3,573.—Crescent *sliding top* saw table. End view showing sliding top and general construction.

the saw will heat on the rim. If the lead out of the log be too much the saw will heat at the center. The least amount that is used is about ⅛ in. in 20 feet.

Soft, touch, fibrous timber usually requires more lead than hard, close grained or frozen timber.

In sawing frozen timber, some sawyers give their saw a little more lead, thinking it will aid in slabbing a log. This is a mistake, for if a saw be lined into the log, after the first or second cut, or after the frozen sap is taken off,

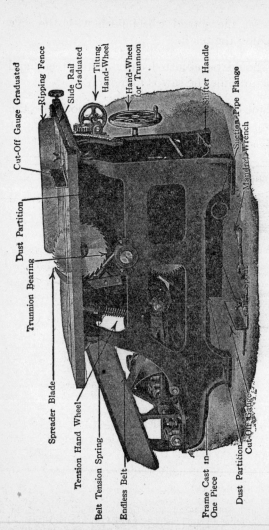

Cut-Off Gauge Graduated

Ripping Fence

Slide Rail Graduated

Tilting Hand-Wheel

Hand-Wheel for Trunnion

Dust Partition

Trunnion Bearing

Spreader Blade

Shifter Handle

Suction-Pipe Flange

Mandrel Wrench

Tension Hand Wheel

Belt Tension Spring

Endless Belt

Frame Cast in One Piece

Dust Partition

Cut-Off Gauge

FIG. 3,574.—Crescent universal saw table, adapted to pattern shops or other geneal use. *It has* two mandrels, so arranged that either one of them can be swung into action by turning a hand wheel. The two mandrels are mounted on a heavy cast trunnion, and a saw may be placed on each of the two mandrels (preferably a rip saw on the one and a cut off on the other). The mandrels are so belted that only the upper saw is in motion when in use, the lower mandrel not being in contact with the belt at all. No changing of belt is required to change saws; simply turn the hand wheel and the trunnion carrying both mandrels will revolve, bringing the desired saw up through the table ready for operation; and this may readily be done while the machine is running. One of the mandrels has the projecting end, or stub, made long enough to admit a groover head 2 inches wide to be placed between the tight collar and nut. The other mandrel is made with a short stub, admitting only a saw, made in this manner, so that this mandrel may be raised to its maximum height when table is tilted to a full angle of 45 degrees, without having end of mandrel to strike against the under side of table. Both mandrels will swing clear of the table when table is level, or when but slightly inclined.

the saw will have a tendency to run into the log and make the lumber thin at the rear end of the cut. To prevent this, the sawyer is forced to guide the saw out a little with the guide pins. The saw will then run out in the first cut worse than before. It will be a trifle full between the rim and the center and will heat at this point, causing to tremble and flutter, and to work badly.

Fig. 3,575.—Yates self-feed circular rip saw. The iron table is raised and lowered by a hand wheel to accommodate different thicknesses of stock. The feed works are designed to provide a positive feed and consist of a spur roll that feeds stock to the saw, and a corrugated delivery roll that conducts the ripped pieces from the saw. The feeding and delivering rolls are mounted independently, and by means of coiled tension springs a firm and even pressure on stock is maintained at all times. Over the saw is a steel spring to hold down the stock, which permits feeding of small stock without danger of kick back. To work thicker stock feeding mechanism may be thrown clear of table and stock fed by hand.

In lining a saw for frozen timber it is advisable to line it in such a way that it will run on the board guide instead of the log guide; that is, after the saw has attained its normal speed, set the board guide so it will touch the saw lightly. Bring the log guide close to the saw but not close enough to pinch the saw in the guides. Any play given the saw should be on the log

FIG. 3,576.—Yates gang ripping machine. *It is designed* for mills requiring a light, accurate gang ripper. Is simple in construction with ample strength to withstand all abuse it may be subjected to. The base is a single piece casting to which both front and rear tables are firmly bolted. The feed works consist of two fluted rolls set close before and after saw. The necessary idle rolls are provided on both tables. The mechanism for spacing saws is controlled from operator's position by means of a set of levers to which is attached a grooved wheel. Taut wire ropes extend over sheaves to the guide, moving saws to desired position when lever is operated. The hold down rolls are raised and lowered by means of screws positioned on the side of each roll. Tables are made of seasoned maple, and are approximately, 3' long. A device is employed to prevent kick-backs. Saws are 14'' in diameter, and will rip material 4'' thick as a maximum. Drive pulley is 8'' in diameter with 10½'' face.

guide. If the saw do not run so it can be guided in this manner, look to the lining and line it so that it can be run on a straight guide.

Lining the Saw.—There are various methods used for lining a saw with the carriage. First, be sure that the mandrel is set perfectly level so that the saw hangs plumb and is perfectly flat on the log side. Then try one or more of the following:

1. Move the carriage until the head block is on a line with the front edge of the saw. Fasten to the head block a pointed stick with the point lightly touching the saw. Move the carriage until the point is opposite the back edge of the saw. Then set the mandrel until the point of the stick clears the saw $1/32$ in. to $1/64$ in. Check by turning saw $1/2$ revolution.

2. Fasten a square edged stick to the head block with the end of the stick $1/8$ in. from the saw at the center. Run the carriage back 15 to 18 feet. Stretch a line from the back of the saw to the stick. Give the saw the lead desired.

3. Take a tapering board the radius of the saw with a hole at the large end. Fit the hole over the mandrel after removing the saw and screw up the collars. Pierce the stick at the small end with a nail, screw, or skewer. Measure from the head block to the nail. Turn the mandrel over by pulling the belt. Run the head block to the new position and measure again. Set the mandrel to give the required lead.

4. Draw a line 10 feet each way from the center of the mandrel and parallel with the "V" track. Fasten a stick to the head block so that it comes up to the line at the end in front of the saw. Run the carriage forward the 20 feet. Move the rear end of the line one inch away from its former parallel position. Then set the mandrel until the saw is parallel with the new position of the line.

5. Stretch a fine line of thread, say 20 feet long, across the face of the saw in a parallel line with the "V" or guide track. This can be done easily by running the carriage back and forth the length of the thread and placing each end of the thread an equal distance from the front head block. The thread being properly placed, with a piece of chalk mark the saw at the front at a point on a level with the carriage and measure the distance between the thread and the marked point on the saw. Then slue the arbor around either way, as the case may require, to give the saw $1/32$ in. lead into the log in the diameter of a 60-inch saw.

The author recommends marking the saw and taking both

Fig. 3,577.—American wire cable drive for saw mill as used on variable friction feed machines.

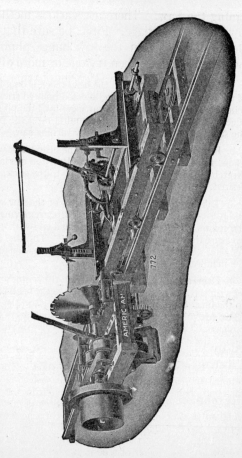

Fig. 3,578.—American variable belt feed saw mill equipped with balance wheel.

measurements from this marked point on the saw as the saw might be a trifle out of true. A measurement taken from the front and back of the saw, without turning the saw over, might not be perfectly accurate.

Feed.—This is the moving of the wood against the saw. Where the saws are small, 46 inches in diameter or less, the feed is usually by hand or in an automatic machine.

Power feed for larger saws is—steam, rope or friction.

Feed is measured by the number of linear inches cut in one revolution of the saw. A 12 in. cant is usually taken as a basis of calculation.

The feed may readily be determined by measuring the distance on the log from the mark made by a prominent tooth to the next mark of the same tooth, indicating one complete revolution of the saw. The feed of larger saws is from 4 in. to 16 in. The more feed desired the greater must be the number of teeth in the saw.

Be careful not to over-feed.

Speed.—Speed is indicated by the number of revolutions per minute made by the saw and also by the number of feet traveled by the rim per minute. The revolutions are measured by an instrument called a speed indicator.

Revolutions.—Light portable mills run 450 to 650 revolutions per minute.

High speed steam feed mills run 600 to 900 revolutions per minute.

Small circular bench saws, hand feed, may run 2,000 to 2,500 revolutions per minute.

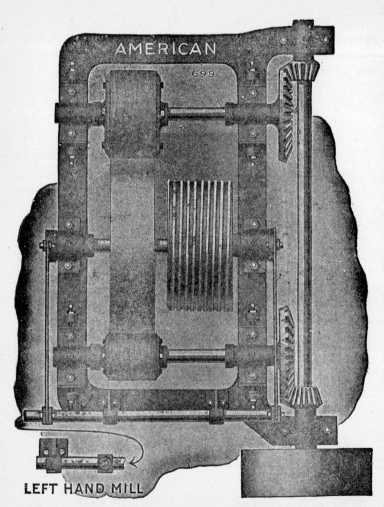

F<small>IG</small>. 3,579.—American band friction mill feed. *It may be driven* from the mill shaft or from the line shaft and cam, if preferred, be placed at end of track, in which case one sheave only is used.

Rim Speed.—Rim speed is the speed of the cutting edge. For mill curcular saws it increases from 8,000 to 12,000 feet per minute. Medium rim speed for the average mill is 10,000 feet per minute.

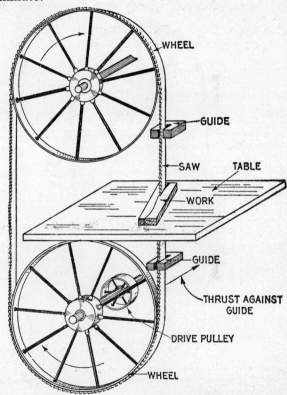

FIG. 3,580.—Essential parts of a band saw showing principle of operation.

Speed must be regular and uniform as determined by the engine and the pulleys.

Test by the speed indicator.

Be careful not to over speed.

The speed must be known before a saw can be hammered to the right tension.

Band Saws.—Saws of this type are sometimes erroneously

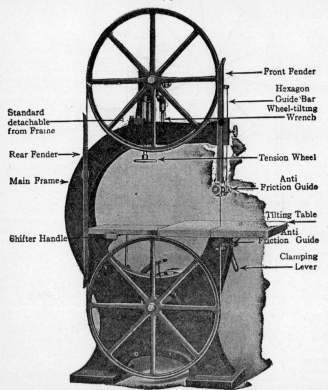

Front Fender

Hexagon
Guide Bar
Wheel-tilting
Wrench

Standard
detachable
from Frame

Rear Fender →

Main Frame →

Tension Wheel

Anti
Friction Guide

Tilting Table

Shifter Handle

Anti
Friction Guide

Clamping
Lever

Fig. 3,581.—Crescent band saw. Side view showing general construction.

called "scroll" saws; the latter variety as later described is quite different from the band saw.

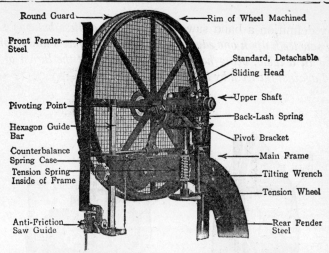

Round Guard — Rim of Wheel Machined

Front Fender Steel

Standard, Detachable
Sliding Head

Upper Shaft

Pivoting Point

Back-Lash Spring

Hexagon Guide Bar

Pivot Bracket

Counterbalance Spring Case

Main Frame

Tension Spring Inside of Frame

Tilting Wrench

Tension Wheel

Anti-Friction Saw Guide

Rear Fender Steel

FIG. 3,582.—Crescent band saw upper wheel mounting showing upper shaft construction with round guard attached. The wheel can be inclined backward or forward, or raised or lowered while saw is in motion. The end of the tilting wrench extends downward so as to be in easy reach of the operator while standing in front of the machine. The pivot bracket is fastened to the sliding head by means of two bolts passing through slotted holes. When these are released the upper wheel may be adjusted sidewise to align with lower wheel (cross line adjustment). A spring near back end of upper shaft holds bearing in proper position, preventing back lash to upper wheel in case saw should break. A tension spring is telescoped over the raising screw as shown.

Tilting Table

Front Table Segment

Saw Blade

Sub Table

Rear Table Segment

Degree Scale and Pointer

Table Stop

Main Frame

Clamping Lever

Adjusting Nuts

FIG. 3,583.—Crescent band saw tilting table. The tilting range is 45°, the angle scale being plainly seen in the illustration; the table is held in angular position by means of an eccentric lever. When setting table level again a stop is provided giving quick precision adjustment.

By definition a bana saw *consists of an endless band of steel with saw teeth upon one edge, passing over two wheels and through a slot in a table, being held in position against the thrust of the wood against the teeth by two guides.*

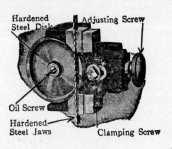

FIG. 3,584.—Crescent band saw fenders. They are so placed as to completely cover the side and front edge of the blade. The front fender is attached to the guide bar so as to raise and lower with it.

FIG. 3,585.—Crescent band saw guides. The back of the saw in sawing is thrust against the pivoted steel disc which turns with the saw reducing friction. Side jaws prevent any lateral movement of the saw. There are two of these guides located just above and just below the table.

These essential elements are shown in fig. 3,580 and the general construction of the small light duty circular saws, in figs. 3,581 to 3,585. Saws of this type are suitable for all kinds

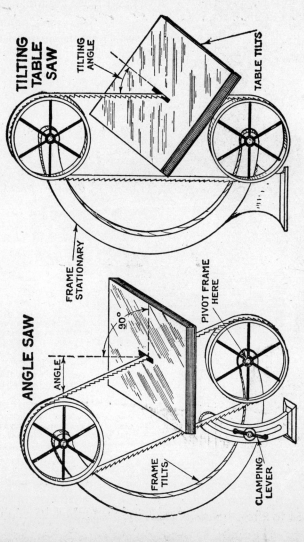

Figs. 3,586 and 3,587.—Distinction between angle band saw and tilting table band saw.

of light and medium duty sawing without regard to the direction of grain of the wood.

The distinction between an angle saw and a tilting table saw should be carefully noted as indicated in figs. 3,586 and 3,587. The actual construction of these two types of saw is shown in figs. 3,588 and 3,589.

FIG. 3,588.—American angle or bevel band saw for shops where heavy stock is to be bevel sawed such as in ship yards and car shops. *In operation*, the table remains stationary in a horizontal plane while the upper wheel shifts to bring the blade at any angle to the table up to 45°.

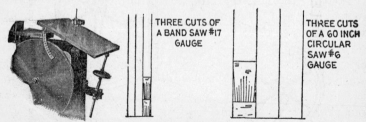

THREE CUTS OF A BAND SAW #17 GAUGE

THREE CUTS OF A 60 INCH CIRCULAR SAW #6 GAUGE

FIG. 3,589.—Fay and Egan quick angling tilting table device with micrometer adjustment for pattern work.

FIGS. 3,590 and 3,591.—Relative cuts of circular and band saw, illustrating saving due to the band saw.

Note the method of tilting frame in fig. 3,586, and compare with fig. 3,588, in which the angular position of the saw is obtained by sliding the upper wheel mounting on the circular shaped top part of the frame.

"Rip" Band Saws or Band Saw Mills.—Formerly band saws were used only for light work such as sawing boards, but because of the considerable saving in lumber due to the thin cut as compared with the circular saws, the range of work performed by the band saw has been greatly increased. In fact recent development has produced band saws up to 18 ins. wide capable of the heaviest duty; they have largely replaced the circular saw in several lines of work. The relative saving due to thinness of the band saw blade is shown in figs. 3,590 and 3,591.

Band saws from 2 to 8 inches in width, are extensively used for ripping and resawing, because, compared with the circular saw, they save kerf, time and power.

This leads to the consideration of the band saw as related to the saw mill. Before its introduction there was a limit in size of timber which could be sawn by circular saws, which could cut only logs of a size slightly less than half the diameter of the saw. The size of the saw itself was also limited; difficulties of management and running arose as soon as the saw diameter was increased beyond a certain point.

Double Mills.—Double mills were used to a great extent in regions where large timber was being cut. By this arrangement, which consisted of two circular saws, one above the other, logs of an ordinary size were sawn with the larger or "main" circular saw, while the smaller, or "top saw," was brought into action when a log exceeded the capacity of the main saw. The band saw obviated all this, for there is practically no limit to the size of logs which can be cut by band saws.

In large band mills, as a rule, the work is brought to the saw upon a carriage driven by feeding devices independent of the saw.

FIG. 3,592.—Fay and Egan band saw mill or "rip band saw."
The carriage with its dogs securely clamping the log travels on a
track in front of the saw. The control of the log is by the levers
shown. The set works are double acting and will set accurately
to ¼ in. An index is in plain sight of operator showing exact set
of the knees. *In operation,* a single throw of the lever either to
or from the operator sets all knees in head blocks quickly and
accurately forward to make next cut. An eccentric stop permits
an accurate set from the saw blade and a taper wedge mechanism
on the lever gives the fractional set to take care of the saw kerf.
A foot treadle or hand lever releases the receding mechanism
which is controlled by a brake convenient to operator.

Continuous Cutting.—Formerly used in sawmills, such as mill, gang, etc. The band saw has the advantage over the reciprocating saws of steady and continuous cutting action,

However, gangs of reciprocating saws, by reason of their ability to cut as many as 30 boards at one time, are still retained in numbers of large mills as an adjunct to the bands.

Fig. 3,593.—Fay and Egan twin band resaw designed to meet the requirements of furniture, box, fruit package and panel makers. The machine will resaw timbers up to 24″ wide and 10″ thick. It will saw a board into three pieces ³⁄₁₆″ thick or three of any other thickness up to 3″ each. It will saw one piece 3″, one 6″ and one 1′: or any combination less than these. By adjusting the movable saw out of the way the machine may be used as a single resaw, sawing up to 3″ on one side and 6″ on the other. The wheels are 54″ diameter proper face to carry 6″ blade. The first rolls of the variable speed friction works are 5″ and second 4″ diameter, and may be set self-centering or can be quickly changed to have one set rigid for sawing from one side of a timber. Right angle bevel gear drive; gears cut steel and enclosed. Motor, 50 *h.p.*, 1200 r. *p.m.*, direct coupled, or any speed belted.

When one considers the value of every $\frac{1}{16}$ inch saved in kerf in the course of a day's sawing of several hundred thousand feet, the great economy in using the thin blade band saw can be more fully appreciated.

Large Bands.—Large band saws for log sawing range from 8 to 18 inches in width. The general width for single-edged bands, *i. e.*, toothed on one edge, is 12 inches, while double-edged band saws are made in a variety of sizes. The majority of these latter, however, are about 14 inches in width, although, as previously stated, some few are made as narrow as 8 inches.

The length of the standard log band saw varies, according to size and make of mill, from 40 to 60 feet.

Double-edged band saws are now used frequently and the log can be cut as it moves in both directions.

The swage set is principally used on log bands and resaws. Swaging the teeth consists of spreading or widening the cutting edge of each tooth so that it extends slightly beyond each side of the blade, giving clearance to the body of the saw while cutting. Sufficient clearance prevents friction and insures free runnings.

> Again, with the swage tooth both corners of the tooth cut, consequently it will not only do twice as much work as a spring-set tooth, which merely cuts half a kerf, but in addition it will stand more feed, thus greatly increasing the capacity of the mill.

> The **band resaw,** which is not extensively used, has been successfully operated in gangs. There are mills in the United States and Canada using gangs containing two or more machines.

The Hand.—The experienced sawyer or mill man is familiar with the "hand" of a band saw, but for the benefit of the beginner it may be stated that a saw is either right or left hand. As you stand facing the mill with the teeth of the saw toward you, if the log pass on the right hand side, it is a right hand saw; if it pass on the left of the saw, it is a left hand saw.

Narrow Bands.—Band saws adapted for certain kinds of cutting are known as "narrow and wide." Machines on which are working saws $\frac{1}{8}$ inch up to $1\frac{3}{4}$ inch are designated as narrow bands. These are used extensively in mills, cooperage shops, furniture factories and other wood-working establishments, for a great variety of purposes. They are employed to cut in addition to wood, slate, fiber-board, paper, bone, meat, hard rubber, ivory, asbestos, magnesia, horn, amber, cloth, bronze, brass, copper, aluminum, nickel, iron, steel, carbon, ice, celluloid, talc, camphor, mica, pearl, shell, and cardboard.

In using small band saws, the work rests upon a table, through the center of which the saw passes, the work being fed by hand. For general work, the blades are made as narrow as $\frac{1}{8}$ inch and from that are graduated up by eighths to $1\frac{3}{4}$ inches, saws up to this width being considered "narrow band saws." The length is usually 18 feet, or longer, according to the size of the machine on which they are used.

Cutting Circles.—The fact that with a narrow band saw, circles or other curved lines can be cut in any desired direction, makes it available for use in cutting intricate and ornamental patterns. Where formerly scroll sawing was done entirely by the reciproacting type—web or scroll saws, working up and down, and compass saws—now the narrow band saw is being widely used with excellent and greater results. Its downward motion carries the sawdust away without the aid of a blower, leaving the lines drawn on the work perfectly clean to the operator.

It is understood, of course, that band saws can be used in this connection only in cases where the pattern is begun on the edge of the stock, for interior designs it is necessary to use a reciprocating saw (jig saw), the end of which can be passed through the interior of the pattern.

Small, narrow band saws are fitted with spring-set. With the spring set the point of one tooth is bent to the right and the next to the left, and so on alternately throughout the length of the saw. This effects the necessary clearance.

The general construction of a band saw mill or "rip band saw," as they are sometimes called, is shown in fig. 3,592.

Scroll or "Jig" Saws.—The distinguishing feature of saws of this type is that the blade moves with a reciprocating motion

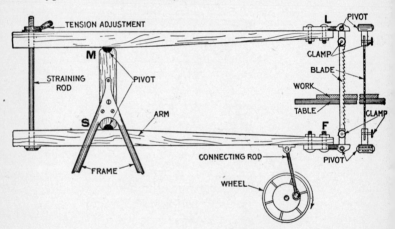

Fig. 3,594.—Essential part of a scroll or bracket saw illustrating working principle. *In operation,* the fly wheel turns in the direction of the arrow (being driven by foot or engine power). A reciprocating motion is given to the arms and saw blade, the latter cutting the wood on each down stroke.

instead of continuously in one direction as in the case of circular and band saws. Accordingly *only half of the distance traveled by the saw is effective in cutting.*

A familiar example of scroll saw is what is usually called a "bracket saw" and looked upon as a toy. The essential features and operation of such device are shown in fig. 3,594.

Here, as seen, the saw is clamped to two heads, L, and F, attached to the arms, the latter being pivoted to the frame at M, and S, and brought in tension by the straining rod and adjusting nut seen at the left end of the arms. This maintains the delicate saw blade in tension and prevents buckling.

A reciprocating motion is given by the familiar connecting rod and fly wheel. The work is placed on the table and fed to the saw in the direction indicated by the arrow.

FIG. 3,595.—W. F. & John Barnes scroll saw with power drive. *Capacity:* pine, 2 ins. thick, 1 ft. per minute; 1 in. thick, 4 ft. per minute; walnut, 3 ins. thick, ½ ft. per minute; 1 in. thick, 2 ft. per minute, and other woods and thicknesses in proportion. Ordinary speed 800 to 1,200 strokes per minute. *Dimensions:* swing, 24 ins.; Length of blade, 7 ins. Table and arms of hard maple; frame cast iron. Weight, 60 lbs. Speed of countershaft, 500 *r. p. m.* Tight and loose pulleys 4 ins. diam. × 2 in. face.

When substantially constructed as in fig. 3,595, it is frequently used for practical service in the workshops of carpenters and builders, cabinet makers and other wood workers.

Fig. 3,596 shows a scroll or "jig" saw designed for heavier work to meet the needs of furniture, car and pattern shop use. Intricate scroll sawing, including external and internal curve work, can be handled to advantage by this type of saw.

Lathes.—By definition, a lathe is *a machine tool for shaping wood (or metal) by causing it to revolve between centers while acted upon by a sharp edge cutting tool held in the hand and supported by a slide rest.*

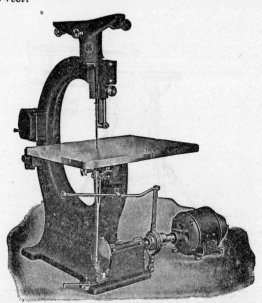

Fig. 3,596.—Fay and Egan scroll saw with direct electric drive. The table may be tilted 30° to right or left and can be securely locked at any angle. The motor is 2 horse power at 1,200 r. p. m. and may be directly connected with friction clutch as shown or any speed belted. 14 in. saw is used. The cast iron housing at the top carries the tension mechanism. An automatic blower is provided which works in conjunction with strain and keeps stock clear of saw dust so that the cutting line of saw is always visible.

The lathe is one of the most widely used wood working machines, being employed largely in many lines of work as pattern making, furniture, carriage and any other work requiring the shaping of wood to cylindrical form.

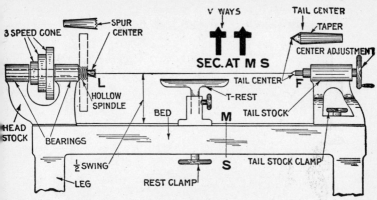

FIGS. 3,597 and 3,598.—Essential part of a wood turning lathe and section of bed at MS, showing V ways which register with V grooves cut into bottom of head and tail stock **and** which

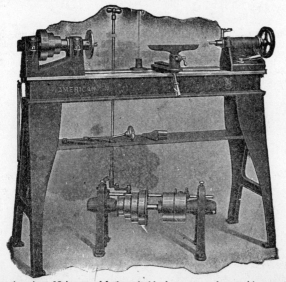

FIG. 3,599.—American 12 in. speed lathe suitable for pattern shop making small patterns. Bed lengths for 19, 26, and 43 ins. between centers. The bed is made of cast iron planed **and** finished giving precision alignment.

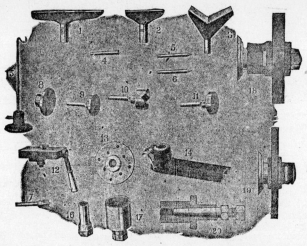

FIGS. 3,600 to 3,619.—Auxiliaries or attatchments used on (American) lathe. ***They are:***
1, 12″ rest; 2, 6″ rest; 3, angle rest; 4, cup center; 5 and 6, conical center; 7, spur center; 8, rosette chuck face plate; 9, rosette chuck with face plate and taper center; 10, crotch center; 11, drill pad; 12, rest socket plate; 13, 6″ face plate; 14, rest socket; 15, print holder; 16, small hollow chuck; 17, large hollow chuck; 18, 1″ × 7″ emery wheel attachment, no emery wheel furnished; 19, ½″ × 7″ emery wheel attachment; 20, speed lathe collet.

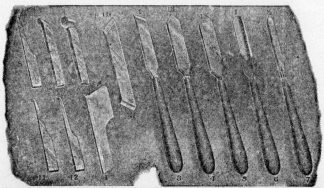

FIGS. 3,620 to 3,631.—American lathe turning tools. ***They are:*** 1, roughing and smoothing chisel; 2, double edge skew chisel; 3, skew edge chisel; 4, spear point chisel; 5, straight chisel; 6, gouge; 7, round nose chisel; 8, 9. 10. 11, 12, tool post turning tools for carriage.

Since the wood is revolved while being cut, the operation is called "wood turning."

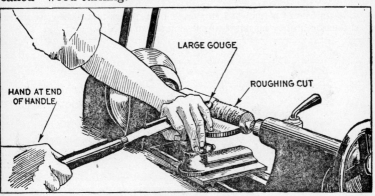

Fig. 3,632.—Roughing cut. Place the large gouge on the rest so that the level is above the wood and cutting edge tangent to the "circle of cut." *In adjusting* rest for this the handle should be well down. Roll gouge over slightly to the right so that it will shear instead of scrape the wood. Lift handle slowly thus forcing cutting edge into the wood. First remove in this way the corners, then the intervening portions. The tool should be held at a slight angle to the axis of the wood being turned with the cutting end in advance of the handle as shown.

Fig. 3,633.—Sizing cut. First set calipers to the required diameter, then with a small gouge held in the right hand scrape grooves about 1 in. apart until to size, frequently testing with the calipers.

The essential features of a lathe are shown in figs. 3,597 and 3,598.

It consists of a rigid bed supported by two legs and having its upper surface accurately machined (to section shown at MS).

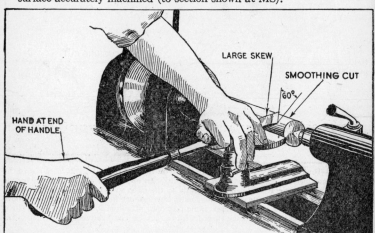

FIG. 3,634.—Paring or finishing cut. Lay the skew chisel on the rest with the cutting edge above the cylinder and at an angle of about 60° to the surface. Slowly draw chisel back, raising the handle until the chisel cuts about ¼ to ⅜ in. from the heel. Begin first cut from 1 to 2 ins. from either end pushing toward the near end. Then begin at the first starting point and cut toward the other end, thus taking off the rings left by the gouge, cutting down to where the scraped sections are just visible. Now take a last cut removing all traces of the rings bringing the wood down to a uniform diameter from end to end. *To test for smoothness* place palm of the hand with the fingers extended straight lightly on the back side of the wood away from the tool rest.

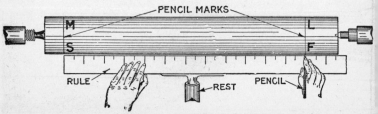

FIG. 3,635.—Marking length of work. Place rule on tool rest holding it in position with left hand very close to work and with sharp pointed pencil mark length to which piece is to be cut off as shown by pencil marks MS and LF.

SMALL SKEW

SQUARING CUT

FIG. 3,636.—Squaring the ends. Place ¼ or ½ in. skew chisel on the rest bringing the cutting edge next to the stock perpendicular to the axis. The heel of the chisel is then slightly tipped from the cylinder to give clearance. Raise handle and push chisel toe into the stock about ⅛ in. outside the line indicating end of cylinder Swing handle still further from cylinder and cut a half V, giving clearance and preventing burning. Continue until cylinder is cut to about 1/16 in. diameter.

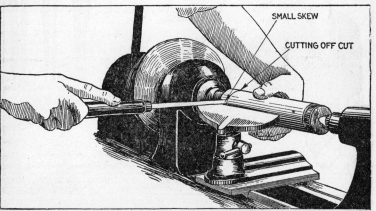

SMALL SKEW

CUTTING OFF CUT

FIG. 3,637.—Cutting off with small skew. After squaring hold chisel in right hand (same position as for squaring) and with fingers of the left hand placed around the stock to catch it slowly face the point of chisel into the stock at the line center end until stock is cut free and cylinder falls in operator's hand.

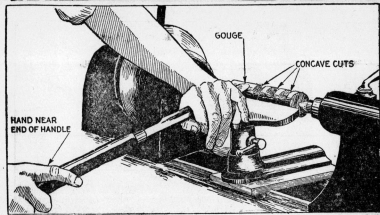

FIG. 3,638.—Concave cut. Place gouge on rest with cutting edge well above the wood. Roll tool to side till grind at cutting point is perpendicular to the axis of the cylinder. Slowly raise handle to force gouge into the wood. When gouge bites force it forward and upward by slightly lowering the handle while rolling back toward its first position. Reverse position of gouge and make a similar cut from the other side to form the other half of the semi-circle.

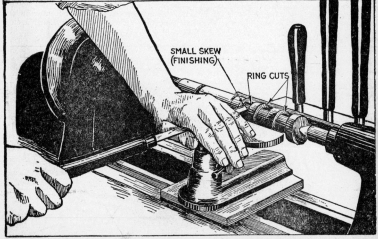

FIG. 3,639.—Ring cut. Mark center of convex surface to be cut which indicates starting point for all cutting. Place ¼ or ½ in. small skew chisel on rest with cutting edge above the cylinder and lower grind tangent to it. Draw back chisel and raise the handle bringing heel of chisel in contact with the cylinder at the marked line. The chisel is then moved to the right (if cutting right side of bead) while being continually tipped to keep the lower grind tangent to the revolving cylinder and also to bead at the point of contact. Continue cut until the bottom of the convex surface is reached.

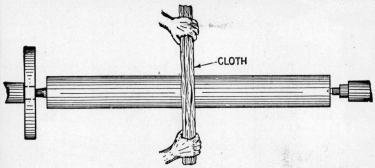

CLOTH

Fɪɢ. 3,640.—Polishing.   *This operation* is done with a cloth after the cylinder has been sanded and while rotating in the lathe.   *In sanding,* use first a fairly coarse grade of paper, No. 1 or 1½, and afterwards a fine grade No. 0 or 00.   Before applying the cloth the wood may be varnished lightly while the lathe is not running, taking care to wipe off all the surplus varnish.   The varnish will assist in giving the surface a fine polish when the cloth is applied.

AMERICAN

ɢ. 3,641.—Face plate turning.   *In this kind of turning* the piece to be turned is held by the screw center chuck, or as shown by the face plate, the rest being fastened in suitable position at that end of the bed as shown.

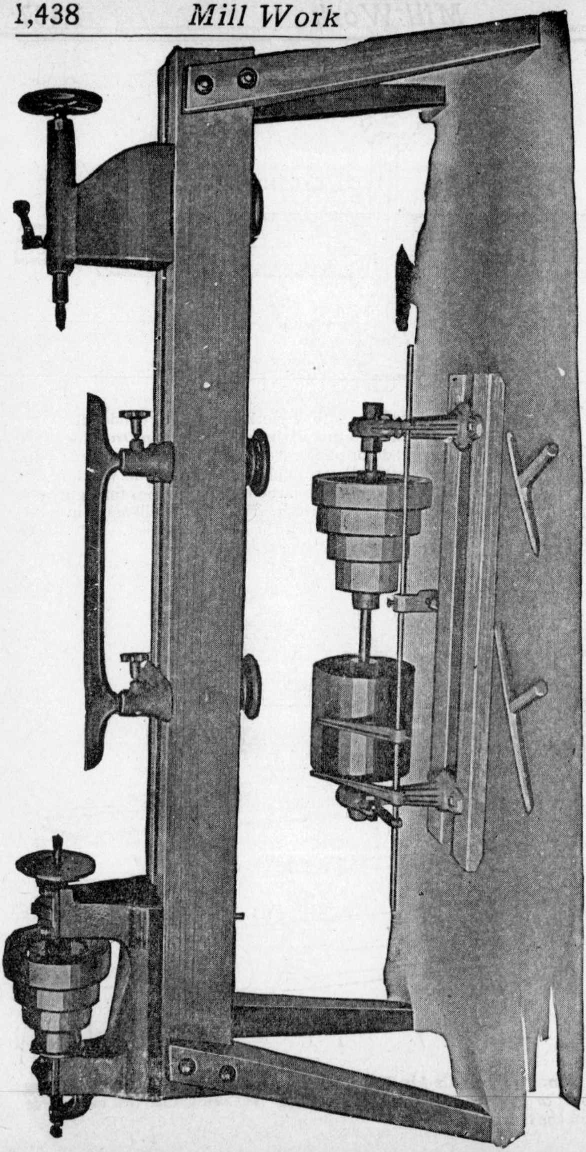

FIG. 3,642.—Superior 12, 16 and 20 in. single head wooden bed lathe. *As seen*, the bed is made of two substantial timbers separated by distance pieces and bolted together at the ends. Alignment of head and tail stocks is secured by lugs projecting down from the bottom face into the slot or space between the two timbers. Of course no such precision of alignment is possible as with the all metal construction (fig. 3,599) but when carefully made and correctly proportioned is much cheaper and accurate enough for ordinary work.

The two "V" ways carry a rigid head stock at one end, and a tail stock, the latter arranged to slide on the "V" ways and to be secured at any point by tightening the tail stock clamp.

The head stock carries a hollow tapered spindle with speed cone between two bearings. Fitting in the taper is a spur center L, which engages one end of the wood to be turned, the other end being secured by the tail center F.

When the spur center is caused to turn by belt drive on one of the "steps" of the speed cone, the spurs of the spur center, cause the piece of wood inserted between the center to turn also.

By resting a sharp edge cutting tool against the T rest the wood is "shaved off" and the surface reduced to circular form.

There are two general classes of lathes, the metal bed type as shown in fig. 3,599, and the ordinary wooden bed lathe shown in fig. 3,642. The latter type is cheaper especially where work of considerable length if to be turned and when the bed is well constructed of substantial timbers, the alignment is sufficiently accurate for ordinary work.

How to Operate a Lathe.—The process of wood turning on the lathe is an interesting one and presents no difficulties when understood and correctly done. The accompanying cut (figs. 3,632 to 3,641) illustrate the general methods employed in wood turning.

Speed of the Lathe.—This should range from 2,400 to 3,000 when the belt is at the smallest step of the cone. At this speed stock up to 3 ins. diameter can be safely turned. Use second step of cone for stock up to 6 ins. diameter and largest step for all stocks over 6 ins. diameter. Glued work should not be run at too high speed owing to danger of it being thrown from lathe by centrifugal force.

Planers.—The various machines known as surfacers, jointers, matchers and moulders, timber sizers, timber dresses, etc.,
are all types of planer being more or less complicated according
to the range and variety of work performed.

In general a planer is *a machine for planing or "surfacing"
wood, especially boards, by means of a rapidly revolving cutter
which chips off the rough surface in minute shavings as the piece
to be planed is passed over (or under) the revolving cutter by hand
or power feed, leaving a smooth or finished surface.*

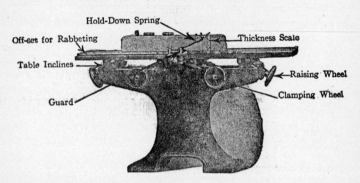

Fɪɢ. 3,643.—Crescent 8 in. jointer. In operation the shavings are delivered to the rear of the
machine by a chute. *In construction,* the table inclines for table adjustment are bolted
to a sliding sashlike casting gibbed into the main frame on a sliding dovetail allowing the
tables to be horizontally withdrawn from the head without disturbing the vertical adjustment. The front and rear tables are of equal length. The tilting fence can be moved to any
position across the table and tilted to 45°. It is provided with a pressure spring to hold the
work down on the table convenient when making the strips.

Lumber thus treated or planed is said to be *dressed*. Lumber may be
dressed on one, two or all sides according as may be desired.

The simplest type of planer is the jointer, sometimes called
hand planer or buzz planer.

It is called hand planer because the work is fed through by hand instead
of by power feed.

A jointer is used for straightening lumber. It will plane one surface straight and out of wind; by the use of the fence it will also bring one surface on dimension stock square with another, or on accurate bevel with another.

It is not intended for surfacing boards to uniform thickness. For such use, a regular planer or surfacer must be used.

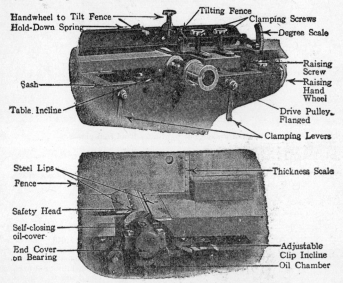

FIGS. 3,644 to 3,646.—Crescent 8 in. jointer. Views showing various details of construction illustrating attachments and control devices. The tilting fence can be moved to any position across the table. It is provided with a pressure spring to hold work down on the table; this is convenient when working thin strips. The tilting fence can be set tilting for fence work and can be set at any angle from 45° to 90°. The tilting of the fence is accomplished by means of a hand wheel and worm gear, a graduated scale being provided to indicate the degrees of angle. A vertical scale on the face of the fence shows in advance the exact thickness the piece will be after the cut is made. For instance, a block of wood is 2¼ inches thick, and it is desired to reduce it to 2 inches in thickness; lay it on the front table and lower the table till the top of the piece is opposite the 2-inch graudation, then make the cut, and the piece will be found to be of the desired thickness. The lower edge of the fence always rests on the rear table, hence the thickness of the piece after the cut is made will always correspond to the graduations on the scale, as shown, before the cut is made.

By use of special cutters, a jointer is often adapted to grooving, making light moulding and other similar work regularly done on a *shaper* (later described).

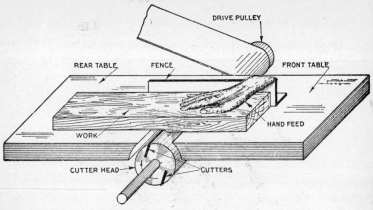

FIG. 3,647.—Essential parts of a jointer or light duty hand feed planer.

FIG. 3,648.—American rabbeting and jointing machine. This is virtually a light duty form of planer designed especially for rabbeting and jointing blinds rapidly and smoothly. *In operation,* the blind is fed on its edge, the bead is worked on the same side with the guide, avoiding the unevenness usually found in beads on blinds; the headstock carrying the rabbeting head is set on a mitre with the face of the blind, which makes a free cut on both sides of the rabbet; the headstock is adjustable vertically and horizontally while in motion by means of screws; both feed shafts are hung in pivoted boxes, and the idler on opposite side of machine is adjustable to take up slack on jointer belt. The blind is jointed on both edges at the same time it s rabbeted and beaded. *Table.* This is long the after part being adjustable in line with the cutters, which insures straight work. The blind is held firmly by means of springs, and is fed through by two rubber rolls, one before and the other after the cutters. The first roll is fitted with a spur, or fluted roll, on the lower end, which operates on the part to be cut out, making a strong feed.

Fig. 3,647, illustrates the operation of a jointer.

In operation the rapidly revolving cutters make a clean cut on the bottom side of the work as it is slowly fed by hand in the direction of the arrow. The depth of cut is regulated by adjusting the table vertically up or down, with respect to the cutter. Actual construction of a jointer is shown in figs. 3,644 to 3,646.

There are two general types of cutter head used on jointers

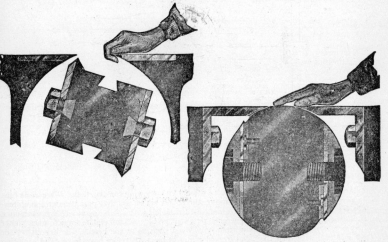

FIGS. 3,649 and 3,650.—Square and "safety" or cylindrical forms of cutter cylinder or head showing how fingers may be accidentally cut off with the square form and how this danger is overcome with the safety form.

and other planers; the square and the safety as shown in figs. 3,649 and 3,650.

A comparison of the illustration will at once indicate why the square form should *not* be used.

A great variety of work can be done on a jointer depending largely upon the knowledge and skill of the operator. A fair idea of the scope of work usually accomplished on the jointer is shown in the accompanying illustrations, figs. 3,652 to 3,662, which show also the appearance of the various cuts.

In operating a jointer never omit using the guard.

A type of planer adapted to larger work than the jointer is known as the *surfacer*.

There are two general types:

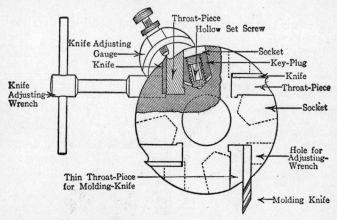

FIG. 3,651.—Crescent safety cutter head; sectional view showing construction. ***Directions for taking knives out of head:*** First loosen the hollow set screws that pass through the center of the key plugs, by giving about a half turn to the left with the hexagon wrench sent along for that purpose. Before taking wrench out, strike a blow on top end of wrench with a light hammer to release the key plug from its wedged position in the head. The key plugs are wedge shape with their thick end toward center of head, therefore have to be driven a blow downward toward center of head to loosen, after screw is released. When all the key plugs are thus released then the knife will be free and can readily be removed. After knife is removed, the throat piece and key plugs can also be removed. To replace the knife, first see that all the dirt and dust is removed from the knife seat and throat piece. See that each key plug is in its proper place according to the numbers stamped on the same. After the key plugs, throat piece and knife are properly placed, then tighten the key plugs very lightly; then adjust the knife to cutting position by use of the special wrench inserted into the holes at back of knife. Use the small gauge furnished, with end of screw over top of the edge of knife to get a uniform setting of the knife edge. When knife is properly set, then tighten the key plugs snugly, ready for use.

1. Single cylinder.
2. Double cylinder.

In both of these the work is passed through the machine by power feed.

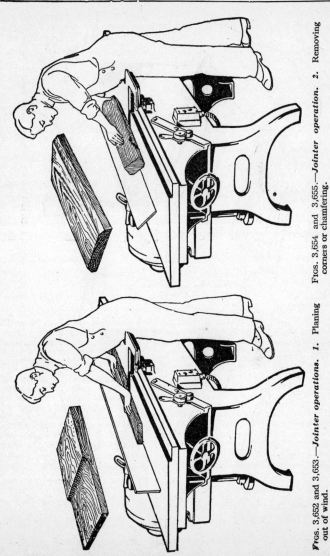

FIGS. 3,652 and 3,653.—*Jointer operations.* 1. Planing out of wind.

FIGS. 3,654 and 3,655.—*Jointer operation.* 2. Removing corners or chamfering.

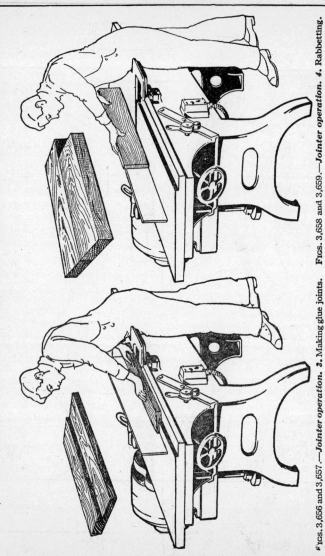

FIGS. 3,656 and 3,657.—*Jointer operation.* 3. Making glue joints.   FIGS. 3,658 and 3,659.—*Jointer operation.* 4. Rabbetting.

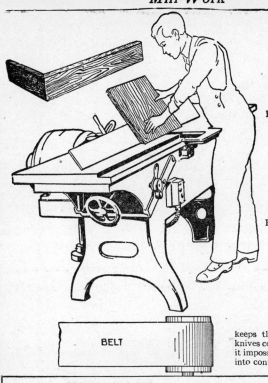

FIGS. 3,660 and 3,661.—
Jointer operation. 5.
Planing a bevel for mitre
work

FIG. 3,662. — Action of
guard on jointer. *In op-
eration,* the nose of the
guard presses against the
work at F, due to the
spring M, and lies over the
portion of the cutter not
under the work. The
guard being pivoted at S,
swings to any opening to
accommodate the width
of the work. As shown it
keeps the unused portion of the
knives covered at all times making
it impossible for the fingers to come
into contact with the knives.

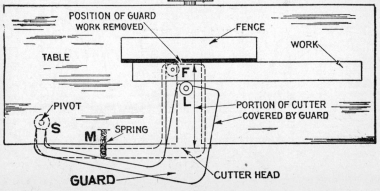

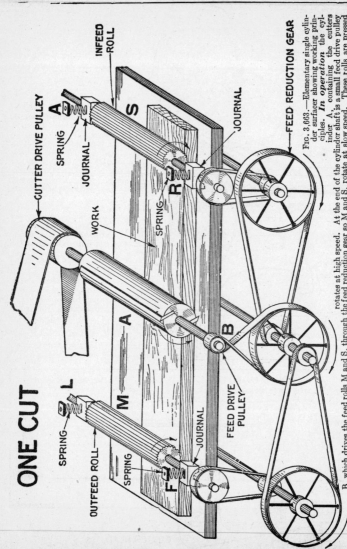

ONE CUT

CUTTER DRIVE PULLEY

SPRING

A

JOURNAL

INFEED ROLL

S

WORK

R

SPRING

JOURNAL

FEED REDUCTION GEAR

FEED DRIVE PULLEY

B

M

A

JOURNAL

SPRING

F

SPRING

OUTFEED ROLL

L

Fig. 3,663.—Elementary single cylinder surfacer showing working principles. *In operation* the cylinder A, containing the cutters rotates at high speed. At the end of the cylinder shaft is a small feed drive pulley B, which drives the feed rolls M and S, through the feed reduction gear so M and S, rotate at slow speed. These rolls are pressed down on the work by the springs L, A, R, F, working through the journals as shown. The rolls being corrugated considerable grip is obtained on the work so that it is slowly pushed along the table in the direction of the arrow while the cut into the work leaves a smooth surface. The reason for two feed rolls is that the work must be fed to the cutters before it is gripped by M. and must continue feeding after the end of the work leaves S, so that the entire board will be planed.

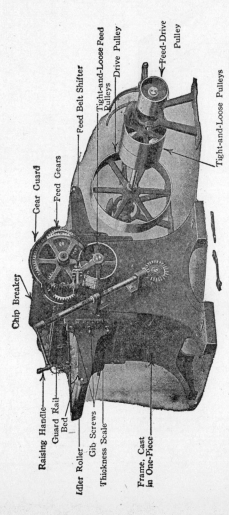

Chip Breaker

Gear Guard

Feed Gears

Feed Belt Shifter

Tight-and-Loose Feed Pulleys

Drive Pulley

Feed-Drive Pulley

Tight-and-Loose Pulleys

Raising Handle

Guard Rail Bed

Idler Roller

Gib Screws

Thickness Scale

Frame, Cast in One-Piece

FIGS. 3,664 and 3,665.—Crescent 18 and 24 in. single cylinder surfacer, and counter shaft. *The feed* is driven from the small pulley on the counter shaft to a pair of tight and loose pulleys on the machine. A convenient belt shifter is provided in the machine for starting and stopping the feed. The rate of feed is 25 ft. per minute. The machine is not made with lower rolls driven, the upper rolls only being driven. The upper rolls are hung with springs. The front and rear rolls are 10 ins. apart between centers and are 2⅝ ins. in diameter. A guard rail is placed in front of the upper front roll to prevent accident to operator when feeding short stock.

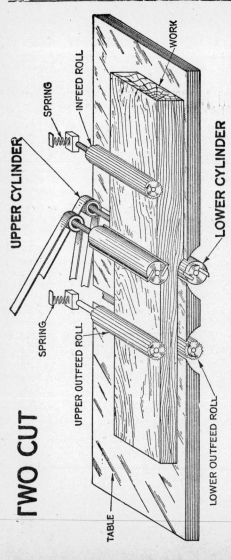

TWO CUT

UPPER CYLINDER

SPRING

INFEED ROLL

WORK

LOWER CYLINDER

UPPER OUTFEED ROLL

SPRING

LOWER OUTFEED ROLL

TABLE

FIG. 3,666.—Elementary double cylinder surfacer showing how both sides of the work are planed at the same time and illustrating upper and lower feed rolls and upper and lower cylinders.

The single cylinder surface planes one side of the wood in one operation, as shown in fig. 3,663, whereas the double cylinder type planes the wood on both side sat the same time as shown in fig. 3,666. These two figures represent elementary machines to show how they work. Actual construction of the machines is shown in figs. 3,664 to 3,667.

A type of single cylinder plane very similar to the familiar moving table planer round in machine shops is shown in fig. 3,684.

An advanced type of planer known as a *sizer* is constructed so as to make four

FIG. 3,667.—Yate's double, or two cylinder surfacer, designed especially for cabinet surfacing at double the rate of feed ordinarily used. *As constructed,* all knives may be ground and jointed without removal from the machine. The feed works consist of four 6 in. rolls, two in feed and two out feed; driven by roller bearing chains over cut sprockets. The bed is adjustable for stock thickness either by hand wheel or power hoist.

cuts at one time, that is the stock is planed top and bottom and on the other two sides simultaneously.

The method of doing this with four cylinders is very clearly shown in fig. 3,685.

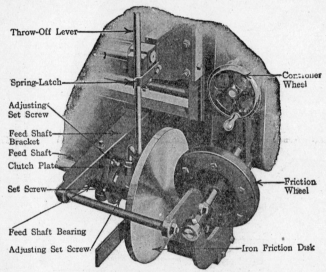

Throw-Off Lever

Spring-Latch

Adjusting Set Screw

Feed Shaft Bracket

Feed Shaft

Clutch Plate

Set Screw

Feed Shaft Bearing

Adjusting Set Screw

Controller Wheel

Friction Wheel

Iron Friction Disk

FIG. 3,668.—Crescent variable friction feed for planers. *In construction*, the front feed shaft is arranged to be driven by a belt from the head. To this shaft the iron friction disc is fastened. It is so arranged with a sliding key that it runs against the side of the disc, the required distance away from its center, to make the desired speed of feed. For faster feeds this friction wheel is moved out towards the rim of the friction disc; and for slower feeds it is moved in closer to the center of the disc; this being readily under control by simply turning a hand wheel to make the required feed. A brass scale and pointer indicates at all times the number of lineal feet per minute that the machine is planing. When rough lumber is to be surfaced, where some pieces are somewhat thicker than others, there is an advantage in using a slower feed for the thicker pieces. In this way it is not necessary to choke the machine down, in heavy cuts, till the belts begin to slip; and yet a normal feed can always be used for pieces of normal thickness. When lumber is to be surfaced as smooth as possible, a slower feed is necessary for the best results; but for ordinary common planing the faster feeds are necessary; to save time or to give greater output. A throw off lever at side of machine is provided for stopping the feed entirely, at any point, by disengaging the contact between the friction wheel and the friction disc. A small clutch plate is fastened, with a set screw, to the bearing of the feed shaft, near the lower end of the throw off lever. When this set screw is loosened, it releases the clutch plate, and it may then be adjusted by two other set screws whose points bear against the feed shaft bracket, until the desired pressure or contact is produced on the friction wheel.

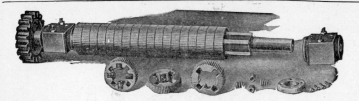

Figs. 3,669 to 3,682.—Oliver sectional feed roll and parts. *It consists of* sections $1\frac{1}{2}''$ wide $\times$ $4''$ diameter. While giving a horizontal drive as positive as a solid roll, they yield vertically independently of each other to the extent of $\frac{1}{16}''$ Each section is composed of an outer ring enclosing four sections or seats placed radially to the center of the roll shaft and carrying a helical spring.

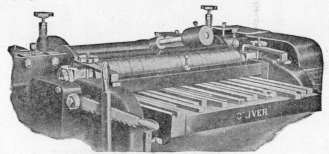

Fig. 3,683.—Oliver sectional feed roll as seen on top of surfacer.

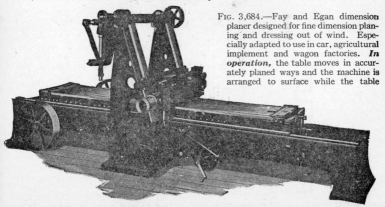

Fig. 3,684.—Fay and Egan dimension planer designed for fine dimension planing and dressing out of wind. Especially adapted to use in car, agricultural implement and wagon factories. *In operation,* the table moves in accurately planed ways and the machine is arranged to surface while the table moves in either direction. The table movement is by gear transmission connecting with a rack under the table. The material is clamped to the table by a dogging apparatus.

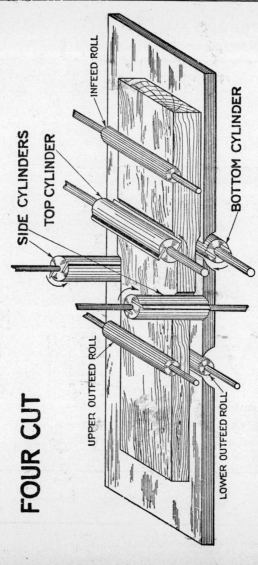

FOUR CUT

SIDE CYLINDERS

TOP CYLINDER

INFEED ROLL

BOTTOM CYLINDER

UPPER OUTFEED ROLL

LOWER OUTFEED ROLL

Fig. 3,685.—Elementary four cylinder sizer showing how four sides of the work are planed at the same time.

Shapers.—The wood shaper or variety moulder is one of the essential machines in a wood working plant.

The style of work done on these machines varies from rabbeting, grooving, and fluting to shaping of every description.

Shapers are usually constructed with one or two vertical spindles which carry the cutter heads. Two spindles revolving in opposite directions is perhaps the most general and useful

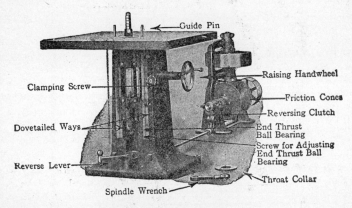

FIG. 3,686.—Crescent single spindle shaper.

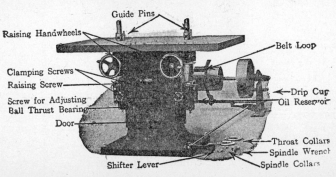

FIG: 3.687:—Crescent double spindle shaper:

form, as with this arrangement one cutter can cut with the grain of the wood running in one direction and the other cutter can operate on the wood with the grain running in the other direction without stopping to reverse the machine.

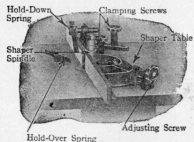

The spindle with suitable cutter attached projects above the surface of an accurately planed table and the cutting edges of the iron should be speeded to travel 5,000 or more feet per minute.

Fig. 3,688.—Crescent shaper fence for single or double spindle shaper. *It is useful* for edging and straightening up lumber, for working casing light mouldings, or other similar work. It is made in two sections to adjust for light or heavy cut. The rear part is to be set flush with the cutting line of the knife, while the front part is to be set over by means of a hand wheel and screw, for desired depth of cut, on same principle as the tables of a jointer. One spring is furnished to hold work down on the table, and another to hold the work against the fence.

Fig. 3,689.—Crescent safety guard for shapers. The shoe is mounted flexibly with a spring. The arm is easily changed in height on the standard for different thicknesses of work and it may easily be swung out of the way when not wanted in operative position.

Borers.—The boring of holes in wood is an important operation that must be frequently performed in any wood working mill. This is accomplished with precision by boring machines or "borers," as they are called. There are two general classes of these machines:

1. Vertical.
2. Horizontal.

The vertical borer very much resembles the machine shop drill, and the horizontal borer is somewhat like a milling machine.

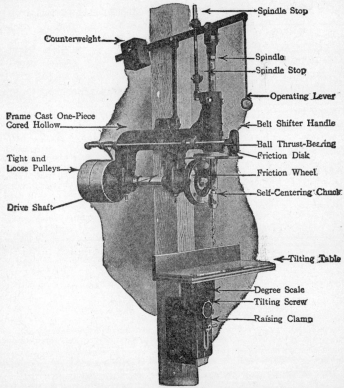

FIG. 3,690.—Crescent post type vertical borer. *In construction* it is provided with a variable friction disc drive instead of the usual belted drive. To change the speed of the bit, loosen set screw in the hub of the friction wheel and move wheel on the shaft until the desired speed is obtained. The spindle travels 8 ins. and stops are provided to regulate the depth of hole. Capacity up to 1¼ in. but in hard wood. The table is adjustable for height to thin or thick stock and will tilt to any angle up to 45°.

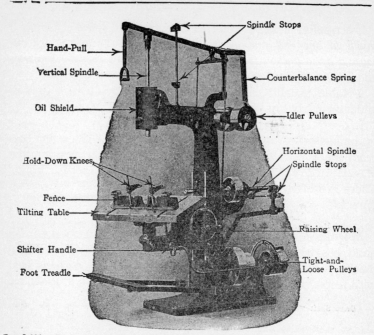

Spindle Stops

Hand-Pull

Vertical Spindle

Counterbalance Spring

Oil Shield

Idler Pulleys

Horizontal Spindle

Spindle Stops

Hold-Down Knees

Fence

Tilting Table

Raising Wheel

Shifter Handle

Foot Treadle

Tight-and-Loose Pulleys

Fig. 3,691.—Crescent heavy duty "universal" or combined vertical and horizontal borer. The treadle is arranged to work both spindles at the same time or either spindle independently as desired. Suitable stops are provided to regulate depth of hole and prevent bits interfering with each other. Vertical spindle has two speeds and can be operated by a hand pull when desired.

Fig. 3,692.—W. F. and John Barnes' horizontal boring attachment for saw table. It has a sliding table on which the work is placed and a stop to govern the depth of hole. The table is adjustable up and down and as the work can be run from side to side between stops, in the usual way, all the adjustments necessary for general use are provided.

Essentially, a borer consists of *a vertical spindle having a chuck at one end and telescoping a splined sleeve to which engages a drive pulley, the assembly arranged to rotate in bearings attached to the frame of the machine.*

A table usually capable of angular adjustment is placed under or in front of the chuck to hold the work.

In operation, the bit held in the chuck is forced into the work by hand feed. The operation is so simple an elementary diagram is not necessary. Fig. 3,690 shows a light duty post type of vertical borer and fig. 3,691 a heavy duty vertical borer. There are many modified forms of borer designed for special purposes.

Mortisers.—The laborious operation of cutting mortises by hand has been overcome by the various types of mortising machines now available. These may be classed, perhaps best with respect to the motion given to the cutting tool or tools, as:

1. Rotary.

    Cutting tool: bit

2. Combined rotary and oscillating.

    Cutting tool: bit

3. Reciprocating.

    Cutting tool: solid chisel

4. Combined reciprocating and oscillating.

    Cutting tool: solid chisel

5. Combined rotary and reciprocating.

    Cutting tools: bit and hollow square chisel

The working principle of the rotary type is shown in fig. 3,693.

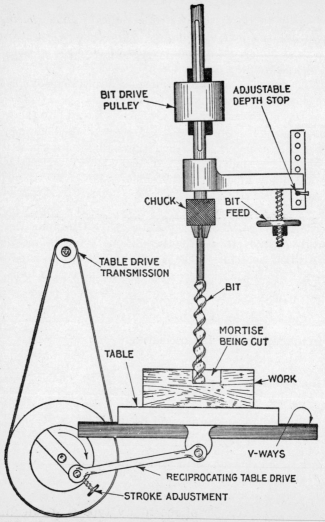

BIT DRIVE PULLEY

ADJUSTABLE DEPTH STOP

CHUCK

BIT FEED

TABLE DRIVE TRANSMISSION

BIT

MORTISE BEING CUT

TABLE

WORK

V-WAYS

RECIPROCATING TABLE DRIVE

STROKE ADJUSTMENT

Fig. 3,693.—Elementary rotary type mortiser showing how the bit is gradually driven into the work while the latter reciprocates the length of the mortise.

FIG. 3,694.—Typical mortising machine bit.

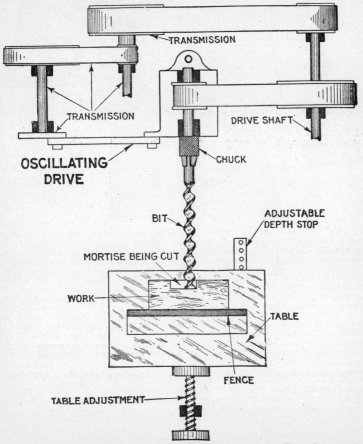

FIG. 3,695.—Elementary combined rotary and oscillating type mortiser illustrating operating principles

Fig. 3,696.—Whitney combined rotary and oscillating (bit) mortiser. **Designed** especially for the routing and mortising done in furniture, chair, desk, cabinet and auto body factories. Such work as corner blocks, cupped work, either round or oblong and similar pieces can be made on this mortiser. **Motor application.** A high speed *a. c.* motor is mounted directly on the spindle in place of the pulley. The motor housing is made a part of the head block that carries the spindle and bearings, all of which slides back and forth as a single unit to make a mortise of the desired size. **Table.** This is supported on a knee that is raised and lowered in dove tailed ways planed on the frame. The knee has a vertical adjustment of five inches, and by means of a handwheel the table can be quickly set for the various sizes of stock to be mortised. The knee can be locked at any desired height. The table is heavily ribbed, having slots through which fixtures can be clamped. It is equipped with a movable fence. Two quick acting clamps securely hold the work. The table can be moved quickly to and from the bit by means of a conveniently placed lever that operates a rack and pinion feeding mechanism. The table is fitted with stops to regulate the depth of the mortise that is being cut. **Head block.** This block carrying the spindle and motor oscillates from side to side through a distance equal to the length of the mortise to be cut. The movement of the sliding head is such that the end of the bit travels in a straight line and makes a mortise of uniform depth the entire length. The head block is driven horizontally back and forth by a motor geared to a crank shaft that drives a connecting rod fastened to the head block. The ends of the connecting rods are equipped with universal joints. The end of the rod that is fastened to the crank shaft can be adjusted to give the desired troke to the head block to cut any length of mortise up to six inches. The crank shaft has a handwheel by means of which the head can be operated back and forth when making a set-up. The head block has two rates of feed, 150 and 200 strokes per minute. The change in the feed is secured by the operation of a lever.

Here the bit is driven into the work gradually by the bit feed, while the work, fastened to the table which travels in "V" ways, reciprocates the length of the mortise, the reciprocating drive having a stroke adjustable to desired length of mortise. An adjustable stop regulates the depth of the mortise.

It should be understood that the bits used in mortises have no screw to draw them into the work, hence there is no tendency for the bit of itself to enter the work.

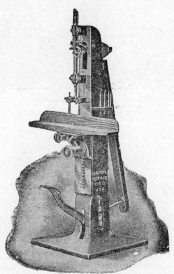

FIG. 3,697.—Fay and Egan reciprocating (solid chisel) foor power mortiser. The table may be raised and lowered to different heights and is adjustable out or in by hand wheel and screw Each machine is provided with five chisels ¼, ⅜, ⅞, ½ and ⅝ in.

Moreover the lips are, or should be, very shallow, so as to minimize the scoring of the wood below the bottom of the mortise. A bit possessing these features is shown in fig. 3,694

The essentials of the combined rotary and oscillating type mortiser are shown in fig. 3,695.

Here, the bit spindle is shown working in bearings on a plate pivoted at its upper end.

The lower end of the plate is connected to an oscillating drive and the table is arranged to approach or recede from the bit controlled by the table adjustment.

In operation the work is placed upon the table and fastened to the fence The wood is forced against the revolving bit by the table adjustment.

While the bit is rotating it is also given an oscillating motion by the oscillating drive which working by suitable gear, casues the bit to slowly

FIG. 3,698.—Fay and Egan reciprocating (solid chisel) mortiser and borer with hub attachment. *Designed* for wagon, carriage, implement and railway shop use. Automatic in operation. Capacity: hubs up to 16 ins. diameter and 20 ins. long. Table has vertical, lateral, transverse, and angular adjustments. The hub attachment is provided with angular spacing device and tipping rig.

transverse the work and return, or oscillate back and forth the length of the mortise.

The mortise may be cut to any length by adjusting the stroke of the oscillating drive. While the bit is oscillating from end to end of the mortise it is gradually forced deeper into the cut by the table adjustment. An adjustable depth stop regulates the depth of mortise.

The reciprocating type mortiser works as shown in Fig. 3,699.

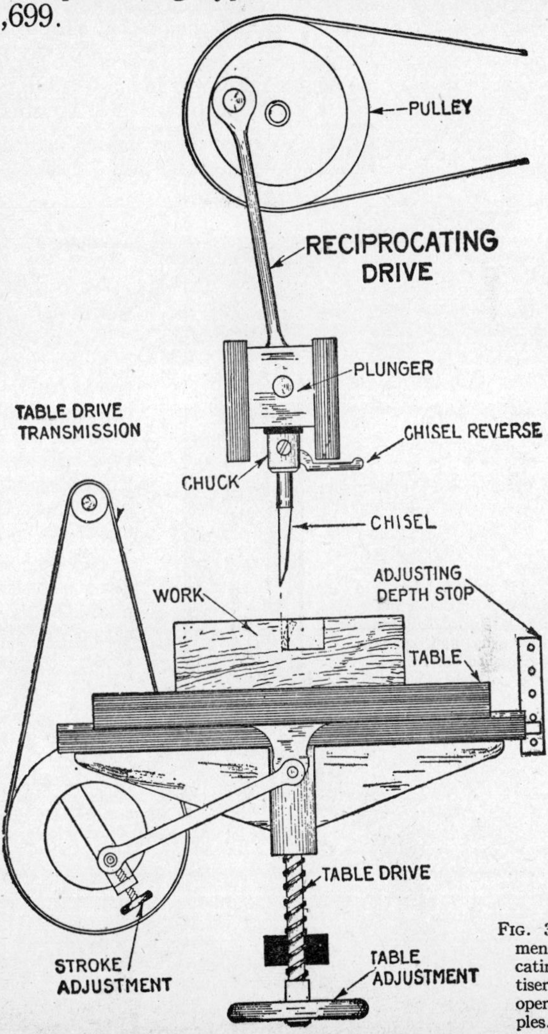

Fig. 3,699. — Elementary reciprocating type mortiser illustrating operating principles.

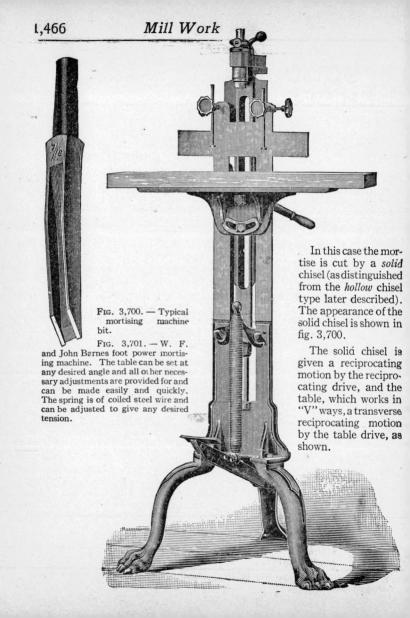

FIG. 3,700. — Typical mortising machine bit.

FIG. 3,701. — W. F. and John Barnes foot power mortising machine. The table can be set at any desired angle and all other necessary adjustments are provided for and can be made easily and quickly. The spring is of coiled steel wire and can be adjusted to give any desired tension.

In this case the mortise is cut by a *solid* chisel (as distinguished from the *hollow* chisel type later described). The appearance of the solid chisel is shown in fig. 3,700.

The solid chisel is given a reciprocating motion by the reciprocating drive, and the table, which works in "V" ways, a transverse reciprocating motion by the table drive, as shown.

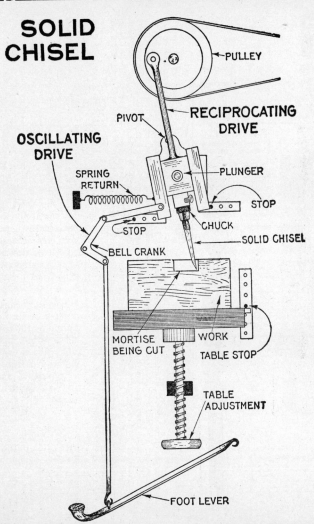

SOLID CHISEL

PULLEY

PIVOT

RECIPROCATING DRIVE

OSCILLATING DRIVE

SPRING RETURN

PLUNGER

STOP

STOP

CHUCK

BELL CRANK

SOLID CHISEL

MORTISE BEING CUT

WORK

TABLE STOP

TABLE ADJUSTMENT

FOOT LEVER

Fig. 3 702.—Elementary combined reciprocating and oscillating type mortiser showing operating principles

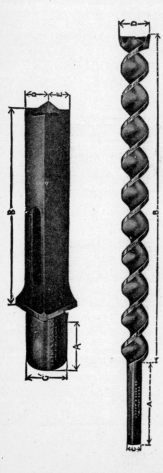

Figs. 3,703 and 3,704.—Fay and Egan hollow chisel and bit for use with combined rotary and reciprocating mortisers. A, length of shank; B', from shoulder to cutting edge, C', diameter of shank; D' and E', length of two adjacent edges; A, length bit shank; B, from shoulder to cutting edge; C, diameter shank; D, diameter of bit. It is of importance that the hollow chisel and bit be accurately fitted to each other, hence both should be made by the same manufacturer. *In sharpening the chisel use the hand file only;* don't sharpen by grinding. Under no circumstance should a chisel be sharpened on the outside. File on the inside only and in such a manner as to leave as much stock as possible on the cutting edges, thereby keeping same sharp and short. The corners should be filed no thinner than the two bevels of the side cutting lips. The stock of a chisel tapers on the inside toward the edge, an angle or about 25 degrees, being slightly less on small chisels and greater on the larger tools with thicker walls and the actual cutting edge is filed back a very short distance to form a greater angle with the side of the chisel, viz.: 32 to 35 degrees. The edge of a chisel should start straight across at the corners for about one-eighth of the width of the chisel at each side and then taper back so as to produce a sheer cut until the two tapers unite in a gentle curve at the center. A sharp angle at this point is liable to cause breakage. The depth of this curve, measured from a straight line down from point to point, should be about 1/32 inch for each 3/8 inch of the diameter of the chisel. The bore of the chisel for receiving the bit reduces the thickness of the walls near the center of each side and a curved line is formed where the bore meets the taper which should not be filed beyond the natural angle. *Setting of the bit.* The bit should be set in the chisel so that the edge of the chisel will not press down on the auger, thereby ruining both. The proper set is to have the cutting point of the auger project beyond the points of the chisel about 1/16 in. *Sharpening the bit.* In general sharpen the bit the same way as any machine bit is sharpened, keeping the side lips on a line with the cutting edge, preserving a straight line for the cutters. The inner edge of the cutting edges should extend past the center of the bit and kept in that position for the reason that these bits have no screw point to open the wood at the center. A bit well filed will be reduced in diameter only from natural wear. When its diameter wears much smaller than the chisel diameter it is no longer serviceable. *In ordering,* specify diameter and length of shank, also diameter and length of blade to the shoulder. Give the size and name of machine in which the chisels or augers are to be used. The illustrations show the dimensions needed in ordering.

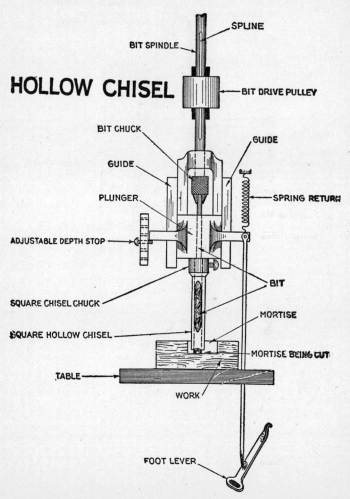

HOLLOW CHISEL

SPLINE

BIT SPINDLE

BIT DRIVE PULLEY

BIT CHUCK

GUIDE

GUIDE

PLUNGER

SPRING RETURN

ADJUSTABLE DEPTH STOP

BIT

SQUARE CHISEL CHUCK

MORTISE

SQUARE HOLLOW CHISEL

MORTISE BEING CUT

TABLE

WORK

FOOT LEVER

FIG. 3,705.—Elementary combined rotary and reciprocating (hollow chisel) type mortiser showing operating principles.

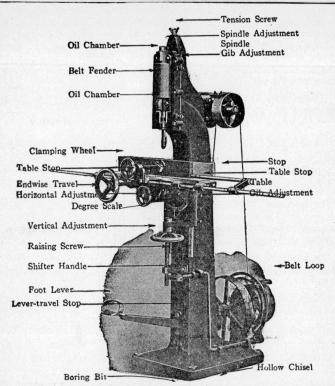

Tension Screw

Spindle Adjustment
Spindle
Gib Adjustment

Oil Chamber

Belt Fender

Oil Chamber

Clamping Wheel

Stop
Table Stop

Table Stop

Table

Endwise Travel
Horizontal Adjustment

Gib Adjustment

Degree Scale

Vertical Adjustment

Raising Screw

Shifter Handle

Belt Loop

Foot Lever
Lever-travel Stop

Hollow Chisel

Boring Bit

FIG. 3,706.—Crescent combined rotary and reciprocating (hollow chisel) mortiser. **Foot lever.** The vertical travel or stroke of the bit is operated by the foot lever maximum stroke $3\frac{1}{2}$ ins. which is depth of deepest mortise that may be cut. By changing fulcrum bolt into another hole in foot lever the stroke is shortened to $2\frac{3}{4}$ ins. and leverage increased, thus adapting the machine for heavy work without excessive exertion by operator. **Lever slot.** This is in the main frame and is provided with an adjustable stop above the lever, to make the travel of the lever shorter when so desired. By shortening the travel of the lever for shallow mortises the work of the operator is reduced, and output increased. **Bits.** The machine is recommended for any size chisels up to $\frac{3}{4}$ in. square, for oak or other hard wood. Bits of the following dimensions will fit the machine. Length of boring bit, over all, 9 ins.; length of twise, 6 ins.; diameter of shank $\frac{1}{2}$ in., or shank to be fitted with bushing to make this size; length of chisel blade, 4 ins.; diameter of shank, $\frac{7}{8}$ in., or to be fitted with a bushing to make this size. In putting a new bit into the machine, a good plan is to fit it so the end of the boring bit shank will bear against the bottom of the hole in the spindle when cutting end is in proper relation to the chisel. This prevents the bit pushing furthe' into the spindle, which would injure the cutting end. Length of bits, as above given, allows for such fitting. The chisel must be firmly fastened to keep it from pulling out, which would likewise

In operation the chisel is pressed into the wood at each stroke of the reciprocating drive and at the same time the wood which is fastened to the table slowly travels back and forth the length of the mortise by the table drive, thus a series of cuts is made during the travel, the chisel cutting deeper into the wood as the "V" ways carrying the table are raised by the table adjustment.

The machine is adjusted to any desired length of mortise by the stroke adjustment.

The essential features of the combined reciprocating and oscillating type mortiser are shown in fig. 3,702.

In operation, the solid chisel is given a reciprocating (up and down) motion by the reciprocating chisel drive, as shown. The plunger to which is attached the chuck carrying the chisel works in guides cut into a casting pivoted at the upper end.

By means of the bell crank gear controlled by the foot lever the chisel is given an oscillating motion limited by the stops which may be adjusted to the desired length of mortise.

When the tool has oscillated to the end of the travel the foot pressure is released and it returns to its initial position by means of the return spring.

The depth of cut is under control of the table adjustment which, in raising the table causes the chisel to cut deeper into the wood.

The depth of mortise is controlled by the adjustable table stop

---

Fig. 3,706—*Continued.*

injure the cutting end. *To use the borer.* When the square chisel is removed, and a regular boring bit used, the machine makes an efficient borer for round holes, up to ¾ in. in diameter, and 3½ ins. deep. *Table.* This is adjusted vertically and horizontally by means of screws, to regulate the depth of mortise to be cut, and the distance of the mortise from the edge of the piece. After table is set to its proper place it remains stationary during use of machine; the bit moves up and down to make the working stroke. When table is arranged to tilt its angular range is 45° to the right or to the left; a scale and pointer indicating the degrees of angle. A late improvement on the tilting table is a stop to gauge the distance from the end of the piece to the mortise. This stop is fastened to a horizontal rod and will adjust for any distance up to 54 ins. from either end or a longer rod can be used when required. On this same rod are two table stops that control the travel of the table to make required length of mortise. The tilting table has a rack and pinion feed, for endwise travel, to make the length of the mortise. The tilting table has a clamp for holding the work against the table fence; it also has a rack and pinion feed, for endwise travel, to make the length of the mortise. The rigid table is for square mortising only. The work is held on the table by hand. Two curved hold down rods are provided, to prevent the chisel lifting the work; these are quickly adjusted and held firmly in place by means of eccentric lever clamps.

The most important type of mortiser or the one most generally used is the combined rotary and reciprocating or hollow chisel mortiser, whose working principles are shown in fig. 3,705.

FIG. 3,707.—Oliver square hollow chisel and bit. Chisel blades are of 4 in. lengths, **except** that the ¼, ⁵⁄₁₆ and ⅜ in. sizes are made extra short or 2¾ ins. for 2¾ in. blades.

In this mortiser, the chisel of square cross section has a high speed bit revolving within it which serves both to bore a round hole and to remove the chips thus bored as well as those cut out by the corners of the chisel.

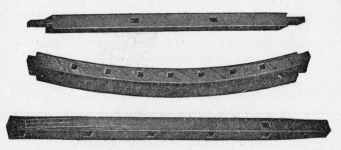

FIGS. 3,708 to 3,710.—Samples of work executed on Oliver vertical combined rotary **and** reciprocating (hollow chisel) mortiser. Fig. 3,708, furniture work; fig. 3,709, chair **work;** fig. 3,710, sash and door work.

Accordingly the two, operating together, accomplish what is equivalent to boring a square hole. That is, the hole is bored and squared at the same time.

By repeating the operation, shifting the work each turn, a mortise of the desired length is produced with square ends and square bottom, leaving no difficult chips to be removed.

In operation, as shown in the illustration, the tool is forced into the work by pressure on the foot lever, a return spring bringing it back to initial spring when the pressure on the foot lever is released. The depth of mortise is easily regulated by the adjustable depth stop.

Figs. 3,703 and 3,707 show appearance of the "hollow" chisel which telescopes the bit.

FIG. 3,711.—Fay and Egan combined rotary and reciprocating (hollow chisel) automatic mortiser. *Designed* for a variety of light and medium duty work in car shops, furniture vehicle and agricultural implement factories. Especially adapted for auto body, passenger and mail coach work. Table has vertical adjustment of 8 ins. by means of a lever provided with stops to prevent making double or triple rows of mortises in the same line. It has an adjustment endwise with suitable stops for regulating the strength of mortise by hand wheel rack and pinion as shown. *The chisel* is fixed to a reciprocating frame moving in planed ways on the top of the column. It is driven by elliptic gears and has quick return at the completion of the mortise. This return movement of chisel is three times as fast as the forward movement, thereby effecting quite a large saving in time in the course of a day's work. Four speeds of feed to ram to cover wide range of sizes in chisels and hard and soft woods. The foot treadle at the base of the machine governs the chisel thrust. The stroke of the chisel is variable by changing the crank pin on the crank arm. The depth of the mortise is regulated either by the adjustment of the table or the adjustment of the stroke. Chisel speeds, 13, 20, 28 and 40 strokes a minute.

Figs. 3,712 to 3,717.—Champion combined rotary and oscillating portable mortiser; its application, and examples of work done.

The foregoing cuts are intended to illustrate simply the working principles of the various types of mortiser and not the actual construction of these machines. By thus eliminating structural details the student can grasp more readily the principles upon which their operation depend.

Actual construction of standard mortisers shown in figs. 3,697 to 3,718, and instructions for ordering and sharpening hollow chisels in figs. 3,703 and 3,704.

FIG. 3,718.—Greenlee combined rotary and reciprocating (hollow mortiser) in operation, showing chips being thrown out of the mortise. *In operation,* the bit cuts slightly in advance of the chisel, boring a round hole where diameter is equal to the chisel size. The edges of the chisel cut the corners, all chips being carried away by the bit. Partial cuts may be taken on the edge of the stock and oblong, oval or other shapes of chisels used for special work.

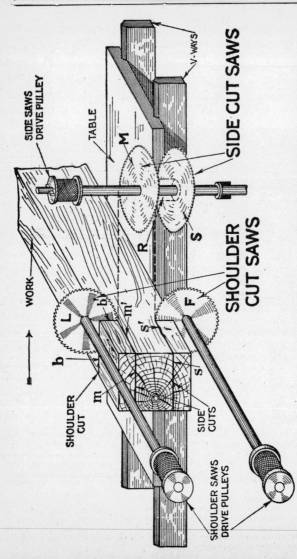

FIG. 3,719.—Elementary circular saw tenoner. There are two pairs of saws: One pair, M, S, mounted on one spindle and separated by a collar R, whose length equals thickness of tenon to be cut; the other pair L and F, mounted on separate spindles parallel, to each other and at right angles to the spindle carrying saws M and S. The table is arranged to slide on the V ways. In *operation* the work clamped to the table in position for desired length of tenon, first passes across the side cut saws M, S, which make the side cuts *mm'* and *ss'*. The table continuing its travel in the direction of the arrow causes the work to pass across the shoulder cut saws L and F, saw L, making one shoulder cut *bb'*, and F, making the other shoulder cut, of which only *f'*, is visible. In *actual machines* various adjustments provided permit cutting a range of tenon sizes, either with line and line shoulders or one side larger than the other.

Tenoners.—Mortising and tenoning are so inseparably connected as being the essential operations in making mortise and tenon joints that following mortisers should come an explanation of tenoners or machines for cutting tenons. There are several types of tenoners, and they may be classed with respect to the cutting tools and their motion as:

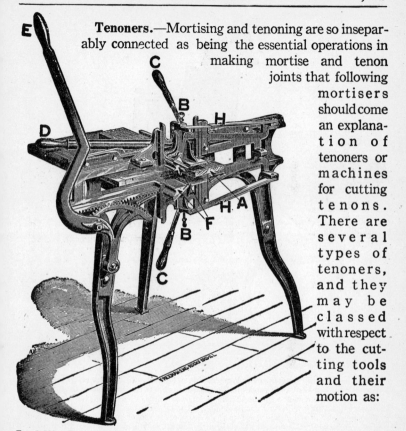

FIG. 3,720.—Barnes hand tenoning machine. *The parts are:* A, tenon being cut; B,B, screws to set depth of shoulder; C,C, handle to raise cutters from work; D, lever to hold work in place; E, lever to drive cutters forward and back; F,F, cutter heads; H,H, spring to press cutter heads against work. *Range.* The machine will cut tenons of any length up to 3 ins. By repeating the cut any desired length can be made. It will work on stuff of any size up to 2 × 12 ins. and can be adjusted to gauge the length, thickness and shoulder of a tenon. It will not cope a shoulder, but will cut one shoulder farther back than the other to accommodate stuff having rabbeted edge, and will cut one shoulder deeper than the other, or both alike as desired. Both sides of the tenon are cut at once, or one side only can be cut. *In operation,* each thrust of the lever E, cuts a shaving similar to that of a rabbet plane; the rapidity of the thrusts and set of the knives (as with a plane), govern the speed of the work. The machine cuts true, smooth, square shoulders and can be set to cut tenons of uniform thickness or distance between the shoulders.

Fig. 3,721.—Whitney circular saw type motor driven tenoner. *In construction* the carriage travels on a V way at right angles to the *side cut* saws. It can be adjusted vertically by a hand wheel to obtain the size and angle of tenon required. *The table* has slots through which various kinds of fixtures can be clamped. The table can be tilted either above or below the center and locked at any angle up to 22 degrees. It is equipped with a movable gauge and an adjustable clamping device to securely hold the work to the table. From a tilted position the table can be quickly set into a horizontal position by means of a positive stop rod. *Yokes.* The top and bottom saw arbors with their bearings and motors are mounted in yokes that are raised and lowered by elevating screws operated by hand wheels at the operator's end of the machine. The yoke carrying the top saw arbor has a horizontal adjustment to line up the top shoulder saw with the bottom saw or to make an offset tenon when desired The yokes can be locked at any desired height. The yoke carrying the vertical arbor and bearings has a horizontal adjustment to move the splitting saws to and from the work. *Saw arbors.* The ends of the saw arbors are detachable and are so made that, when screwed down in position against the shoulders of the arbors, they center themselves and come in perfect alignment with the saw arbors. *Shoulder and cut off saws.* The bottom (horizontal) arbor carries the cut off saw in addition to the bottom shoulder saw. It has vertical adjustment. The cut off saw can be adjusted to make tenons up to 6½ ins. long. *Side or "splitting" saws.* The vertical saw arbor carrying the side cut saws is mounted in a

Fig. 3,722.—Fay and Egan rotary cutter type automatic vertical cut tenoner. *Designed* for heavy duty railway car and bridge shop service to make single, double or triple tenons on heavy timbers without reversing. Special work can be done by using irregular knives. The long lip tenons of side sills can be cut either by using heads of large diameter, or with regular heads by clamping the sills forward on the table to clear the spindle. The spindle can be fixed in position and side sills scarfed by feeding them under the cutters. A salient feature in the construction of this machine is that it is entirely self-contained and can be belted from any direction or direct connected to motor. Will work timbers up to 20″ × 16″. After one end has been tenoned on down stroke of head the timber is moved forward to opposite table, brought to position, and the other end tenoned on up-stroke. By working two men on this machine, one on each end, an extremely large output can be obtained. *Cutter heads* are carried on heavy spindle, mounted in our new high speed side wing angle clamp boxes. Carriage raised and lowered by means of a double rack and pinion operated by friction is controlled by lever at front of machine.

Fig. 3,721.—*Text continued.*

yoke that has a horizontal adjustment operated by a hand wheel. The entire top of the arbor can be removed with the saws. The side cut saws can be adjusted together or independently. *Adjustments.* A quick and accurate adjustment of the horizontal and vertical saws as well as the knee supporting the carriage is secured by hand wheels placed within easy reach at the operator's end of the machine. The small knobs for locking the yokes that carry the shoulder saws are also at the operator's end. All adjusting screws are equipped with thrust ball bearings.

1. Reciprocating planes.
2. Circular saws.
3. Rotary cutters.
4. Hollow auger.

An example of the reciprocating plane type is the Barnes hand tenoning machine shown in fig. 3,720, the operation being sufficiently simple as not to require an elementary diagram.

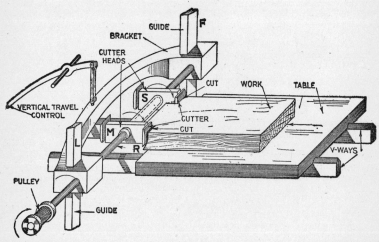

FIG. 3,723.—Elementary rotary cutter tenoner showing operation. *The essential parts are* the rotary cutters attached to heads M and S, revolving on a spindle R, whose journals are carried by a bracket having vertical movement along guides L and F. The work is clamped to a table which moves on V ways at right angles to the spindle R.

The first mechanical device for cutting tenons employed an arrangement of circular saws working at right angles to each other.

One pair of saws running parallel to the grain of the wood cut the sides of the tenon, and another pair running at right angles, cut the shoulders.

The two saws cutting the sides of the tenon are of the same diameter and are mounted on the same spindle, a collar being placed between them to regulate the thickness of the tenon.

The saws forming the shoulders are mounted on separate spindles running at right angles to the pair of saws which cut the sides.

The elementary circular saw tenoner, shown in fig. 3,719, illustrates this method.

The rotary cutter type of tenoner is largely used, its working principle being shown in fig. 3,723.

Fig. 3,724.—Greenlee rotary cutter vertical car tenoner designed for making single, double or triple tenons on car sills or other heavy timbers without reversing. Special work can be done by using irregular knives, side sills can be scarfed by feeding them under the cutters while the carriage is stationary, and long lip tenons can be cut by clamping them forward on the table to clear the spindle. All adjustments are complete and stops are provided to gauge the stroke and to lay out the length of tenons. Transverse adjustment of the spindle yoke is provided. The power feed has three speeds and is perfectly controlled by the feed lever.

Here two cutter heads, M and S, similar to planer cutters are placed on a spindle R, whose journals are carried by a sliding bracket having a vertical movement along the guides L and F.

The cutter heads may be placed any distance apart, corresponding to thickness of tenon to be cut by placing on the spindle between them a collar whose length equals thickness of tenon.

The table slides on "V" ways at right angles to the spindle so that when the work is clamped on the table it may be brought into position under the cutter for the desired length of tenon.

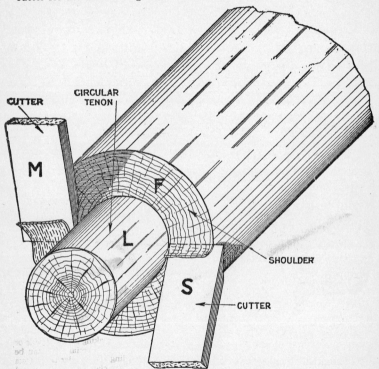

FIG. 3,725.—Elementary circular tenoner or "hollow auger," showing principle of operation.

With the cutters raised above the work, the latter is pushed under the cutters in direction of arrow to desired length of tenon to be cut, and the cutters, which are revolving rapidly, slowly passed across the work by lowering the bracket with the vertical control, thus planing off the sides and forming the tenon, no separate operation being necessary for cutting the shoulder.

So far the tenoners considered are types which cut tenons of rectangular cross sections. There are numerous instances where tenons of circular cross sections are necessary, as in carriage and furniture factories, etc.

Circular cross section tenons, known as circular tenons, are cut by a form of tenoner fitted with a hollow bit, whose principle of operation is indicated in fig. 3,725.

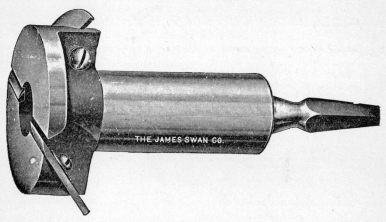

FIG. 3,726.—Ames hollow auger. The side screws permit adjustment of the cutters to the precise size desired.

Essentially there are two cutters, M and S, secured in a hollow frame and adjustable radially for tenons of various diameters.

The work which may, for instance, consist of a wheel spoke or other light member is secured in a suitable clamp or chuck centered with the cutter spindle and fed forward toward the cutters, M and S.

The latter revolving at the same time removes a ring of stock from the work, thus forming a circular tenon L with shoulder F. It is, as seen, essentially a boring operation.

The accompanying illustrations figs. 3,719 to 3,729, show construction of the various types of tenoners, whose principles of operation have just been described and illustrated by the elementary machines shown.

Sanders.—The economic value of sandpaper is becoming

Fig. 3,727.—Fay and Egan rod machine. *Designed* for turning stretchers, curtain poles, flag sticks and other kinds of rod works, up to 2″ in diameter. Feed consists of three pairs of rollers to suit each size of rod head, powerfully geared and driven from one belt. Two speeds of feed, 12′ and 24′, for small stock, and 7′ and 13′ for large stock furnished. Reverse feed provided. Furnished with three heads and cutters and three sets or feed rolls, the sizes selected by purchaser. Tight and loose pulleys, 10″ × 4½″, 750 r. p. m. Motor, 5 to 7½ h. p., belted to counter shaft.

more apparent every day and its application to the pattern-makers' art is one of its most useful qualifications. The only difference between grinding iron and wood on a disc sander is that the wood can be ground many times quicker than the iron.

Five minutes of sanding on a piece of wood will frequently accomplish more than an hour would any other way. It smooths up end grain and puts

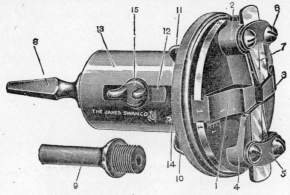

FIGS. 3,728 and 3,729.—Swan universal hollow auger and parts. This auger can be adjusted to cut circular tenons to any size from ⅜ to 1½ ins: in diameter. When set to size, with the back screw properly set up, a perfect adjustment and rigid hold are secured. A depth gauge regulates the length of the tenon, and the face is graduated so it can be readily set to any size desired. *To cut a smooth tenon*, keep the knives ground to the line on the face, and the knives set up so they will not project beyond the center hole.

FIG. 3,730 —Fay and Egan drum hand feed papering machine designed for all kinds of flat surface sanding.

draft on it. It sands out saw marks. In repairing patterns the **broken** piece that is usually thrown away, because it is full of brads or nails, **may** be sanded nails and all and saved.

A large disc is more desirable than a small one because the sand **paper** farthest from the center does the most work.

Sanders may be divided into three general classes:
1. Drum.

FIG. 3,731.—Fay and Egan inverted disc, column, sash and door sander showing operation of sanding a door.

2. Disc.
3. Endless belt.

The type used to best advantage will depend upon the **kind** of work to be polished by sanding.

Fig. 3,732 shows a combination drum and disc sander **and** fig. 3,733 an endless belt sander.

Knives for Wood Working Machines.—When ordering knives, state number of knives wanted, number of sets, number in set, length, width, thickness, name and make of machine, and kind of wood to be cut.

The cutting edge always constitutes the length of the knife.

Fig. 3,732.—Combined drum and disc sander. Considerable "forming" can be done on a sander but its principal use is to smooth or polish surfaces. In the illustration the man at the left is *forming* a mitre, while the one at the right is *smoothing* a surface.

When possible, furnish a pattern. Place the knife face down on the paper, mark around to show the length of the knife and size and position of slots, and be sure to state the width and thickness; also state the number of knives in set, and the temper required, whether high, to grind only, medium, to file slowly, or low, to file easily.

The manufacturer will make a wooden pattern like each paper pattern sent, stamp the same with name of party ordering and date the order is received, and preserve for future use. It is well to send an old knife or a pattern showing the holes or the slots. This is particularly true in ordering planer knives, paper knives, barker and chipper knifes, etc.

The varieties of temper adapted for planer knives, paper knives, veneer cutting knives, leather knives, tobacco knives,

Fig. 3,733.—Fay and Egan endless belt sander showing method of ' ironing" method of sanding. *Designed* for sanding panels and large, flat surfaces, as well as moulding, concave, convex and other irregular work that is now being done by hand. Bulky work, such as refrigerators, desks, phonograph cabinets, etc., can be quickly and easily sanded on this machine by removing the table. It is adapted for furniture or piano factories, nterior finish plants, schools, etc. In fact every shop that does any hand sanding can use this machine to advantage.

hog knives, as well as other knives, are determined by experience. At the same time, much attention should be given to the balancing, grinding and finishing of all knives, that they will prove satisfactory.

In knives, as well as in all other edged tools, good steel is the fundamental part, without which it is impossible to get a satisfactory cutting edge.

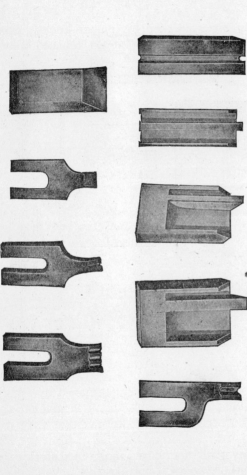

FIGS. 3,734 to 3,742.—Various Simonds' knives for planing and moulding mills, box factories, etc.

High speed steel usually contains sufficient amounts of the elements tungsten, chrome, and in the better grades, vanadium, in addition to the usual constituents of high grade tool steels. These, of course, always contain a large amount of selected iron, etc., to produce a mixture when melted that will result in a steel that will stand "after treatment," high speed and fast feed even to a point of great heat without affecting the temper.

High speed steel air hardened, or as it comes from the rolls, will undoubtedly stand more crowding than ordinary steels. So will ordinary steel when it comes from the rolls stand more work than just iron.

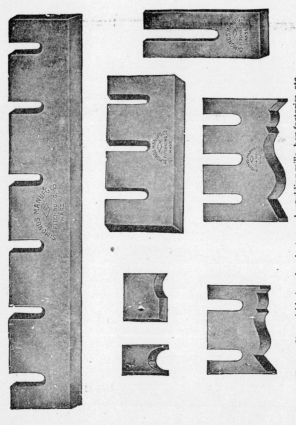

FIGS. 3,743 to 3,749.—Various Simonds' knives for planing and moulding mills, box factories, etc.

Proper treatment of high speed will, however, increase the efficiency to such an extent that a comparison between the one properly treated and the air hardened or as it leaves the rolls, will convince anyone of the economy of the former.

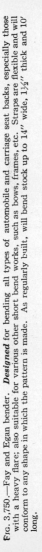

Fig. 3,750.—Fay and Egan bender. *Designed* for bending all types of automobile and carriage seat backs, especially those with a heavy flare; also suitable for various other short bend works, such as bows, frames, etc. Straps are flexible and will conform to any shape in which the pattern is made. As regularly built, will bend stock up to 14″ wide, 1½″ thick and 10′ long.

Fig. 3,751.—Fay and Egan automatic bender. *Designed* for bending felloes, hames, chair and wagon material, etc. Will bend material up to 9″, 12″ or 14″ wide and 3′ thick. Felloes for wheels from 30″ to 60″ in diameter may be formed on this machine. Bending arms are solid.

FIG. 3,752.—C. H. & E. portable saw rig with gas engine drive. *In construction,* the frame is made of structural steel. The table top is a ¼ in. steel plate 42 × 56, bound around the edges with a 1¼-inch angle. The frame of the band saw is a one piece casting channel section, the wheels are of iron, turned true, and perfectly balanced. The boring and mortising attachment is a heavy ribbed one piece casting securely bolted to the saw frame. The jointer is built along the lines of the standard shop machine with the main frame rigidly fastened to the side of the saw table. The jointer head is of the cylindrical safety type and carries four knives 6¾ inches long.

FIG. 3,753.—Rogers automatic feed knife grinder. *In operation,* it grinds straight or concave bevel. It is especially adapted to grinding planer knives and all knives of medium weight.

FIG. 3,754.—Rogers combined automatic knife grinder and saw gummer.

"Crescent Grinding" of Saws.—The Simonds Saw Mfg. Co. have a method of grinding cross cut saws in crescent lines parallel to the cutting edge of the saw, which they call "crescent grinding." The advantage given by them is an even thickness throughout the tooth edge and a gradual taper from the tooth edge to the back which is less set to the teeth and less kerf to cut.

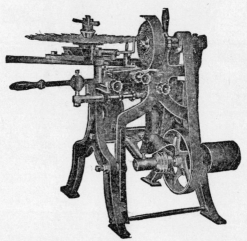

Fig. 3,755.—Rogers automatic circular saw sharpener.

Their crescent ground cross cut saws have five gauges taper from the middle of the saw to the back, and two gauges taper from the ends of saw to the back.

Lumber in the Making.—The following interesting account of methods employed in the making of lumber is here given by courtesy of The Long Bell Lumber Co. of Kansas City, Mo.:

The appraising eye of the lumberman sees in standing trees many qualities that are hidden from the casual observer, and it is this ability to judge that guides him in choosing the field of his forest operations.

Density of growth, the frequency with which high winds may visit a certain locality, climate and soil—all have an influence on the structure of wood in trees, and all these conditions are considered by the lumberman before he begins operations for the manufacture of lumber.

When trees stand uniformly upright with few leaning from the perpendicular, and with dead branches remaining on the tree, the lumberman knows high winds are rare and, because of the dead limbs remaining in place, the lumber made from such trees will be knotty.

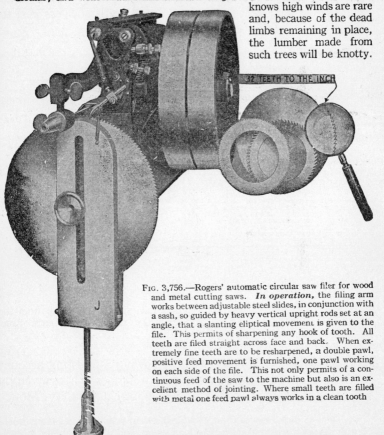

FIG. 3,756.—Rogers' automatic circular saw filer for wood and metal cutting saws. *In operation,* the filing arm works between adjustable steel slides, in conjunction with a sash, so guided by heavy vertical upright rods set at an angle, that a slanting eliptical movement is given to the file. This permits of sharpening any hook of tooth. All teeth are filed straight across face and back. When extremely fine teeth are to be resharpened, a double pawl, positive feed movement is furnished, one pawl working on each side of the file. This not only permits of a continuous feed of the saw to the machine but also is an excellent method of jointing. Where small teeth are filled with metal one feed pawl always works in a clean tooth

FIG. 3,757.—Interior of saw mill showing the log carriage which carries the logs to the saw. It is a ponderous piece of mechanical equipment, spectacular in operation. The carriage is manned by a crew of four to six workmen.

NOTE.—The forests of America were at one time formidable and forbidding wildernesses. The pioneering home seeker was compelled to labor long and patiently to effect a "clearing" for the cultivation of farm crops—and for many years thereafter maintain a constant battle to prevent the re-encroachment of the wilderness upon his reclaimed area. He was able to convert to useful ends very few of the trees he chopped down—his purpose was to destroy them in the quickest and most effective manner possible. The commercial lumberman, on the contrary, has felled trees for the purpose of utilizing every portion of them that could be manufactured into useful forms; and in his operations the lumberman has saved the farmer a prodigious amount of labor in removing trees from millions of acres of land most useful for agricultural production. The manufacture of lumber has attained the rank of the second largest manufacturing industry in America, because forest products—wood in all its countless forms—are absolutely essential to our daily life. Wood for shelter, wood for fuel, wood for implements and weapons, wood for furniture, wood for vehicles of transportation on land and water—every moment of our lives, from the cradle to the grave, we are using necessities or conveniences of wood.

NOTE.—It is impossible for the human mind to comprehend the magnitude of the lumber industry today. Only a vague understanding is conveyed by the statement that the total production of lumber in this country amounts to nearly 40,000,000,000 board feet annually—approximately 1,600,000 capacity carloads. Of this stupendous quantity of lumber, something like 15,000,000,000 board feet, or 660,000 car loads, is of one variety alone—Southern Pine, the most useful and most adaptable of woods. One-third of the total population of the South is directly or indirectly employed in the production and merchandising of Southern Pine lumber, and 5,400 saw mills were engaged in manufacturing that material last year. In addition to some 30,000 saw mills in the United States engaged in converting the raw material —sawlogs—into various forms, there are more than seventy-five thousand kindred industries employed in converting saw mill products into more highly manufactured articles.

NOTE.—The unavoidable waste of raw material in the manufacture of lumber has always been most pronounced in the forest. There is still waste there, and there always will be until the consumers of forest products will accept material that can be made from this waste and in such quantity as to justify its conservation. While to the casual observer the tree tops left in the woods might seem wanton waste, to the lumberman they are reluctantly relinquished portions of his property, sacrificed to freight rates and lack of market; the lumberman is too good a business man to deliberately abandon material that might be utilized at a profit, or even at cost. As it is all waste is being eliminated as rapidly as possible. Time was when the lumberman placed so little value on standing timber and was limited to such primitive and crude devices for the manufacture of lumber that he attempted to utilize only the choicest portions of the best trees, frequently felling many that he later deemed unworthy of making any use of whatever. Today the lumberman has the keenest appreciation of the value of the tree, and equipped with a great variety of marvelously efficient machinery, he strives constantly to devise new means of utilizing even the most insignificant portions of the trees he fells.

In the great Southern pine forest the trees that grow in stiff, compact earth are in their structure harder, heavier and more pitchy than trees which grow in loose, sandy soil, because the firm earth holds the tree roots rigidly and the trees sway and bend above the stump when disturbed by winds. The denser the growth of pines, the fewer the branches on the trees, because the growth energy under such conditions is expended principally in the struggle to reach upward to the sunlight

The first step in extensive lumbering operations is to build a railroad from the saw mill to the timber land, this serving as a main line to which spurs and lateral lines will be joined as the work progresses.

The main line is of more or less "permanent" construction, but the lines running from this artery are constantly being shifted, so that in "logging" Southern pine forests railroad lines are constantly being torn up and relaid.

After the railroad builders, come the logging crews, the workmen who actually fell the trees and assemble them for their journey to the mill.

The log cutters work in pairs, a right handed and a left handed man in each pair. The implements with which they work are a cross cut saw, an axe, an assortment of thin wooden wedges, and a bottle of kerosene with which to oil the saw. The trees are first "notched" on the side toward which they are to fall, that the tree may not split as it starts to descend. That done, the saw is started into the tree on the opposite side. If the tree settle in its position and "pinch" the saw, the wedges are introduced to relieve the pressure, and the sawing continues until the tree is severed and crashes to the ground.

The giant trunks, comparatively free of limbs, produce a peculiar and far reaching sound as they strike the earth; a resonant and sonorous "boom," like the muffled report of a cannon shot far away. When a large gang of loggers is cutting down trees the incessant "boom-boom" of the falling trunks, reverberating through the forest aisles, is more suggestive of a distant battle than of the progress of a peaceful industry.

The log cutters trim the branches from the fallen trunks with the axe, and saw off the small tops. Frequently the long main trunk is sawed into two or more lengths, according to requirements for the class of material being manufactured at the mill.

Hard upon the heels of the log cutters comes the skidding and loading crew. Methods differ in this work, according to the topography of the country, the class of timber and density of undergrowth, but the most economical and most efficient operation is to assemble and load the logs by machinery.

Fig. 3,758.—Gang saw. This machine is used largely in the production of boards and other light dimension lumber.

Frequently one ponderous machine, a combined skidder and loader, which "straddles" the logging railway, supplies the power for both operations. Long steel skidder cables, with "grabs" like ice tongs attached are hauled from the skidder to the fallen logs by stout horses, ridden by boys; or by the most modern method, the cables are steam hauled on trolleys by what is known as the "re-haul." The grab is attached to a fallen log by a "grab setter," a signal is passed to the operator known as the "drum puller" on the skidder, and as the steam power is applied a drum or winch reels in the cable and the log races to the side of the skidder. There the logs are seized by a cable from a loading boom, hoisted into the air, and deposited

FIG. 3,759.—Edger or edging machinery which removes the bark edges and rips the stock to size.

FIG. 3,760.—Trimmer. The machine is composed of many circular saws which cut out knots and remove other defects.

FIG. 3,761.—Soda dipping of common grades of air dried lumber to prevent discoloration or sap stains.

NOTE.—The accompanying illustrations show operations in Long Bell lumber plant.

Fig. 3,762.—Interior of Long Bell planing mill showing lumber in the various stages of manufacture into many forms.

on log cars set to receive them. As each car is loaded to capacity it is pulled forward to make way for an empty car, the operation being repeated until a train load of logs is made up.

Prosy description can give little idea of the spectacular and strenuous activity of logging forces at work in the woods. Horses and men rushing to and fro, seemingly in constant and imminent peril from falling trees; giant logs, with skidder cables attached, plunging through the undergrowth on their way to the skidder, there to be tossed into the air and whirled dexterously into place on the log cars; the "boom-boom" of falling trees, the roar of steam exhausts, engines puffing, workmen shouting warnings and instructions—all contribute to a medley that makes the forest seethe with motion and resound with a confusion of noises.

When train loads of logs hauled from the woods reach the mill, possibly twenty miles or more distant, they are automatically dumped into the mill pond. This pond is common to all Southern pine saw mill plants, for the reason that logs can be handled, sorted and stored in water more economically than in any other way, and are there preserved against decay and injury from wood destroying insects while awaiting their final journey to the saws.

The logs make their entrance into the mill over an inclined chute equipped with an endless spiked chain conveyor. The logs are floated into place until one end is brought into contact with the conveyor, when they are caught by the chain spikes and lifted from the water and up the chute.

As they enter upon the "log deck" inside the mill they pass under the inspection of a scaler and deck saw man, skilled in judging the size and quality of the logs and their fitness for conversion into certain forms of lumber.

If a log chance to be of very large size, free from imperfections and dense in its structural fibre, the deck sawyer may permit it to pass on its way, to be squared and dressed into a great timber suitable for use in heavy construction. If it might better serve some other purpose, the deck sawyer halts the progress of the log, and with the pressure of a lever a giant circular saw descends, cutting the log in two with the speed and seeming ease of a knife cleaving new cheese.

From the log deck the log or each of its sections is "kicked" by steam driven steel arms onto a skidway, down which it rolls to a resting place in front of the band saw carriage.

The band saw, the carriage and all of the "rig" pertaining thereto are highly important parts of saw mill equipment, under the control of one of the most important and highly skilled workmen in the mill—the sawyer. A good sawyer not only must know the anatomy of a tree and be able to judge it at a glance, but he must be extremely sensitive to the amount of

FIG. 3,763 —Long Bell export timber booms at a Southern gulf port.

force at his command, represented in the complex mass of powerful. steam driven machinery he controls, and be able to divide his attention into three or four channels at the same time and all the time he is on duty. He directs and regulates the speed of the log carriage, using both hands and feet in applying and cutting off steam power; manipulates the log on the carriage as it travels to and from the saw; determines the size of every cut made from the log, and meanwhile is constantly "sizing-up" and classifying the log as c it after cut is removed—all simultaneously.

A crew of three to six men ride on the log carriage and manipulate the "setting" device and the "dogs" which hold the log in place while it is being sawed. These workmen take their orders from the sawyer, receiving them in the form of signals made with the fingers, since the incessant roar of ponderous machinery moving at top speed makes speech inaudible.

The log carriage moves to and from the band saw at a rate that makes riding upon it seem precarious work, requiring close attention to the business in hand, and at each trip a slab or plank is ripped from the log.

The slabs, or outer cuts of the log, fall upon running rolls and are hurried to a machine called a slasher, which cuts them into four-foot lengths for lath stock.

Planks or boards cut from the logs pass over conveyors to the edger, a machine which, at the direction of the operator, may merely trim the bark edges from the planks or may rip them into various combinations of widths.

From the rear table of the edger the boards drop to conveyors which carry them to the trimmer, where they have faulty ends removed and defects cut out. This accomplished, the resulting product is finished rough green lumber, and the first important step in the manufacture of logs into building material is completed.

The portion of the lumber that is to be kiln dried drops into a conveyor on live rolls and is carried to the drop sorter, where it is automatically separated as to lengths, and is loaded on small trucks, or kiln cars, of about four thousand feet to the car, by which means it is conveyed to the dry kiln.

The portion that is to be air dried drops from the trimmer into another conveyor on live rolls and is carried to a long sorting table, at which point it is separated as to grades and lengths, and loaded on trucks for conveying to the yard for drying.

When the sawyer in control of the band saw decides that a log is best suited to manufacture into a structural timber, the log is merely stripped of slabs and squared up before it leaves the log carriage. These timbers are dropped upon live rolls and conveyed to the back end of the mill, where they are carefully trimmed to proper lengths and graded. From this point they pass to the timber dock and from there are loaded directly to railroad cars for shipment.

In other instances the log is squared and then sent to the gang saw, where it is converted into a number of boards at one operation. These boards pass over conveyors to the edger and from there follow the same course as the boards cut by the band saw

The better grades of Southern pine lumber are usually kiln dried, and at some plants all the lumber products, except timbers, are so treated. The kiln drying is actually a rapid seasoning process by which the material is made fit for building use in from three to six days and as completely seasoned as can be done in the open air in many months.

The process of kiln drying lumber intended for manufacture into highly finished products is an operation requiring painstaking care in the regulation of heat and moisture. Safe limits of temperature and humidity differ widely for different kinds and thicknesses of wood. Valuable high grade material where joints, mortises, glued construction, re-sawing and shaping are involved must not only be free from check, splits and warping, but must be free from brittleness, case hardening and internal stresses, and therefore dried to a uniform moisture content.

For uses in which the highest quality of material is not essential or desired, or when certain reduction in quality is permitted, somewhat different degrees of temperature and humidity are used to produce more rapid drying, according to the requirements and judgment of the operator.

From the kilns the lumber is run into cooling sheds, where it is allowed to stand until the moisture content of the lumber has been equalized with that of the surrounding atmosphere. After this cooling process the lumber is removed from the kiln cars, assorted as to sizes and lengths, and is ready to be sent to rough sheds for storage, or to the planing mill for manufacture into the finished forms for which it may be best suited.

The planing mill is an important and necessary part of a lumber manufacturing plant, and special machines work the material into a multitude of products required for general building purposes, from plain dressed boards and dimension to flooring, ceiling, siding, moulding, partition, casing, base, window and door jambs, etc.

Planing mill products generally are ready for shipment as soon as they complete their journey through the mill, and usually are loaded on cars direct.

CHAPTER 57A

Termite Protection

In order to successfully prevent damage to buildings or materials of cellulose origin from termites, it is necessary, first, to be able to identify this type of insect; second, to know as much as possible about their propagation requirements, *i.e.*, the conditions which make for a better or *richer life* for this attacking enemy. It is only after this knowledge has been acquired, that plans for their elimination can be successfully attained.

Termites and Their Identification.—Termites or so-called *white ants* are social insects which live in colonies made up of different forms or castes. True ants are enemies of the termite. At certain seasons, usually spring or fall, but varying with the species and the locality, males and females, white-winged, but with black or brown bodies, swarm from the outdoor colonies, or in buildings to which their work has extended, to seek favorable points outdoors for the establishment of new colonies.

These swarming, or flying, termites do not attack wood or other articles in houses and must reach the open if they are to be successful in establishing new colonies. It is the descendants of these winged migrants, *the workers*, which are *cream-colored white ants*, that are known as the wood-mining and destructive members of the colony.

They are *blind, shun the light,* and conceal themselves in runways or behind a protecting shell of wood, and are only seen when the wood in which they are working is removed or broken up.

FIGS. 1 and 2—Represents winged adult and mature workers. Enlarged eight and three times respectively.

The invasion of buildings by termites practically always has its source from outdoor communities through foraging tunnels made by the workers in any direction under the surface of the ground. Thence chance contacts made with buildings of wood or with the structural wood of masonry buildings supplies a rich "granary" of food. Entry through basement timbers is immediate, although the invasion may not be recognized by the owners for several years.

In case of the better type of wooden buildings constructed on stone or concrete foundations, the worker termites can bridge over such foundations by means of earthlike shelter tubes built of earth and wood particles. The workers are also able to build buttressed tubes reaching, without support, up from the ground, rarely more than a foot, in the effort to contact with structural timbers.

FIGS. 3 to 6—Metal shields inserted in various types of construction to protect against termite invasion. Note—method of capping of drain pipes and joist support to impede their progress.

In the usual type of masonry buildings with concrete foundations and full basement covering of concrete, a common means of entry is through cracks which are very likely to develop in the often inferior concrete used as base for joists for basement flooring. Such joists are moistened by the concrete with some resulting decay and then, when made accessible through cracks, furnish an ideal start for the termites.

Proper Method of Construction to Prevent Termite Damage.
—Termites must maintain contact with the ground to obtain
the *moisture necessary for their existence*. Hence the first consideration should be to build in a manner which will prevent the
entry of termites from the ground.

Construction of Foundations.—The foundations of buildings
should be constructed of masonry, of approved pressure
treated, or naturally termite-resistant lumber. Where a basement is provided the foundation walls should be of masonry
construction. If unit block construction be employed, as brick,
tile, cement blocks, etc., all joints should be well filled with
mortar and the wall topped with a 2-inch cap of cement. This
should be reinforced to prevent cracking when over open type
units as cement blocks or vertical opening tile. The ground
within the basement should be sealed over with concrete; posts
should not extend through the floor into the soil, but should rest
on concrete footings that extend at least two inches above the
floor.

If foundations be built over an earth fill or naturally loose
earth, subsequent settlement may cause the joint between the
concrete basement floor and foundation wall to open up. Such a
joint is a probable source of termite entry and should be
guarded against by installing a mastic or a metal expansion
joint between the wall and floor.

Concrete for basement floors and walls should be a dense
mixture and the walls reinforced with steel rods at the corners
and intersections to tie them together. Improper construction
of the basement floor and walls may cause cracks to develop
through which termites may gain free access from the earth.

Window sills and frames in the basement should not come in
direct contact with the ground, nor should leaves or debris be
allowed to collect and remain in contact with them.

Buildings which have no basements should have the sills set a minimum of 12 inches, and preferably 18 inches, above the excavated ground or natural grade at all points, to afford the necessary clearance and good ventilation. On the exterior,

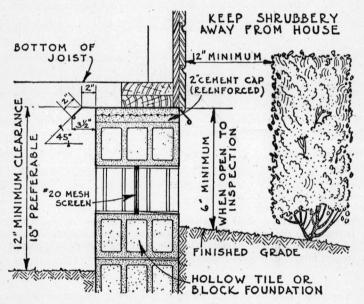

FIG. 7—Illustrates termite shield capping for a hollow foundation wall in a building having no basement.

the ground clearance to woodwork may be reduced to 6 inches above the finished grade line, provided the foundation walls permit access to occasional inspection for shelter tubes by the home owner. In the case of solid foundations, ventilation should be provided by allowing not less than two square feet of net open area for every twenty-five linear feet of wall. Openings should be screened with 20 mesh non-corroding screening. All lumber which comes in contact with the ground should be pressure treated with a preservative, or be the heartwood of a termite-resistant material.

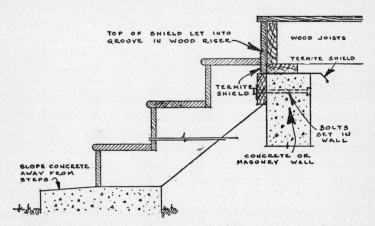

FIG. 8—Illustrating location of termite shield between wood steps and porch. It should be remembered that the support of porches or steps should not be laid directly on the ground, but should rest on solid masonry or pressure-treated lumber of termite-resistant material.

Termite Shields.—As previously pointed out termites require constant access to soil moisture and unless they stay in a moist atmosphere they soon die. Because of this need for moisture, termites construct shelter tubes of earth or waste material to carry moisture and to act as passageways between the ground and their food supply when it is not in contact with the soil.

Destroy or prevent this *ground contact* and the termites cannot damage the building.

These shelter tubes may be constructed over the face of stone, concrete, brick or timber foundations and along water pipes or similar structures. Such contacts may be prevented by means of a metal shield barrier. This is called a "termite shield" and consists of non-corroding metal firmly inserted and pointed into a masonry joint or under the sill, projecting horizontally at least 2 inches beyond the face of the wall and then turned downward an additional 2 inches at an angle of 45 degrees. All joints should be locked (and preferably soldered also) with corners made tight, and the outer edge rolled or crimped to give stiffness against bending as well as to eliminate a sharp edge.

The termite shield should be used on each face of all foundation walls, except that it may be omitted from a face, either interior or exterior, which is exposed and open to easy and ready inspection. However, around houses and places where shrubbery may partly conceal the wall and inspection is likely to be infrequent, a modified shield may be used. Here the horizontal projection is omitted and the 2 inch projection bent downward at 45 degrees is employed. A satisfactory metal for a termite shield is 16 oz. copper.

How to Determine Presence and Locate Damage of Termites.—Except at swarming time, termites are invisible unless their galleries or passageways are broken open. The earth colored shelter tubes offer a ready means of recognizing their activities. Their work can usually be detected in wood by striking it with a hammer. Solid wood rings clear, while timber or woodwork eaten out by termites will give a dull thud when struck. Striking with an ice pick also determines weakened wood.

Clean-cut holes in books, papers and clothing are good indications of the presence of termites. Springy basement floors or the softening or weakening of woodwork suggest termite, or other damage.

How to Stop Termite Damage.—The means of stopping termite injury in a building are substantially the same as those to be employed in new construction to prevent the entry of termites. Inasmuch as contact with soil moisture is absolutely essential to the life of ground-inhabiting termites, reconstruction of a type which permanently breaks and makes impassable the ground connections maintained between the parent soil colony and any building will result in the prompt dying of any termites remaining in the woodwork or furniture or contents of the building, even if they have reached the second or third floors. However, if through water leakage or other source such woodwork is kept more or less permanently moist, termites cut off in the building may continue to work as long as this condition exists, and this applies particularly to damp corners of basements or similar conditions which may result from leakages of water pipes in bathrooms, kitchens, etc.

The Two Best Remedies.—The most lasting and effective remedy, as already indicated, is in the replacement of wood in or near the basement of the building with concrete. Second, in order of effectiveness and durability, is in replacement of such wood with treated wood or timbers, and, in regions of excessive termite damage, to employ under both methods protective shields. By this means contact between colony and building is permanently broken and relief from termite damage is assured. This means that joists imbedded in concrete and the basement floor and baseboards should be replaced with any type of plain or ornamental concrete. In basement rooms so constructed, movable furniture of wood, and also built-in furniture, particularly if resting on concrete footings, can be employed with safety.

Capping and Facing.—To give the capping and facing to basement walls of frame buildings, it is rarely necessary to jack up the building, but usually it is possible to remove the upper tier of brick or upper portion of the masonry unit in sections and replace with portland cement mortar and suitable capping of slate or mortar. Where poor grades of mortar have been used in masonry walls below the ground, it may be necessary to coat the outside, and if necessary also the inside, of the wall with portland cement or concrete to keep termites from boring through.

Application of Soil Poison.—In the case of masonry or concrete walls or piers, which have disintegrated or cracked, or are of a type of construction that cannot be sealed off by capping with concrete on top of the foundation, thus permitting termites to construct their earthlike shelter tubes on the inside, it may be necessary to use soil poisons as a more or less temporary measure for preventing termite damage.

An economical soil poison is one part creosote oil to 2 or 3 parts kerosene or mineral spirits (dilution depends on density of soil). If the odor of creosote be objectionable (it will disappear in a short time if there be proper ventilation) orthodichlorobenzene (full strength) or paradichlorobenzene crystals may be used.

In the northern states it is well to use these crystals only during warm weather when soil temperatures are relatively high. The chemical should be applied in a shallow trench about one foot wide (it is well to also loosen the earth as deeply as possible below the trench) against all walls, piers, pipes and on the exterior and interior sides of all exterior walls, step and stair foundations, etc. The creosote mixture should be used at the rate of one gallon per 10 lineal feet of trench; orthodichlorobenzene at the rate of one gallon per 10 lineal feet of trench and paradichlorobenzene at the rate of 5 pounds of crystals per 10 lineal feet of trench. All wood and other debris, termite shelter tubes, etc. should be thoroughly removed from the soil and walls before applying chemicals. Orthodichlorobenzene is harmful to living vegetation.

It is well to inspect the work about 3 to 4 weeks after the poisoning is completed, and re-poison if there be any indications of continued termite activity. The building should be regularly inspected about 4 weeks after the semi-annual "flying time" (in spring and fall, varies according to species of termites and locality) and re-poisoning done if there be evidence of new infestation.

CHAPTER 58

Paints

By definition, paint is *a mixture consisting of finely divided substances, called **pigments** held in suspension in a liquid called the vehicle.* In this condition it is capable of being spread on the surface to which it is to be applied by a brush or sprayer. When the surface has been thus covered it is said to have received a *coat* of paint.

Usually two or three coats are applied, the second or third coats being applied after an interval of time sufficient for the preceding coat to dry. It should be noted here that three coats of thin paint will last longer than two coats of heavy paint and will require less material.

As stated, the different solids which are used in paints are called pigments and they do not become paint until mixed with the thinning material or vehicle.

Paint may be obtained in two forms:
1. So called unmixed or paste
2. Mixed

The so called unmixed paints consists of the pigment ground in just enough of the vehicle to form a paste, the painter adds to this more of the vehicle to properly thin the paint.

The mixed paints are mixed by the manufacturer, and as a good vehicle is expensive, the buyer is taking a chance on getting paint with a poor substitute for the vehicle, resulting in a poor job which will not last. Accordingly: *Mix your own paint.*

Pigments.—The principal white base pigments are white lead and zinc white. In addition to these are several other white pigments which are variously regarded as inert pigments or *extenders*. Among these are barytes, whiting and gypsum.

White Lead.—In making white lead, pig lead is melted by means of a specially designed machine and subjected to a blast of superheated steam, which reduces the metal to its finest possible state of subdivision.

This process partly hydrates and oxidizes the comminuted lead which passes thence into cylinders fitted with agitators and containing water through which a current of air is passed.

The sub-hydroxide of lead is here further oxidized into lead hydroxide which is then treated in other cylinders containing water with a stream of purified carbon dioxide gas which converts it into basic white lead of ideal composition after which the completed product goes to specially designed drying beds.

Sublimed White Lead.—This is a lead sulphate that is white in color and is produced by a fire process.

It is used to a considerable extent in ready mixed paint making, and is inferior to the genuine white lead.

Zinc White.—This is oxide of zinc made by blowing a current of air through molten zinc. It is free from poisonous qualities which render white lead objectionable for an indoor paint and is not acted upon by sulphur or gases, which darken white lead.

Zinc white spreads more rapidly than white lead, but does not cover so well, so that it will require four or more coats of zinc white to equal the covering obtained by three coats of white lead.

It is generally used in combination with white lead on exterior work.

Barytes.—This is sulphate of barium and is a native rock, which is very finely ground and is used as an inert extender of paint. It has no affinity for linseed oil, and absolutely no covering power. Four coats of barytes mixed with linseed oil will not hide a surface to which it is applied, and the film is practically transparent. The same is true of *silica*, which is another so-called "inert pigment."

Whiting.—This is pulverized chalk, calcium carbonate, and is lighter in weight than barytes, and possesses a decided affinity for linseed oil. Mixed with oil in a paste form, it becomes **putty.** It has very little covering power in itself.

Vehicles.—The best vehicles or thinning agents are linseed oil and turpentine, to which in the mixing of paint must be added a small proportion of one of the *driers*, to cause the paint to dry in a reasonable time.

In *enamel* paints the vehicle is varnish, and in kalsomine and other cold water paints it is a solution of glue, casein, albumen, or some similar cementing material. The cementing material is sometimes called the *binder*. A vehicle for outside paint of the best quality will generally consist of from 90% to 95% linseed oil, and from 10% to 15% of japan drier.

Linseed Oil.—This, the principal vehicle, is the oil expressed from the seed of the flax, and is remarkable from the fact that it unites with oxygen to dry to a waterproof film.

It is this fact, that it is a drying oil, that gives it its great value in paint. Linseed oil is adulterated with various mineral oils, resin oil, corn oil, and fish oil. The first named are the most common adulterants. Accordingly, buy only from reliable dealers.

Linseed oil may be obtained either
1. Raw (not boiled)
2. Boiled
The object of boiling linseed oil is to drive off part of the moisture which the raw oil contains. After boiling, some form of

drier is added to hasten its drying. The result is a heavy body, partially oxidized oil.

When *genuine* boiled oil is used the paint dries rapidly on the surface but the under part of the paint film remains soft and tacky for a long time. If the final coat be applied too soon the pulling influence on the soft under coat (as the upper coat hardens) causes it to shrivel up and crack. In most cases blistering will occur.

Do not use boiled oil on exterior work.

It should be noted that there are a lot of fake "boiled" oils on the market.

A great deal of the oil which is sold as boiled oil by unscrupulous dealers has never been boiled but consists of raw oil overloaded with driers. Such oil is known to the trade as *bunghole dried*, and while it dries quickly, it causes paint made with it to perish rapidly because it hastens unduly the oxidation of the oil.

A reliable test for both raw and boiled linseed oil is the flash test, the temperature at which pure linseed oil flashes being 470° Fahr., while mineral oil which is the chief adulterant of linseed oil, flashes at about 400° Fahr., and resin oil still lower, thus rendering it a simple method to detect these adulterants.

Another test for the purity of linseed oil (apart from chemical tests) is to examine its drying properties; this may be done by spreading a very thin layer of oil upon a glass plate, and exposing it in a warm situation.

Boiled linseed oil will be dry in twelve hours or thereabouts, but raw linseed oil will require two or three days. Prepared boards may be also used for the purpose, in which case the time will be somewhat shortened. It is a good plan to compare the samples with undoubtedly genuine boiled or raw oil.

If it be desired to ascertain the amount of these adulterants in linseed oil, take any weight of the suspected oil, place it in a beaker or any suitable vessel, and add a small quantity of caustic soda, alcohol, and a little water. The contents of the vessel should then be boiled for some time, with constant stirring, after which the oil will be found saponified while the adulterants will be unchanged. The mass is then poured into a separating vessel

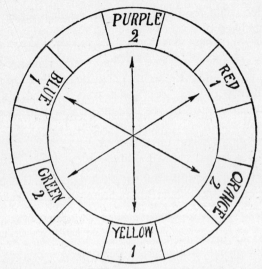

FIG. 3,764.—The primary colors 1 and the secondary colors 2 derived from them. The arrows show the complementary colors one with another. The diagram shows a circle on which are placed in equal divisions apart the primary colors of red, yellow and blue and the resulting secondary ones of orange, green and purple that are the result of the proper combinations. In order to arrive at a correct knowledge of complementary colors, or those that more harmoniously relate, one to the other, it is only necessary to carry the eye directly across the circle through its center to the opposite color. For example, it will be noted that the complementary color to red is green, to blue, orange, and to yellow, purple. There is more or less confusion in the mind as to what constitutes a gray color. Gray to the uneducated is merely a mixture of black and white, whereas properly speaking the gray of any color is the addition of its missing primary or secondary. For instance, as seen in the figure the complementary or graying color of blue is orange. Blue being a primary color we must add the missing primaries to gray it, and in this case the missing primaries are red and yellow, or orange. The same will hold true through the entire range of primary and secondary colors. In order to illustrate what is meant by the graying color, suppose that a panel two feet square has been painted a vivid red and that over half of this has been laid a board to cover it, and the panel placed where it can receive the direct or bleaching action of the sun. In the course of a few weeks, if the board covering be removed, it will be found that the original vivid red is still there, but where the sun has acted on the uncovered portion it has grayed the red color. Now if it became necessary to produce this gray color the question arises what must be added to the original red. As found above the complementary or graying color of red is green, or a combination of yellow and blue. So then if the proper proportion of green be added to the original red, the grayed tone of the superimposed piece of board will be exactly duplicated.

and agitated with benzine until it takes up the mineral or resin oil, which afterwards comes to the surface of the vessel. The bottom layer is then run off and the top portion is well washed with warm water until all traces of the saponified oil have disappeared. The residue, which is mineral oil, is then placed in a vessel and weighed.

Turpentine.—This vehicle is the distilled sap of the long leaf pine. It is used to make paint more fluid, and hence to make it spread easier. It dries by evaporation, leaving a slight, gummy residue. Owing to its price it is likely to be adulterated with the lighter mineral oils.

Benzine.—As an adulterant for diluting paint, this petroleum distillate is used by disreputable painters and dealers.

It dries by evaporation without residue. Owing to the high price of turpentine the temptation is great to adulterate turpentine with from 10 to 20% benzine. Better use benzine entirely or wood turpentine made by the destructive distillation of pine wood.

Driers.—In order to cause the paint to dry within a reasonable time, oxidizing agents or *"driers"* are mixed in the paint. They usually consist of salts of lead or salts of manganese. Some driers are also called *japans*. Not more than 10% by volume of any liquid drier should be added to oil. Excess of drier makes the paint less durable. Cheap driers often contain resin.

Paint mixtures.—There are three kinds of mixtures of color:

1. Oil
2. Flatting
3. Distemper

The first is bright and glossy; the second is perfectly flat or dead (without gloss); and the third is like the second in effect, but without its durability.

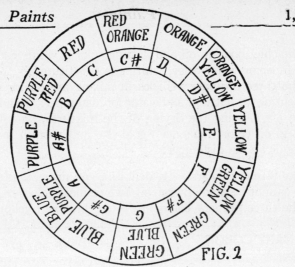

FIG. 2

Fig. 3,765.—Arrangement of the primary, secondary and tertiary colors, as relating to the chromatic scale in music. The diagram shows the three primaries, their secondaries and what may be called the tertiary colors. Opposite each of these there has been placed one of the notes of the chromatic scale forming a perfect octave. It is interesting to note that the claim has been made, and with much insistence, that any scheme of color that may be selected and which may be struck as a chord will, if the chord be harmonious, become a harmonious scheme of color, but if this chord produce a discord of music, there will be a discord of color in the picture. It will be interesting to those who are musically inclined to experiment in this matter and it is believed that much entertainment and instruction will result therefrom.

NOTE.—*Poor quality paints.* There is undoubtedly much prepared or mixed paint on the market which is largely made up of makeweights and extenders, and which possesses little real paint value. Such paint is usually offered for sale at a low price, and, like all cheap things, is apt to be of poor quality. In buying cheap paint, or in hiring a cheap painter, the property owner must expect to get as poor results as he would obtain if he buy cheap clothing in which cotton masquerades as wool. Good paint, like everything else that is good, commands a fair price, and cannot be bought cheap. Good results can be obtained by first class mixed paints, and just as good results can be obtained by the shop mixed paint of the experienced and honest practical painter, but the ready mixed paint and the shop mixed paint will differ materially in composition. The painter as a rule, prefers a paint made of white lead and linseed oil, with the necessary tinting colors for light tints and such driers as may be required. The manufacturer finds it practically impossible to put up a pure white lead and linseed oil paint in cans ready for use, because such a paint will almost invariably become "fatty" and unfit for use after standing in stock for some time, and the result obtained from its use in that case would be anything but satisfactory. The use of forty per cent or more of zinc white in a mixed paint seems to prevent this tendency to become fatty; and as its use may be defended on other ground also, it follows that prepared paints are all based to a greater or less extent on zinc white, some of them containing no white lead at all. The best prepared paints are made up of white lead and zinc white, with such colors as may be needed to produce the desired shades, and contain none of the so called "inert pigments." The use of as much as thirty per cent of barytes is strongly urged by many paint experts.—*Radford*

The chief body in oil and flatting color is white lead; but in distemper or water-color, whiting is substituted.

The three ordinary vehicles in mixing are oil for oil color, turpentine for flatting, and water for distemper. In addition to these for insuring the drying of the mixtures, patent drier is used in oil color, japanner's gold-size and varnish in flatting, and glue size in distemper.

The Primary Colors.—By definition, primary colors are those that cannot be made by mixing two or more colors together.

The three primary colors are: Red, blue and yellow.

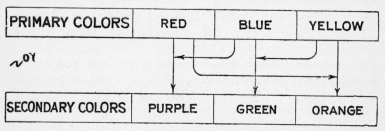

FIG. 3,766.—Diagram of primary and secondary colors. These relatives are shown in the diagram.

The colors got from mixing any two of the primary colors together are called secondary colors. There are three secondary colors, called purple, green and orange.

Red and blue gives purple.

Blue and yellow gives green.

Red and yellow gives orange.

By mixing any two of the secondary colors together we get what are called the **tertiary** colors, citrine, olive, and russet. Thus, orange and **green** gives citrine, green and purple gives olive, orange and purple gives russet.

NOTE.—If you must use ready mixed paints do not use the kind put up in cans without the name of the manufacturer on the label: there is a reason.

Black and white are not regarded as colors.

A good black can be produced by mixing the three primary colors together in proper proportions.

By adding white to any color you produce a tint of that color. By adding black to any color you get a shade of that color. That is the difference between "tint" and "shade."

The use of black subdues or lowers the tone of any color to which it is added.

To preserve the richness of colors when you wish to darken them use the primary colors instead of black; for instance, to make a yellow darker use red and blue; to blue add red and yellow, and so on.

Every shade or tint of color required by the painter can be made from red, blue and yellow with black and white.

To make any of the umbers or siennas lighter in color and to preserve the clear richness of tone, always use lemon chrome instead of white. If you want a subdued or muddy umber or sienna color then use white.

The most useful primary colors are:

Yellows—lemon, chrome, deep ocher.

Reds—Vermilion, Venetian red, crimson lake.

Blues—Prussian blue, ultramarine.

Gold and silver leaf harmonize with all colors, and with black and white in small quantities; can be used to bring into harmony the most glaring colors.

The old-time heraldic painters knew the value of outlining their strong primary colors with gold, silver, black or white, so as to bring them into harmony one with another. The ancient Egyptians and other peoples made use of the same knowledge in their decorative schemes.

Yellow ocher is the most useful color the painter possesses. In its pure state it is admirable for large wall spaces, and if you are in doubt as to what color to use to complete a color scheme you will find ocher or one of its shades or tints will in nine cases out of ten supply the missing link.

Red on walls makes a room look smaller and absorbs light.

Yellows give light and airiness to any room and reflect light.

Useful colors in large quantities for churches, public halls, etc., are:

Primrose red.
Terra cotta (white, burnt sienna, lemon chrome).
All tints of ocher.
Flesh color (white and burnt sienna).
Pea green, apple green.
Grey green (white, paris green and touch of black).
Ivory shades (white, lemon chrome or ocher)
Old rose (white, ocher, Venetian red or pure Indian red and black).
Nile blue and Nile green (white, Prussian blue, lemon chrome).
Light citrine, light olive, light russet.

For ceilings the best tints are the creams and ivory tints and greys.

Creams and ivory tints are made from white tinted with one or more of these colors, lemon chrome, orange chrome, ocher, raw sienna; and to produce a warmer tone the addition of a small quantity of burnt sienna, vermillion or Venetian red. To produce a colder tone use a little green, black, raw umber or blue.

Greys are made from white tinted with either black, black and green, blue and umber, black and red, red and blue, burnt sienna and blue.

Light colors are always to be used for ceilings in preference to darker colors. Contrasting color is better for a ceiling than a lighter tint of the wall color.

CHAPTER 59

Painting

Priming Coat.—The first coat applied to the bare surface is called the *priming coat*. For wood, it consists chiefly of oil and is usually equivalent to a gallon of ordinary paint thinned with a gallon of raw linseed oil. For structural metal the paint is not thinned.

In all wood work, nail holes and other defects are filled with putty after the priming coat has been applied. If the wood be resinous, knots and resinous places must be covered with shellac varnish before the priming coat is put on.

Pitchy woods, such as southern yellow pine and cypress do not readily absorb oil, and turpentine should be substituted for part of the oil.

Red lead is successfully used as a primer (2 parts to 1 of white lead) on such woods.

Outside Painting.—After the priming coat has been largely absorbed by the wood, a second and third coat of paint should be applied.

On best jobs no ready mixed paint will be used. Get the best white lead ground in 8% of oil.

One hundred lbs. of this is equal to 2.8 gals. in volume and is commonly mixed with $3\frac{1}{2}$ gals. of raw linseed oil, 1 qt. of turpentine, and 1 pt. of drier to make $6\frac{2}{3}$ gals. of paint for the second coat, or with 4 gals. of oil, 1 pt. of turpentine and 1 pt. of drier for the finishing coat.

If white zinc be used 9½ lbs. of dry zinc oxide and 5.7 lbs. of oil make 1 gal. of paint. To this turpentine and dryer should also be added.

Colored paints are commonly made by adding colored pigments to lead or zinc, but some dark paints contain only iron oxides, ochers, etc., as pigments. These weigh from 12 to 14 lbs. per gal.

Painting should always be done in dry weather and no painting should be done until the inside plastering is dry. Paint should not be applied to lumber that is not dry. A week or more should be allowed between successive coats.

In painting the outside of a house, the trim should be painted first; then the body color can be laid neatly against it. The final brushing should be in the direction of the grain of the wood.

It is good practice to have the successive coats (except for white paint) vary a little in color, to facilitate inspection. White, light blue and light green are less durable colors than yellow, gray, or dark colors in general, owing to the fact that the chemical rays of light penetrate the former more easily.

A gallon of paint will cover from 400 to 600 sq. ft. of surface, depending upon the character of the surface. Roof paints should contain a larger proportion of oil, and a smaller amount of drier or none at all.

Three coats are desirable.

Tin roofs and galvanized iron work should be thoroughly scrubbed and then dried before painting.

The shingles on the walls and roofs of a house are sometimes stained with creosote stain, which consists of a pigment suspended in creosote or some similar liquid. The creosote has some preservative effect.

Inside Painting.—Door frames and window frames should receive a priming coat of paint in the shop; if they are to be finished in varnish this paint will be applied to the back only. As has already been said, before any painting is done any resinous knots should be varnished with shellac.

All interior surfaces which are to be painted should be puttied after the priming coat and the putty should be applied with a wooden spatula, not a steel one, to avoid marring the surface. The paint for the second coat should contain as much turpentine as oil, that is, its vehicle should be half oil and half turpentine.

The effect of this is to make the paint dry with a dull instead of a glossy surface, *flat surface* being the painter's term. To this the next coat will adhere well. If the next be the final coat, it may be an ordinary oil paint. When thoroughly dry the gloss may be removed by lightly rubbing it with pumice and water.

Enamel paint consists of pigment with varnish as a vehicle. It is harder and makes a finer finish than oil paint. It is also more expensive.

It is usual to apply it over oil paint, in which case the last coat of oil paint should be lightly sand papered when quite hard and dry. A coat of enamel paint is then put on, and when it is dry it should be sand papered or rubbed with curled hair. The final coat of enamel is then laid on and it may be rubbed in a like manner if a flat surface is desired, or it may be left with the gloss.

It is also common practice for painters to make a final enamel finish by adding varnish to white lead or white zinc, very little oil being used in this case. The best varnish for this purpose is a spar varnish from a thoroughly reliable maker. The quicker drying varnishes will crack and alligator.

Specifications for Inside Finish on Wood.—First the wood work must be in proper condition, then be primed with paint to the consistency of 17 lbs. to the gallon; of white lead and half and half of raw linseed oil and turpentine and a very little drier.

The density or kind of wood to be done may vary the proportions of turps and oil, if very hard a little more turpentine will improve its value.

When thoroughly dry putty (use lead putty) all nail holes and imperfections and after hard, rub to a smooth surface with a material that, in smoothing the surface will not scratch or cut into the wood.

For the second coat use more body with less oil. If it is to be tinted add the color to this and to the third coat, which will contain about 1 part oil to three of turps.

If the finish is to be white and in three coats, the last coat shall contain two-fifths zinc white and three-fifths lead and no oil but white. If a varnish instead of fourth coat is to be used, use one-half lead and one-half zinc, varnish according to the gloss required and turpentine. Or, if it be the last coat, use all zinc, white varnish and turps. However, it should be noted that the skill of the painter will not enable him to better prepare the proper ingredients than the high grade, standard manufacturers.

Four coats of white lead and zinc with the last two rubbed, applied 7 to 10 days apart, finished over with two coats of one of the best grades of prepared enamels, makes a high grade and lasting job in a bathroom or wherever required. Will not be injured with water.

In rubbing down do not use coarser than 00 or 0 sand paper. Coarse sand paper cuts through the finish.

Painting Iron Work.—It is cheapest to use the best material for the work in hand. There is no cheap substitute that is just as good. Where structural iron is to be permanently concealed and subject to chemical action, too much care and consideration cannot be given to its covering. One gallon covers a large amount of surface applied to metal as compared with wood, hence there is no excuse for the use of cheap paints.

The painting of iron work, until recent years has been one of the most neglected, though most important factor in its preservation. Now, since mechanical and structural engineers devote much time and thought to it, *specifications* more generally and specifically state the grade and kind of materials and how the work shall be done. Thus after years of experiments it is a conceded fact that pure dry red lead mixed when wanted for use with well settled raw linseed oil, preferably Calcutta, applied as quickly as possible after mixed so that oxidization takes place after applied, is the best and most durable for structural iron work and steel ship bottoms.

If exposed to the air (oxygen) too long after mixed it rapidly loses that quality of oxidizing that should take place when drying, thus losing an element that will render it but little better than ordinary oxide of iron paint so much offered for sale for that purpose.

If the work to be done cannot be allowed to stand for several days before using, and drying must be hurried, an amount of strictly pure oil of japan drier that contains no gum may be added up to about 4% without very material injury, but, if possible avoid it.

Gloss on Machinery.—Take prepared iron filler which comes in paste form, and if the casting, pipes or any part thereof be rough, thoroughly clean down to the iron, thin the paste and apply with spatula sufficiently thick to make a smooth, even surface, wetting the spatula occasionally with turps or benzine.

When all such surfaces have been filled, dip a stiff brush into turpentine and go over it all until smooth. This is only necessary when the job is rough.

Finish with two coats of japan, black or green, or as desired. Free the japan with turps so that it will flow on smooth.

Stains.—There are numerous kinds of stain, the principal varieties being:

1. Water
2. Oil
3. Alcohol
4. Spirit
5. Acid
6. Alkali
7. Pigment or wiped
8. Wood dyes
9. Fuming process

The color of open grained wood, like oak, ash, chestnut, etc., may be modified by coloring the paste filler by adding some pigment to it.

In addition to the above methods of staining, all of which are used by the painter and hard wood finisher, there are large quantities of stains sold that are intended principally for the use of the amateur who wants to stain and finish in one operation and who does not possess the mechanical skill or technical knowledge needed to use a true stain.

A great variety of water stains are possible, made from aniline, alizarine and other vegetable products. To give the formula for each would be more exhaustive than the practical working painter will care to digest, beside, most stains now used are either oil, acid or spirit, and can be purchased ready for use.

Alcohol and water stains are least used except when, for effect, it is desired to raise the grain of the wood above its dressed surface, when it produces an etched appearance.

Water stain is generally made up as wanted and the few following formulæ will suffice for a guide:

Mahogany.—Combine Bismark brown, one ounce, with 3 quarts of boiling hot water. Regulate its density by the amount of rubbing out. Use cold.

Light Oak.—Quercitron bark (citron or oak bark), 2 ozs.; water 1 gallon, macerate (steep soak) for about 2 weeks, filter and use.

Dark Oak.—For dark oak double the quantity of Quercitron bark.

Walnut.—Dissolve 1 oz. of permangenate of potash; 1 oz. of Epsom salt in one quart of water. Strain for use. More than one coat may be required for sufficient density.

Also it may be made by boiling together 3 ozs. of crushed nutgalls; 4 ozs. of concentrated lye and 8 ounces of dry Vandyke brown. When boiled down to one-half and cold it is ready to be applied, preferably with a cloth.

Cherry.—One pound Spanish anetto; 1 oz. concentrated lye. Boil for concentration, or gamboge (yellow gum resin) will concentrate it.

Ebony.—Three pounds extract of logwood; 1 pound concentrated lye; 7 pounds of water. Dissolve by boiling. When stain is dry go over it with a strong solution of vinegar and iron. Also it may be made by boiling together (slowly for about 3 hours) ½ lb. sulphite of iron; 2 ozs. of Chinese blue; 3 ozs. of nutgalls; 2 lbs. of extract of logwood; 1 gallon of vinegar and ¼ lb. of carbonate of iron.

Rosewood.—Any water mahogany stain will make rosewood by applying it over and over until the proper depth of color has been attained. Then go over very lightly with ebony stain.

The Chalking of Paint.—If white lead be not broken up well and thoroughly mixed with the oil, the oil and lead will not be equally distributed. This is the reason why the paint will begin to chalk on one part of the job before it does on another and before the time it should begin to do so. There is not enough of oil to bind the pigment properly.

To break up and mix a considerable quantity of lead and oil properly with a paddle by hand is a tiresome operation.

The best way to do it is to take two suitable vessels, a larger and smaller one. Put a hundred pounds or less of lead, ground in oil, in the smaller one, add a little oil, a half gallon, for instance, and thoroughly work it into the lead. Keep on adding a little oil in this manner, working thoroughly into the lead until the mass is of such a consistency that the paddle will move freely through it.

Pour into the larger vessel and proceed in like manner until there is enough to do the job, or, at least one coat. Stir this mass thoroughly until you are sure the oil and lead have been equally distributed. Don't be afraid of stirring it too much.

Painting Old Brick Walls.—The principal difficulty in the painting of an old brick wall is the liability of the paint to come off, owing to a bad condition of the bricks. Hence the first thing to do is to make the wall as clean and solid as possible, scraping and brushing off all loose material, finishing with a broom sweep down.

This must be done when the wall is dry, indeed the entire job from start to finish, should be done in dry weather. A wire brush is an efficient tool when the bricks are rotten in places. Plaster may be necessary to fill up cracks and holes where the brick has rotted away. If this part of the work be done right the result will be just as good a surface for paint as if the surface were wood instead. And just the same kind of paint is used.

The first coat should be thin, raw linseed oil colored with whatever pigment will best suit the finish, ochre or red, for instance.

Let the surface take in all it will absorb, use a flat wall brush, one having medium long bristles, but working the paint in criss-cross with the ends of the bristles. Care should be exercised not to miss places.

After the first coat has become dry, putty all cracks that may remain after the plastering, and of course there will be some, then it is ready for the second coat, to be followed by the third.

Use driers in each coat of paint. There are two finishes, flat or lusterless, and gloss. The former is only used on fine jobs, new work mostly, for it does not look well when the bricks are old and uneven.

A gloss-finish is simply paint that is made with oil only, no turpentine. Three coats of such paint will give good wear. On new bricks, the fronts of houses, the flat paint, that made with turpentine, will also give excellent wear.

The priming coat on the old brick wall may be made upon this formula:

Dry Venetian red, 20 lbs., raw linseed oil, 10 gals., with driers—say a pint. It will be an advantage to allow this coat a *week for drying*.

The second coat may be made with 75 lbs. Venetian red in oil, 25 lbs. white lead in oil, and 3 lbs. of Indian red, in oil. Mix stiff and let the mass stand 24 hours before thinning for use. Do not thin it until ready to use. Don't add driers until ready to use.

As the next and final coat is to have a full gloss, add a little turpentine to the second coat, to dull the gloss a little; it is a fact in painting that if an oil paint be applied to an oil surface a partly dead effect is obtained and not a full gloss. Hence the rule to have the undercoat somewhat dull if the finish is to be a gloss, and vice versa.

For better brick painting there are a wide series of colors, ranging from cream, through the buffs, on to the light and dark reds, the latter up to a decided purple-red. These colors are effected by the use of ochre and Indian red, the darkener being Prussian blue. Milwaukee or buff brick color is made from white lead, yellow ochre and a little raw sienna.

Coming back to the old brick wall, if there be green mould or mildew on it, it should be washed with water made sour with hydrochloric (muriatic) acid. Use a stiff fiber scrub brush. In places where much soft coal is used and the walls are black with soot, the soot may be removed with this preparation:

To one gallon of good soft soap add two pounds of pulverized pumice stone, about 00 or F, and one pint of liquid ammonia. The soot should first be swept off as much as possible with a stiff broom.

The soap preparation should be left on about one-half hour; after which scrub the wall, now and then dipping the brush in the clear water, a bucket of which should always be accessible. Finally wash off with a hose, or sponge. Paint after dry.

Old paint may be removed in the usual way, with burner or alkali, washing off then with acid water. A 20 per cent acid solution is about right. Finally wash down with clear water. Efflorescence may be removed with muriatic acid water, first removing all loose salts by means of a stiff brush. It is difficult to prevent efflorescence once it appears; the best one can do is to remove it, and lessen the evil by filling the bricks full of oil. On such a wall it would be best to apply straight oil, rather than a thin paint primer.

Whether to use boiled or raw oil is debatable; some prefer the one, some the other, while still others add a little turpentine to the oil. The turpentine causes the oil to penetrate better, especially if the boiled oil be used. Boiled oil has a thicker body, hence does not penetrate as well as the raw oil does.

Paint or oil stains on the brick work, where the old surface is to be renovated, may be removed by a paste made of whiting two parts, soft soap one part, and potash one part, with some hot water to reduce the mass to a paste. Apply this, let it stand a half hour, then wash off and scrub with soap and water, to remove any part of the stain not taken off in the first place. Finally wash clean with water.

Painting Cement Surfaces.—One of the foremost authorities on cement has been painting with oil paint over cement for many years with the best results. All non-drying oils are more or less destructive to cement, and if the cement wall should be saturated with raw linseed oil, the oil would slowly disintegrate the cement, but, oil paint will dry on the surface without affecting the cement.

Experts hold that cement surfaces, properly executed, clean and dry, are no more dangerous to oil paint than the modern wall plasters.

Most of the trouble is caused by the painting being done before the cement is dry. Cement dries very slowly. The opinion of men who are experts in the use of cement say that a cement wall must stand at least over one summer before painting with oil can be commenced and accomplished.

The first thing required is to wash the surface thoroughly with a 7 to 8% solution of muriatic acid, followed with a good wash of clean water. The surface must then be given time to dry perfectly.

In painting, it is well to use considerable more turpentine than is ordinarily the case and very little driers. Boiled linseed oil is considered preferable to raw. For priming, the paint should be used thin, and contain so much turpentine that it is almost flat, increasing the amount of oil for succeeding coats. Each coat must be given ample time to dry before the next one is applied.

For water color or calcimine, washing with muriatic acid solution, followed by clean water, should be done if first class work is to be expected. When the surface is thoroughly dry it should be given a coat of alum size, or still better, a coat of flat paint, and when the size is dry the surface is ready for calcimining.

A contractor, who does a great amount of work in the east, makes a size of equal parts of acetic acid and alum. His formula is one pound of acid, one pound of alum and two gallons of water.

There is a considerable amount of alkali in cement, which has to be counteracted before any paint is applied to the surface, also it is very essential that all work should be thoroughly dry before painting. The cement should stand at least six weeks to two months.

Cement acts on the paint by eating through and softening the paint, and turning it into a very gummy substance first, so that if a heavy rainstorm should beat against it, it would be washed off in many places.

Best Way of Treating Cement.—First, take about half a bushel of alum lime to twenty-five gallons of water and thoroughly shake the same; when cold add six gallons of the best cider vinegar and about five pounds of English Venetian red; strain through a fine strainer, use it about the consistency of thin cream. Apply one coat of this to the cement work; let it stand at least twenty-four hours, so that it may become good and hard. Then give it one good coat of red lead and linseed oil, with enough of japan drier to dry it. Then paint any color desired.

To Prevent Paint Peeling.—For a treatment that will keep paint from peeling or chipping off galvanized iron generators and galvanized iron pipes, apply a solution, which, when premitted to dry, will allow any paint to adhere firmly to the metal under all conditions. This wash consists of a solution of two ounces each copper chloride, copper nitrate and sal ammoniac, dissolved in one gallon of soft water in an earthen, porcelain or glass or other acid proof vessel, to which solution is added two ounces of commercial muriatic acid.

It has proven successful in every instance, that the best medium or binder for aluminum bronze to be applied to a heated metal surface is the so called banana liquid, a mixture of gun cotton, anylacetate and benzol or benzine; of course it must be applied while the metal is either cold or only moderately warm and not near an open flame.

Paint for Hot Water Pipes and Radiators.—Most every paint and varnish manufacturer makes a paint suitable for the purpose named.

First make sure that the surface is free from scale, rust and grease. Paint them while warm, so that the paint may bake on, because when applied while cold and the paint is allowed to dry and the hot water or steam turned on suddenly, the paint is liable to blister or scale off.

Where white is required, do not use white lead, but zinc white only.

For black use ivory black, and for tints also use zinc white as the base.

Yellow ochre, sienna raw and burnt, burnt umber, Venetian red, ultramarine blue and zinc yellow are the only pigments that will not change color appreciably when used on heated surfaces.

Most paint dealers carry a stock of radiator and other enamels, bronze and baking or baking varnishes which will probably give satisfactory results and save time.

Natural Wood Finish.—Some light colored hard woods are finished their natural colors or may be stained to represent dark woods, and often softer grained woods such as pine, cedar, cypress, and white wood are stained to represent darker woods.

Natural color of woods may be preserved by using white shellac instead of oil fillers—oil darkens wood—orange shellac on yellow cast woods. Use copal and light color varnishes.

Open grained woods such as oak, ash and chestnut must have the grain filled before varnishing. Where the closer grained woods are not to have a rubbed finish, they too should be filled, if only with a liquid filler. Mostly every dark colored wood may be represented by staining lighter and less expensive wood. Cypress and birch take mahogany, walnut and cherry stains. Cherry, fir and white wood will represent walnut, light mahogany, rose wood and red gum. Spruce takes a red cedar color.

Fuming.—Sometimes the treatment known as *fuming,* is resorted to especially for antiqueing oak. This is done by putting in a tight box or as small room as will take the amount in and placing on the floor porcelain or glass receptacles scattered about and filled with 26 degrees ammonia. Allow it to remain over night or until the desired tone is reached. Weathered or Flemish effects are thus easily produced. Then finish as desired.

It is of course readily understood that the surface to be fumed must not be covered by another board, but must be unobstructed. It is also well to know that the quicker it is done after dressing, the more tonic acid is present to be acted upon and the result better.

Besides ammonia, which may also be applied with a mop instead of vaporizing, there are the following compositions that by application will produce age tones:

1. One oz. of bichromate of potash dissolved in hot water and when cold diluted with water until the brownish tone desired is reached.

2. Dissolve iron filings in sulphuric acid and dilute with water and repeat applications until right tone is had.

3. A thick solution of caustic lime and water well worked into the surface with a brush and allowed to dry will, when brushed off leave a dark brown tone.

Oil Stains.—The amount of color for all stains is governed by the kind of wood. Soft woods take in the color more than hard or more dense. The following formulæ cannot be depended upon to give the exact tones desired; this must be determined by staining samples of wood.

Mahogany.—Use burnt sienna in quantity to produce the desired density.

Illuminate with red lake. For old dark mahogany add a little drop black. Add turpentine and japan drier to suit. Or, instead of red lake use rose pink and black.

Cherry.—To 3 pounds of burnt sienna add a half gallon each of spirits of turpentine and raw linseed oil, and one quart of best brown japan. Sometimes, if the sienna be very red, the tone may be improved by making one-third of it raw sienna.

Light Oak.—Two pounds of raw sienna, half pound of raw umber, half gallon each of turps and raw oil and one quart of brown japan.

Dark Oak.—Add to the light oak formula a small quantity of burnt umber.

Rosewood.—To one pound of rose pink add one pint each of good asphaltum varnish, brown japan and boiled oil, and one quart of turpentine. It may be lightened with more pink or darkened with the varnish.

Walnut Stain.—One pound of burnt umber, one quart each of *boiled* oil and turpentine and one pint of brown japan. If wanted blacker, add Vandyke brown. Make lighter by reducing the umber and adding burnt sienna.

Golden, Antique and Red Oak.—These imitations may be produced in beautiful effect on yellow pine and cypress. The dark grain of these woods are very soft and when wet readily raise above the surface, thus avoid water stain, unless, mentioned elsewhere, an embossed or etched effect is wanted. For golden oak, add one pint of asphaltum, half pint of brown japan to one pound of burnt umber ground in oil and bring to consistency of thin varnish with turps. By testing it will be found that a little chrome yellow will help to golden. When the stain is set, rub off with a cloth to bring out the hard (light) grain to the desired prominence. Antique may be made by adding Vandyke brown and drop black to the above.

Red oak is made with Venetian red, subdued as required with drop black. Flemish oak is made as mentioned, by fuming, and blackening with sulphate of iron or like acids, sold for the purpose, and which cannot in this particular case be done with oil or water pigments.

Graining.—This is a method of reproducing natural wood in appearance over a painted surface, for which graining tools are sold with full instructions.

First the surface is oil painted the color of the light grain of the wood.

When dry it is painted over with an oil and dryer paint the color of the dark grain. While the paint is wet the student will, from a sample of the wood before him proceed to form and fashion the grain by wiping off, brushing and combing it with said tools. When dry it is varnish coated, either light or dark as wanted.

Flat or Dull Finish.—Any interior finish, either over stain or enamel may be finished flat by using flat enamels and "lac-lustre" varnishes, or by the additional work; either in gloss finish may be rubbed to a dull or eggshell finish.

Rubbing is what smooths and hardens the surface to receive the better grade of finish varnish.

An excellent rubbing material is ground pumice and rubbing with oil or water.

If lemon oil were not so expensive it could be recommended as an excellent element; by rubbing on high gloss varnish it quickly produces the same result as mossing, pumicing or hair rubbing.

Hard Oil.—This is a substitute for varnish for interior work only, when cheapness is to be considered. It is composed of rosin or cheap copal or both, heated into drying oil and thinned with turpentine, its substitute or benzine.

Floors.—The treatment of floors is the same as that for standing trim except that a regular floor varnish is used for glossing finish.

New floors are sometimes treated with oil and drier to intensify the grain and shellac finish. Sometimes waxed over the shellac. When the oil is

NOTE.—The mechanic wishing to turn out a first class interior job on new work will try to have the builder place in his hands the standing trim so that he may stain, fill and rub it before set, ready for the final coats.

thoroughly dry the wax may be applied directly over it and rubbed or burnished.

It is difficult to varnish over wax. It first should be removed.

Wide joints in floors are unsightly and should be filled.

A good filler can be made by kneading into pure linseed oil, whiting putty and white lead to which may be added brown japan and a little turps to free it.

Where the cracks are wide 20% fine sawdust may be added. Color it to match floor color and in paste form press and rub it into the joints after they have had a coat of boiled oil. With a putty knife remove all from the surface of the boards and thus level the joint.

Varnishes.—There are two principal kinds of varnish classed as:

1. Spirit.
2. Oleoresinous.

Of the spirit varnishes, shellac is the most important and which consists essentially of a resin dissolved in a volatile solvent. The resinous ingredient of oleoresinous varnishes is combined with linseed oil and this compound is dissolved in turpentine or benzine.

The oleoresinous varnishes are commercially the more important, and are largely used in interior finishing. A gallon of varnish covers 500 sq. ft. one coat.

Surfaces to be varnished are treated in the following manner:

If the wood be open-grained, as oak, chestnut, or ash, it first receives a coat of paste filler. Liquid fillers are not desirable, as they form a poor base for subsequent work. A paste filler is really a sort of paint, the pigment being silex, or ground quartz, and the vehicle is a quick drying varnish made thin with turpentine or benzine.

This is rubbed strongly in on the grain of the wood with a short stiff brush, and as soon as it has set, usually within an hour, it is rubbed off with a harsh cloth or a handful of excelsior, the rubbing being hard across the grain of the wood. If it be desired to stain the wood, the oil stain may be mixed with the filler, but if a close grained wood be used, which needs no filler, the oil stain may be thinned to the desired color with turpentine or benzine and applied as a wash.

In cleaning the filler out of mouldings, corners, etc., a suitably shaped stick, but not a steel implement, may be used. If any puttying be necessary it is done next. After two days the first coat of varnish is applied; after five days it should be rubbed with curled hair or fine sandpaper to remove the gloss, so that the next coat will adhere well; then one, two or three more coats of varnish are added, five days or more apart, each coat being rubbed. The last coat may be rubbed or left with the natural gloss. Outside doors, window sills, jambs, inside blinds, and all surfaces exposed to the direct rays of the sun, should be varnished with spar varnish and left glossy. If shellac varnish be used as the interior finish it is applied in the same way, but at least six coats should be applied.

Floors which are to be varnished should be treated as has been described; but if they are to be waxed they should receive one or two coats of shellac varnish, then five or six coats of wax, at intervals of a week, each coat being well polished with a weighted floor brush made for the purpose.

Floor wax is not bees wax, but is a compound wax made for the purpose. Shellac is a good floor varnish; it discolors the the wood less than any other varnish, and dries rapidly.

Fillers.—These are used in painting or finishing woods. There are two classes of filler:

1. Liquid.
2. Paste.

Liquid fillers are sometimes used for first coat on close grained woods where cheapness is desired and where shellac is considered too expensive. These fillers are not intended for use on open grained woods, as they are not fillers strictly speaking. The covering capacity of liquid fillers ranges from 250 to 400 sq. ft. per gallon.

Paste fillers vary in consistency according to the kind of wood to be filled, the more open grained woods requiring the filler to be heavier in body than the close grained woods.

The following rule for *reducing paste fillers* is often used: For oak, chestnut, ash, and other very coarse-grained woods, use 7 to 9 pounds of filler to the gallon. For walnut, mahogany, butternut, and other similar grained woods, a mixture of 6 pounds of paste filler to the gallon may be used.

The covering capacity of paste filler reduced for use is about 300 sq. ft. to the gallon on work in which there is no waste.

Painter's Tools

Palette Knife.—This is a long and very flexible knife with blunt edges and rounded at the end.

As its name implies, it is intended for mixing color, or scraping it off the palette. In using the palette knife it should be held as flat as possible, so as to avoid making indentations in the palette.

Stone Knife.—This knife is similar in shape to the palette knife but is larger and is used in connection with the slab.

Stopping Knife.—A knife used for stopping cracks, etc., with putty.

This knife is shorter in proportion than the palette knife, is spear shaped, broad and stiff, so as to be adapted to bear the force necessary to press the stopping into the crevices, etc.

Paint Brushes.—The brushes used for applying paints are of various sizes and kinds. The largest are called pound brushes. The large brushes are also termed "four O," "six O," and "eight O," the latter being the largest. These are made both round and flattened, or elliptical.

It is a common error to call this form *oval*. Oval means egg like in shape that is, broader at one end than at the other, whilst an ellipse has both ends equal. These elliptical brushes are found very convenient in practice, as they take less time to work into the shape required for spreading the paint.

Paint brushes are bound either with string or with copper wire. They are sometimes used as dusters before being put into oil, by which they become softened; but this plan is not to be recommended.

The smaller brushes are called "tools," or "sash tools," and may be obtained in about a dozen different sizes, some bound with string, others fixed in tin. The smallest hog-hair brushes are called "fitches," and are used for putting in small work, where the tools would be too large.

The smallest brushes are the camel's hair, with long or short hair, accord= ing to the work to be done.

Varnish Brushes.—These may be had in different sizes, and are also made flat and of different breadths, for varnishing pictures and other fine work.

Dusting Brush.—These brushes for removing dust from surface to be painted have longer hairs than painting brushes; the hairs are so bound that they spread outward at their points, which are thus prevented adhering and the dust is more easily shaken from them.

Palette.—By definition a palette is *a thin oval or oblong tablet with a hole for the thumb, upon which artists lay their colors for painting.*

Painters use the palette when only a small quantity of color is required—as in painting a narrow moulding or beading—a very small brush or camel's hair pencil being used. It is, of course, employed by the marbler and the letter painter to the entire exclusion of the paint pot.

Palettes are made of mahogany, or of satin or other light woods, which are to be preferred to those made of mahogany whenever light tints are to be mixed on them. They should be of as little weight as possible, and should diminish in thickness towards their distant end. The oblong form is to be preferred to the elliptical, as it affords more room for colors.

New palettes should be prepared for use by rubbing raw linseed oil repeatedly over them, until they will absorb no more, the last coat being allowed to dry in, as much as possible, and the palette being then well rubbed, it will not after this be stained by absorption of color.

The palette should be carefully cleaned each time it has been used, and paint must not by any means be allowed to harden upon it. When all the color has been scraped off with the palette knife, carefully observing not to make scratches or indentations, the surface should in the first place be washed with a small quantity of turpentine, and should then be rubbed with a piece of silk rag dipped in nut oil, the edges being well attended to, so that no accumulation may take place.

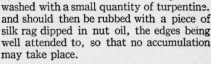

Should it be desired to save a small quantity of the color for the next day's use, it may be scraped up from the palette, and placed in a little heap in a saucer and covered with water, which may subsequently be poured off and the paint will be found ready for use. Or the paint may be placed in a small piece of tinfoil, which may then be folded up, forming a temporary metallic tube in which the color may be preserved for several days.

Mahl Stick.—This is used in connection with the palette as a rest for the hand in letter painting, or other fine work. It consists of a stiff smooth stick having a ball of wool covered with a piece of kid or wash leather at the end.

Bridling Brushes.—Before using a new long bristle, body paint brush it should be bridled, which is wrapping

FIG. 3,767.—Method of bridling a paint brush. Starting at 1, make loop 2, pass the cord through the brush and wind and when wrapped far enough, by 1 pull 2 up about half way under wrapping. Cut both ends off at edge of wrapping and the job is secure.

the brush from the shank down about one-third the bristle length with a hard laid twine of about $1/18''$ diameter as shown in fig. 3,767.

This bridling is left on until the bristles wear too short, and then removed, renewing the life and value of the brush. Sometimes the cord is half-hitched around then fastened the same way.

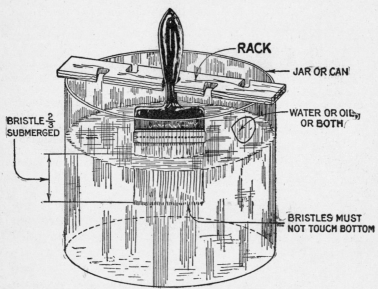

RACK

JAR OR CAN

WATER OR OIL OR BOTH

BRISTLE ⅔ SUBMERGED

BRISTLES MUST NOT TOUCH BOTTOM

Fig. 3,768.—Method of suspending brush in can of water so that it will not rest on bottom of can.

Care of Brushes not in Use.—When not in use the brush should be wiped out and suspended in a pail or can with the handle lodged in a slot of a bar, either of wire or wood laid across the top with the bristles two-thirds submerged in water or oil as shown in fig. 3,768. To rest the brush on the bottom of the pail is to curl the bristles and spoil it.

It is claimed that a brush cannot be properly cleaned in gasoline, especially if it has been used in colors containing turpentine. The turpentine will liven up and form a mass that will cling to the brush.

One method is to use soap powder or kitchen or laundry soap. Work the brush into the lather and put away with the lather on it. When brush is to be used again wash off the soap.

Treatment for Hardened Brushes.—Soak the hardened brushes for twenty-four hours in raw linseed oil, then place

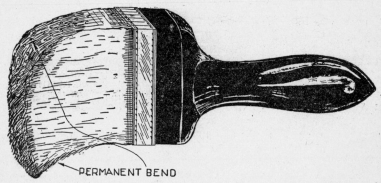

PERMANENT BEND

FIG. 3,769.—Permanent distortion of bristles caused by allowing brush to rest on bottom of can.

them in a pot of benzine and after awhile work the bristles with the hand till separated when the paint will finally soften so that it will wash out.

Practical Points on Painting

Two thin coats over an old finish, well brushed out is better than one heavy coat, and that repainting should not be delayed until the undercoats are too near exhausted.

Too much driers and cheap rosin japans are prime causes of many paint failures.

It is quite unreasonable to expect a first class job with two coats over new work.

An amateur may make a good job painting his house with patent paint if he follow the instructions printed on the can.

Estimating Quantity of Paint Required.—An approximate

FIG. 3,770.—Swelling or enlargement of bristles caused by allowing brushes to remain suspended in water or oil too long. When a brush is not to be used for a long interval of time it should be thoroughly cleaned and put away where not too warm, else it may shrink apart.

calculation of the quantity of paint required to paint a house may be made as follows:

Measure girth of house and height to eaves, if there be gables; to half way up them; multiply one by the other and divide the result by the number of sq. ft. assumed a gallon will cover (approximately 600 sq. ft).

If a second coat, double the quantity. If you mix the paint, the average *formula* per gallon is:

Pure white lead.............................15½ lbs.
Pure raw linseed oil........................ 4½ pints
Pure turpentine............................. ½ pint
Pure drier................................. ½ pint or less

If for priming a good proportion is 100 lbs. lead, 4 gallons oil, 2 gallons turpentine and not over 1 pint drier, together about 9 gallons. Here again the painter must use his judgment or make tests, as conditions of surface to be painted, the season, etc., may call for a greater or lesser amount of oil. Or he may find that a preparatory coat of thinned oil to be a necessary preliminary to priming.

If it be a job over old paint he will decide that two well brushed out coats are best, requiring less oil and an aid to oxidization by adding a larger percentage of drier.

For the second coat he will use a gallon more oil and the total will make about 7 gallons and will cover 4,000 or more feet.

He will make his deductions for trim colors according to the approximate amount of surface to be done, and having determined the amount of labor required, he should be able to give a very fair estimate.

CHAPTER 60

First Aid

The importance of a general knowledge of common remedial measures and first aid treatment cannot be overestimated by anyone who values human life. It isn't so much the size of an open wound (which may be anything from a pin scratch to a major accident) but the number of germs that flock in through the broken defence in the skin.

The tiniest scratch is sometimes more dangerous, if neglected, than a large cut with copious bleeding to cleanse the injured part. Hence treat a wound as soon as possible.

There are a number of good antiseptics, some of which should be in every household.

Antiseptics

Grain Alcohol.—The 95% pure grain alcohol is the antiseptic most widely used. It bites and smarts quite a little on an open wound, but it is a good germ killer. Ordinarily it may be diluted with one to three parts of water but for a "first dressing," the pure juice is best.

Caution.—Great care should be taken not to use wood alcohol (methylated spirits) instead of the ethyl or grain alcohol, because of the danger of absorption into the system resulting in blindness.

Bichloride of Mercury.—An extensively used, and, as claimed by some, much over-rated antiseptic. When poured into or over a wound it loses 80% of its germ destroying power because of the insoluble compounds it forms in conjunction with the blood and other body fluids. Bichloride is very dangerous on account of its "flat taste" and generally harmless appearance. It should only be handled by a physician.

Saleratus or Baking Soda.—The common variety of kitchen baking soda, is much safer around the house than bichloride, carbolic acid, or any active poison. While soda has no germ-killing power outside the body, it exerts a discouraging influence upon ambitious germs when brought into contact with living tissues. Bicarbonate of soda, through its alkalinity, probably prevents the formation of the local acid condition, lacking which the germs are unable to flourish.

Iodine.—This is a dependable and much used antiseptic. Its use has undoubtedly prevented thousands of cases of tetanus (lock-jaw) from wounds sustained and necessarily dressed under unsanitary conditions.

Hydrogen Peroxide.—This is a reliable antiseptic and has the advantage of being harmless.

Chlorazone.—This is a new antiseptic which now can be obtained from most druggists. In its action dead tissue, even large sloughs, treated with Dakin's solution, as it is called, are quickly "digested" away, the surface becoming smooth, clean and bright red in color. The antiseptic is now put up in tablets.

Treatment of Wounds.—Every wound, no matter how trivial, should be immediately washed and treated with some reliable antiseptic. It should then be covered with a layer of absorbent cotton and bound snugly with lint, gauze, or some other sterile bandage. The main idea in treating any wound is to clean it, be sure that it is uncontaminated, and then let it alone. Nature will do the rest.

Every wound, however, made by any animal's claw or tooth, or punctured by a rusty nail, should be referred to a physician for cauterization, or for such other treatment as will insure its being sterile. Take no chances with anything that might subsequently develop into "lock-jaw."

In treating cuts and wounds, the chief points to be attended to are:

1. Arrest the bleeding.

2. Remove from the wound all foreign bodies as soon as possible.

3. Bring the wounded parts opposite to each other and keep them so.

This last item is best done by means of strips of adhesive plaster, first applied to one side of the wound and then secured to the other; these strips should not be too broad, and space must be left between the strips to allow any matter to escape. Wounds too extensive to be held together by plaster must be stitched by a surgeon, who should always be sent for in all severe cases.

For washing a wound, to every pint of water add 2½ teaspoonfuls of carbolic acid and 2 tablespoonfuls of glycerine—if these be not obtainable, add 4 tablespoonfuls of borax to the pint of water—wash the wound, close it, and apply a compress of a folded square of cotton or linen; wet it in the solution used for washing the wound and bandage down quickly and firmly.

If the bleeding be profuse, a sponge dipped in very hot water and wrung out in a cloth should be applied as quickly as possible—if this be not to be had, use ice or cloth wrung out in ice water.

Wounds heal in two ways: 1, rapidly by primary union, without suppuration, and leaving only a very fine scar. 2, slowly by suppuration and the formation of granulations and leaving a large red scar

Bleeding.—This is of three kinds: 1, from the arteries which lead from the heart; 2, that which comes from the veins, which take the blood back to the heart; 3, that from the small veins which carry the blood to the surface of the body. In the first, the blood is bright scarlet and escapes as though it was being pumped. In the second, the blood is dark red and flows away in an uninterrupted stream. In the third, the blood oozes out. In some wounds all three kinds of bleeding occur at the same time.

The simplest and best remedy to stop the bleeding is to apply direct pressure on the external wound by the fingers. Should the wound be long and gaping, a compress of some soft material large enough to fill the cavity may be pressed into it; but this should always be avoided, if possible, as it prevents the natural closing of the wound.

Pressure with the hands will not suffice to restrain bleeding in severe cases for a great length of time and recourse must be had to a ligature; this can best be made with a pocket handkerchief or other article of apparel, long enough and strong enough to bind the limb.

Fold the article neck-tie fashion, then place a smooth stone, or anything serving for a firm pad, on the artery, tie the handkerchief loosely, insert any available stick in the loop and proceed to twist it, as if wringing a towel, until just tight enough to stop the flow.

Examine the wound from time to time, lessen the compression if it become very cold or purple, or tighten up the handkerchief if it commence bleeding.

Some knowledge of anatomy is necessary to guide the operator where to press. Bleeding from the head and upper neck requires pressure to be placed on the large artery which passes up beside the windpipe and just above the collar bone.

The artery supplying the arm and hand runs down the inside of the upper arm, almost in line with the coat seam, and should be pressed.

The artery feeding the leg and foot can be felt in the crease of the groin, just where the flesh of the thigh seems to meet the flesh of the abdomen and this is the best place to apply the ligature. In arterial bleeding the pressure must be put between the heart and the wound, while in *venous* bleeding it must be beyond the wound to stop the flow as it goes towards the heart.

In any case of bleeding, the person may become weak and faint; unless the blood be flowing actively this is not a serious sign, and the quiet condition of the faint often assists nature in staying the bleeding, by allowing the blood to clot and so block up any wound in a blood vessel.

Unless the faint be prolonged or the patient be losing much blood, it is better not to hasten to relieve the faint condition; when in this state any thing like excitement should be avoided, external warmth should be applied, the person covered with blankets, and bottles of hot water or hot bricks applied to the feet and arm-pits.

Frost Bite.—No warm air, warm water, or fire should be allowed near the frozen parts until the natural temperature is nearly restored; rub the affected parts gently with snow or snow water in a cold room; the circulation should be restored very slowly; and great care must be taken in the after treatment.

Broken Bones.—The treatment consists of: 1, carefully removing or cutting away, if more convenient, any of the clothes which are compressing or hurting the injured parts; 2, very gently replacing the bones in their natural position and shape, as nearly as possible, and putting the part in a position which gives most ease to the patient; 3, applying some temporary splint or appliance, which will keep the broken bones from moving about and tearing the flesh; for this purpose, pieces of wood, pasteboard, straw, or firmly folded cloth may be used, taking care to pad the splints with some soft material and not to apply them too tightly, while the splints may be tied by loops of rope, string, or strips of cloth; 4, conveying the patient home or to a hospital.

The bearer then places his arm behind the back of the patient and grasps his opposite hip, at the same time catching firmly hold of the hand of the patient resting on his shoulder, with his other hand; then by putting his hip behind the near hip of the patient, much support is given, and if necessary, the bearer can lift him off the ground and as it were, carry him along.

Poultices.—These outward applications are useful to relieve sudden cramps and pains due to severe injuries, sprains and colds. The secret of applying a mustard poultice is to apply it hot and keep it so by frequent changes—if it get cold and clammy it will do more harm than good.

A poultice to be of any service and hold its heat should be from one-half to one inch thick.

To make it, take flax seed, oatmeal, rye meal, bread, or ground slippery elm; stir the meal slowly into a bowl of boiling water, until a thin and smooth dough is formed. To apply it, take a piece of old linen of the right size, fold it in the middle; spread the dough evenly on one-half of the cloth and cover it with the other.

To make a "mustard paste" as it is called, mix one or two tablespoonfuls of mustard and the same of fine flour, with enough water to make the mixture an even paste; spread it neatly with a table knife on a piece of old linen, or even cotton cloth. Cover the face of the paste with a piece of thin muslin.

How to Carry an Injured Person.—In case of an injury where walking is impossible, and lying down is not absolutely necessary, the injured person may be seated in a chair, and carried; or he may sit upon a board, the ends of which are carried by two men, around whose necks he should place his arms so as to steady himself.

Where an injured person can walk he will get much help by putting his arms over the shoulders and round the necks of two others.

A seat may be made with four hands and the person may be thus carried and steadied by clasping his arms around the necks of his bearers.

If only one person be available and the patient can stand up, ιet him place one arm round the neck of the bearer, bringing his hand on and in front of the opposite shoulder of the bearer.

To get at a broken limb, or rib, the clothing must be removed, and it is essential that this be done without injury to the patient; the simplest plan is to rip up the seams of such garments as are in the way. Boots must be cut off. It is not imperatively necessary to do anything to a broken limb before the arrival of a doctor except to keep it perfectly at rest.

To carry an injured person by a stretcher (which can be made of a door, shutter, or settee—with blankets or shawls or coats for pillows) three persons are necessary. In lifting the patient on the stretcher *he should be laid with his feet to his head,* so that both are in the same straight line; then one or two persons should stand on each side of him, and raise him from the ground, slip him on the stretcher; this to avoid the necessity of any one stepping over the stretcher, and the liability of stumbling.

If a limb be crushed or broken, it may be laid upon a pillow with bandages tied around the whole (*i. e.,* pillow and limb) to keep it from slipping about. In carrying the stretcher the bearers should "break step" with short paces; hurrying and jolting should be avoided and the stretcher should be carried so that the patient may be in plain sight of the bearers.

Burns.—These should be treated the same as any other wounds, only more so, because there usually is a much larger surface from which the natural protection of the skin has been removed.

A most thorough cleansing, followed by a good liberal dusting with baking soda, and a snug bandaging is all they usually require.

Perhaps the best treatment for a severe burn, however, is to thoroughly cleanse the parts with an antiseptic solution, and then coat them over with the wax-like preparation discovered by Dr. Barthede Sandfort, of France, put up by pharmaceutical chemists under the name "Parresine."

Shock.—Loss of blood is one of the things which may produce shock. Don't confuse shock with apoplexy. In shock the skin is cold and clammy, the breathing shallow, the pulse feeble and irregular with little beads of perspiration standing out on the forehead. A patient in shock is not usually unconscious, but appears stupid or apathetic.

The thing to do with the patient is to get him flat on his back, preferably in bed and warm him no matter how hot it might happen to be. Then give him a half teaspoonful of aromatic spirits of ammonia or a cup of strong black coffee, and keep him as quiet as possible. Rub the limbs, stroking always in the direction of the heart. Be careful not to uncover the patient.

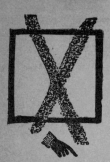

MAIL ORDER

THEO. AUDEL & CO., 49 W. 23 St., New York 10, N.Y.

Please mail me for 7 days' free examination the books marked (X) below. I agree to mail $1 in 7 days on each book or set ordered, and to further mail $1 a month on each book or set ordered until I have paid purchase price.

If I am not satisfied with Guides I will return them.

Check NOW!

You Can Look Over Any Guide In Your Own Home

—

Start the Easy Payments If Satisfied

MAIL THIS TODAY